Teaching Science Through Conservation

McGRAW-HILL SERIES IN EDUCATION

Harold Benjamin, Consulting Editor-in-Chief

ARNO A. BELLACK
Teachers College, Columbia University
CONSULTING EDITOR
CURRICULUM AND METHODS IN EDUCATION SERIES

HAROLD BENJAMIN
Director, Connecticut Study, Role of the Public School
CONSULTING EDITOR
FOUNDATIONS IN EDUCATION SERIES

HARLAN HAGMAN
Wayne State University
CONSULTING EDITOR
ADMINISTRATION IN EDUCATION SERIES

NICHOLAS HOBBS
George Peabody College for Teachers
CONSULTING EDITOR
PSYCHOLOGY AND HUMAN DEVELOPMENT SERIES

CURRICULUM AND METHODS IN EDUCATION

Arno A. Bellack, Consulting Editor

BROWN, LEWIS, AND HARCLEROAD · A-V Instruction: Materials and Methods
MARKS, PURDY, AND KINNEY · Teaching Arithmetic for Understanding
MUNZER AND BRANDWEIN · Teaching Science Through Conservation

Teaching Science Through Conservation

MARTHA E. MUNZER

PROJECT ASSISTANT IN EDUCATION
THE CONSERVATION FOUNDATION

Formerly Instructor of Chemistry
and Chairman of General Activities
Fieldston School, New York City

PAUL F. BRANDWEIN

DIRECTOR OF DIVISION OF EDUCATION
THE CONSERVATION FOUNDATION

Formerly Chairman, Department of Science
Forest Hills High School, New York

McGRAW-HILL BOOK COMPANY, INC. 1960

New York Toronto London

TEACHING SCIENCE THROUGH CONSERVATION

 Library of Congress Catalog Card Number 59-13209

44048

The Conservation Foundation

Foreword

If we consider conservation in its widest sense, it can be said that all teachers are engaged in promoting it. Every educator strives, in one way or another, to create an environment in which his pupils will make the wisest use of their own personal resources. Because conservation is so pervasive a subject, it must inevitably deal with human resources as well as with natural resources, whether animate or inanimate.

Approaching the matter from another point of view, it is also correct to say that all teachers of science teach science through conservation. Teachers may not perhaps be always wholly conscious that they are doing this. Nevertheless, wherever a teacher deals with science as it transforms the environment or as it helps man better to understand his environment so that he may live more in harmony with the earth and its resources, that teacher is dealing with conservation.

Because it is so broad a subject, the meaning and purposes of conservation are frequently not clearly defined, and its teaching is often impaired by the careless use of terms and words. Regrettably, too, conservation is often thought of in too limited a way, since the tendency has been to associate it merely with practices and technologies related to farms and foods. Actually, the subject encompasses all the knowledge, skills, and attitudes through which man accepts his responsibility for stewardship of the earth's resources—renewable, nonrenewable, and even those still to be developed in the future. Through conservation, man assumes a trusteeship of the riches of the natural world not for himself alone but for countless generations still to come.

Although the contents of this book are rich and varied, it has but a single purpose. It deals with the things a science teacher can do to affect directly the wisdom with which resources are used and developed. Thus all science teachers, whether concerned with general science, biology, chemistry, physics, or earth science, use certain demonstrations or laboratory experiments or develop areas of discussion that deal in an immediate way with the vast area of conservation. This book covers a great many of the source materials and teaching approaches available to the science teacher.

The Conservation Foundation feels a great satisfaction in sponsoring this book, which has been written with such care and thoroughness by two authors of unusually wide experience and knowledge. Their careful work has been impelled by a vivid realization of the importance of conservation in the lives of all people. They would be the first to recognize, of course, that no one book on such an all-encompassing topic can be considered complete. Nevertheless, we share with them the belief that it is sufficiently broad in scope to strengthen the science teacher's conviction that his subject deals with one of man's most essential and personal problems: *Am I discharging my responsibility to the great gift of resources upon which all life depends?*

Fairfield Osborn
PRESIDENT, THE CONSERVATION FOUNDATION

Preface

Paul Sears, past president of the American Association for Advancement of Science, has this to say:[1]

> It is proverbially the youngest baby in the family who raises the most hell, and man is nature's youngest. . . . The Old Lady was already well set in her ways when he appeared. Repeatedly he has wrecked his home, repeatedly he has been spanked, but stubbornly he persists in having his own way which he calls "The Conquest of Nature." It is my own suspicion that it is time for him to learn the House Rules. . . . The question, of course, is, "What can be done?" Personally, I think much can be done, but the problem is so big that it must be taken in small portions at a time, just as we do with any big and complex problem. These portions are the local communities in which each of us lives, where we have a chance to see at first-hand what is happening, and a chance as free men and women to do something about it. This is not only good technical conservation, but good political doctrine, too, for as Lincoln suggested, a duty dodged is a privilege lost.
>
> It is precisely at this point that teachers enter the picture. . . .

There is a single purpose to this book. It offers to science teachers, who know what is happening to our resources, selected and practical classroom, laboratory, and field study procedures in the teaching of science, within the intent and content of the area of conservation, as we have used it synonymously with resource use. In one specific way or another these procedures illuminate various aspects of conservation.

The chosen procedures have been culled from many sources—our own

[1] "The Appraisal of Natural Resources," *The Science Teacher,* vol. 21, no. 4, September, 1954.

experience, other teachers, all kinds of literature, both in science and in conservation. Some techniques are the result of visits to experiment stations, industrial plants, research centers, as well as consultations with experts in a variety of fields. All the procedures have been tested in actual teaching of high school students in general science, biology, chemistry, and physics.

You will find a dual table of contents, for two reasons: first, in order to suggest the range of natural resources and the thread of ecological relationships that ties them together; second, to indicate where, in the traditional high school biology, chemistry, and physics courses, consideration of each of these resources fits into place. Clearly the connections of conservation to chemistry and physics are quite as far-reaching as those of conservation to biology.

The index should provide an additional way of helping the teacher to find the particular conservation concept appropriate to a given science lesson. Thus, if a chemistry class is studying the law of conservation of matter or the metallurgy of iron, conservation connections may be found by looking up these topics in the index.

The first two chapters, dealing with the scope and sequence of conservation, may be of interest not only to science teachers but also to high school administrators and those concerned with planning the curriculum. Teachers of science have always been teachers of conservation; courses of study in science are rich in the materials from which the principles of conservation and resource use draw meaning.

This book is meant to be, therefore, a practical aid to teachers of science. To the experienced teacher, the techniques to be found here will no doubt confirm his approach. To the new teacher of science, these techniques may suggest ways of dealing with one of the most important problems of our century.

Our population is increasing at an unforeseen rate. Whether or not we maintain the standard of living to which our present population is accustomed depends on the wise use and intelligent development of our natural resources—renewable, nonrenewable, "inexhaustible," new and to-be-developed ones.

Are we wise enough to do this? The answer lies in part in our schools; in short, the answer lies, as much as anywhere else, in teachers and what they consider to be their function.

For careful and critical reading of the entire manuscript we are indebted to Dr. Phyllis Busch of New York; Lorenzo Lisonbee, science consultant, Phoenix High Schools, Arizona; Dr. Howard Michaud, Purdue University, Indiana; Dr. Richard L. Weaver, University of Michigan; Dr. Harold Benjamin, Connecticut Study of the Role of the Public Schools; Dr. Arno A. Bellack of Teachers College, Columbia.

For the critical reading of the chemistry, physics, and biology sections, respectively, we wish to thank Dr. Saul Geffner and Harvey Pollack of Forest Hills High School, New York, and Dr. Jerome Metzner of Bronx High School of Science, New York.

We should also like to express our appreciation to C. W. Mattison of the Forest Service and to Adrian Fox of the Soil Conservation Service of the U.S. Department of Agriculture and Jack Culbreath of the Fish and Wildlife Service, U.S. Department of the Interior. Through their efforts most of our photographic illustrations were assembled. Other government agencies, as well as a number of industrial concerns, supplied us with additional pictures that we have acknowledged in the text.

We extend special thanks to Dr. Lucile Lindberg, Queens College, New York; Dr. Roscoe Eckelberry, Ohio State University; Dr. William H. Stead, Committee on Economic Development, New York; John Shrawder, Supervisor of Conservation Education, Department of Natural Resources, California; Fern Kent, Meany Junior High School, Seattle, Washington; and Dr. T. R. Porter, State University of Iowa, for the many valuable suggestions they made after reading an early draft of the manuscript.

We have also had advice and encouragement from the participants in a workshop on conservation sponsored by the Joint Council on Economic Education.

For the assistance of our editorial board, from the inception of the project to its completion, we are deeply grateful.

It is our hope that teachers who use this book will get in touch with us to discuss specific procedures that prove unclear or difficult. We should be delighted to include in a revised edition better techniques or suggested improvements, with appropriate credit.

Martha E. Munzer
Paul F. Brandwein

Contents *(According to Interrelationships)*

Contents *(According to Subject Areas)*

Biology, General Science, and Conservation

Chemistry, General Science, and Conservation

Physics, General Science, and Conservation

PART I

Scope and Sequence

I

The Science Teacher and His Commitment to Conservation and Resource-use Teaching

This book is addressed to teachers of science. Teachers of science have considered the problems relating to conservation (i.e., resource use) of sufficient importance to include them in every course of study in science. Hence, these topics are being taught pervasively throughout science.

An analysis of courses of study throughout the country substantiates the idea that conservation and resource use is taught by almost all science teachers. More than 200 courses in the elementary, junior, and senior high schools were examined by the education division of The Conservation Foundation. Although these courses varied in the sequence of their topics and in some cases in their scope, an area of common agreement was readily discernible. In addition, fifteen widely used texts in general science, eighteen in biology, eleven in chemistry, and ten in physics were studied with the purpose of discovering what areas in conservation and resource use were included.

The results of this survey form the basis for the topics selected for inclusion as classroom, laboratory, and field-study procedures in science teaching that make up the body of this book.

The conservation topics that emerged from the examination of curriculums and texts fell naturally into the different chapters of this book. They may be found in the first Table of Contents. The second Table of Contents shows where these same topics appear in the traditional subject-matter areas of biology, chemistry, and physics. When considered together, the topics thus assembled comprise the present curriculum in conservation in the high school.

THE EMERGING CONSERVATION CURRICULUM

Conservation and resource use is apparently so significant an area in American life, the solution of the problems with which it deals is of so overriding an importance, that it has found an enduring place in all areas of science. Furthermore, if we assigned to one year of study the problems, topics, and subject areas listed in the first Table of Contents, we should have a course in conservation and resource use. However, the development in curriculum planning has not been toward a one-year course, perhaps wisely so. Instead, we have a curriculum in conservation that theoretically, at least, pervades the student's entire career in high school.

The net effect of this development is to confront the student with a constant study of conservation and resource use throughout his high school career. As he grows in knowledge and wisdom, he faces problems of increasing complexity. These develop from a study of the resources of his environment, in general science and biology (his early years in high school), to the more complex study of winning, sometimes wresting, his material and energy resources from nature, in chemistry and physics or physical science (his later years in school).

The result is what is usually considered an effective curriculum structure. First, there is an ascending development of complexity of concepts in ever-widening scope, based on an introductory course (general science), where the concepts are originally introduced and sufficiently developed on that level. Secondly, the general area (conservation and resource use) is considered at every grade level from a different point of attack. Hence as the central concept of resource use, wise and efficient management of our resources is taught in different contexts. Thirdly, conservation and resource use, introduced into existing courses of study, does not compete as a specific course for curriculum time.

It is clear that resource problems cannot be solved by science alone. Economics, government, politics, and social institutions all play exceedingly important roles, even when science and technology have made their full and necessary contribution. Resource-use teaching is therefore becoming pervasive in school life, one likes to think, because it pervades every area of life of the people of these United States.

This notion leads teachers to deal with soil, water, fuels, minerals, etc., from the first grade through the twelfth. It leads teachers to deal with conservation and resource use in the kindergarten to sixth grade curriculum, and in general science, geography, history, civics, biology, chemistry, economics, physics, English—in all the areas of school life within the classroom (structured as lessons) and out of the classroom (structured as assemblies, field trips, clubs, and forums). It leads teachers to look at the nature and the nurture of *all* our young people, and leads them not to neglect the nourishment of those whose inventiveness, ingenuity, and devotion to civilization will yield us our new and to-be-developed resources.

This approach tends to emphasize not only the renewable resources—plants and animals and their resource base—but lays clear stress on nonrenewable, "inexhaustible," and future resources in their scientific, economic, and cultural aspects. Humans and what they do to their resource base (their economy) are clearly as important as the preservation of feeding areas for certain birds.

CONSERVATION: AN AREA OF HUMAN BEHAVIOR

Teachers, in short, are beginning to accept conservation and resource use as an area of human behavior. Their educational objective is to change human behavior so that it will fulfill the goals of civilized human beings. The human behavior they are specifically concerned with applies to the wise use and intelligent development of all our natural resources—renewable, nonrenewable, "inexhaustible," new, and to-be-developed. If we deal with renewable and nonrenewable resources only, we mine, in a sense, only the land, the sea, the air. If we look to our future resources, unknown at present, we mine a fruitful source of goods and services—the human mind. If we look to all our resources, we educate for "compassion as well as sophistication."

The essence of conservation is an attitude toward the world and toward people. It helps people to use the materials of the world wisely and to develop them intelligently. Similarly, it gives them the environment to develop to their fullest potential, so that they may use themselves wisely and well.

A better world is, after all, the objective of conservation teaching. And a better world cannot be had without a human commitment. What people are and what they do speak louder than what they say.

2

The Science Teacher and His Approach to Conservation

A study of curriculums throughout the country shows, as we have said, that conservation is taught *pervasively* throughout the courses of study. Nevertheless, conservation teaching has certain trends in "structural" characteristics as shown in teachers' approaches. It should be emphasized that these are merely trends, but rather distinct and noticeable ones.

DEFINITIONS OF CONSERVATION

In Chapter 1 we started by equating conservation with resource use but quickly modified the statement to include "wise" use. We noted that conservation signifies an attitude, a way of looking at life, leading to a definite kind of behavior with specific goals in view. All these ideas and others are inherent in the word conservation. That is why a brief definition is difficult. A generally acceptable one concerns itself essentially with a statement of policy, i.e., conservation is the wise use, intelligent development, and efficient management of our natural resources.

Some scholars have tried other types of definition. Charles Lively, for example, especially conscious of the role of new and to-be-developed resources, products of the inventiveness and skill of man, defines conservation in this manner:[1] "Conservation consists of equating the use of natural resources with the varying demands of population, so that resource supplies will not become exhausted before adequate supplies of

[1] Charles E. Lively and Jack J. Preiss, *Conservation Education in American Colleges*, The Ronald Press Company, New York, 1957.

equally useful resources are either discovered, invented or otherwise reproduced."

Many other definitions are to be found in the literature of conservation. Whatever the definition, one thing is certain; each concerns itself with the use and care of our natural resources.

The economist, Edwin G. Nourse, offers us one classification of the pillars of our modern economy. These are natural resources, labor, capital, private management, and government. Whatever classification is preferred, natural resources are basic. Without them there is no economy.

What, then, are our natural resources? If we accept what is taught in our schools, we find essentially that the area covered falls into the following groups. Although arranged somewhat differently, these groups confirm the classification of *Resources for Freedom* (Sec. 19-2*f*).

Renewable Resources. Those which can be replenished when properly managed

Materials. Plant and animal life, forests, soil (as far as it can be replenished), water (as far as it be recycled), land for scenery and recreation, air (as far as it can be kept clean)

Energy. Water power, wood as fuel, animal power

Nonrenewable Resources. Those which become unavailable when used

Materials. Minerals, metals, nonmetals, chemicals, industrial byproducts, land in natural condition

Energy. Fossil fuels and lubricants (coal, oil, gas), atomic energy (fission)

"Inexhaustible" Resources. Those which are at present so abundant that they seem limitless

Materials. Ocean, sun, certain rocks

Energy. Solar energy, winds, tides, temperature differentials, atomic energy (fusion)

Whether this classification is useful or not, it includes the major areas with which our schools deal. Add to this a fourth category:

New and To-be-developed Resources. Those which depend on the brains and skill of *specially trained* persons for discovery and development. Materials and energy may be drawn from any of the other three categories of resources.

These resources still to be discovered and developed are decidedly a part of the conservation picture. Our presently unknown resources are unpredictable; whatever they are will be the result of the inventiveness of the human brain. Thus, nylon fiber was an unknown resource in 1925; we might then have been concerned with the conservation of the silkworm and mulberry trees. Other once unknown resources, such as butadiene rubber, orlon, polyethylene plastics, come to mind.

These new products, made of existing raw materials in new chemical configurations, depended for their discovery and development on human inventiveness. From the creativity of still other individuals will spring our resources of the future. In any event, in considering the resource-use outlook, we do not conceive of it as excluding the undiscovered or still to-be-developed resources.

It will be seen that our own selections in this handbook include the same broad emphasis, covering nonrenewable and "inexhaustible" resources quite as fully as the renewable ones, and devoting a section to the human potential upon which depend our new and to-be-developed resources.

Our selections also cover a large range of practices in regard to resources, such as protecting, restoring, reusing, recycling, allocating, substituting, and planning—each a significant conservation measure.

THE CURRICULUM IN CONSERVATION AND RESOURCE USE

From additional surveys of curricular practice in the United States, three notions may be derived:

1. In general, the present approach to conservation education consists of its integration throughout the elementary and high school curriculums. In the vast majority of instances, a separate course in conservation is not given.

In those elementary schools where the program is centered around the experiences of the children, direct contacts with conservation occur as they are motivated. This is not to assume that planning does not occur. Generally speaking, however, conservation activities per se enter into what are recognizably the science and social studies areas. However, art and English (at all school levels) may deal with topics that could be considered conservation.

2. In the high school, the general practice is to have work in conservation as part of a specific topic in a given course. In general science, topics such as "soil," "water," "electricity" are common. In biology, chemistry, and physics, the practice is to include resource-use education as part of more specific topics (e.g., soil and water in relation to photosynthesis, the resources of specific metals in relation to the study of their chemistry, the resources of oil within a unit on hydrocarbon chemistry, water resources within a study of electricity in physics), or as specific units with such titles as Conservation (in biology) or Farm Problems (in social studies).

3. As has been indicated previously, if we consider all the areas that are taught in high school science throughout the four years in which science is given (general science, biology, chemistry, physics, and earth science) and extract from those the areas that are clearly conservation and

resource use, we find, in *essence,* a course of study in conservation. The course of study consists plainly of the topics in our Table of Contents. Were these topics taught *in a single year,* we should have a full-year course titled Conservation or Resource Use, which derived its materials from all science areas. For those who are interested in such a course within the objective of general education, this handbook may serve a significant purpose.[2]

Any teacher who has studied methods of devising curriculums will recognize in the method we have used to *derive* our "course" in conservation and resource use one valid way in which courses arise. That is, a course may be born when there is recognition that the materials "scattered" throughout the entire curriculum need to be brought together. This happens when it is realized that grouping is necessary not only because the concepts serve one aim, goal, or purpose, but because it is least wasteful of administrative, teaching, and learning time. Clearly, *one could make a strong case for placing resource-use and conservation materials in one course of study.* Clearly, the course serves the purposes and goals of general education or of liberal education. Just as clearly the time is not yet ripe for the more widely spread inclusion of such a course, if only for the reason that our public schools in the United States are in the throes of a great experience, if not experiment. That experience is to make a full education from elementary through high school available to all who wish it. Curriculums, methods, and administrative devices are in ferment in the truest sense of the word.

For the present, then, most schools include resource-use teaching pervasively throughout the curriculum. There is no evidence whether this is not as effective, less effective, or more effective than teaching resource use in a single course. As educators turn to experimentation in the real sense, the evidence may be forthcoming.

An Example

Be that as it may, there are many examples of the way school systems are proposing to include resource use in their curriculums, one of which is offered here. It is submitted strictly as an example of curriculum planning and is not meant to invite comparison with other plans. Other plans (again only a few) are listed at the end of this chapter.

Our purpose is to point only to the curricular device adopted: Resource use is made pervasive through the years and pervades also various subject-matter areas. Resource-use education is not restricted to renew-

[2] The "course of study" is derived, as has been said, from a study of some 200 science curriculums in use in representative centers of population. The topics included are also represented in the procedures and techniques that are the body of this book.

able resources but includes the nonrenewable as well. No attempt is made at a critical analysis of the "outline" [3] which follows, but it is an example of an effort in the direction of which we speak.

LEARNING TO USE NEW HAMPSHIRE'S RESOURCES:
A Guide to Secondary Schools, 1953

SOIL RESOURCES[4]

Plan of Integration

Appreciating that each course has more or less to offer for conservation, it is suggested the following be stressed or reviewed from the standpoint of soil conservation.

- I. General Science and/or Physics
  - A. Study of Mechanical Effects
    - 1. On the various types of environment
      - *a.* Water velocities (motion)—soil carried at different speeds
      - *b.* Alternate freezing and thawing (heat)
      - *c.* Glacial action (friction)
  - B. Water-holding Capacity—Tests
    - 1. Surface tension
    - 2. Capillary action—treatments for increasing water-holding capacity
  - C. Other Contributions Such as:
    - 1. Insulation
    - 2. Conduction
    - 3. Expansion and contraction
- II. Chemistry
  - A. Soil Chemistry
    - 1. Analysis of soil samples—various types
    - 2. Study of fertilizer analyses
      - *a.* Necessary chemical factors—sources
      - *b.* Limiting elements in nature—supply methods
      - *c.* Formation of organic matter
  - B. Study of Agricultural Station Work
    - 1. Fertilizer experiments
    - 2. Nutrient sources in nature
    - 3. Nutrient loss prevention
  - C. Basic Reactions
    - 1. Chemical exchanges
    - 2. Chemical freeing of bound useful nutrients

[3] By permission from the State Department of Education, Concord, N.H. The subjects covered in the guide include our four great renewable resources: water, soil, forests, and wildlife. Human resources and mineral resources are also touched upon. We have chosen only a portion of one of these topics, namely, soil, to show how it is developed.

[4] The section on soil resources includes also "Specialized Concepts, Topics, and Information," with emphasis on New Hampshire's particular conditions and problems.

Conservation Teaching in Geneva Public Schools (1952), Junior and Senior High Schools, Geneva, N.Y.

Suggestions for Conservation Education, Intermediate and Upper Grades, Alameda County Schools, Oakland, Calif.

Teaching Conservation and the Wise Use of the Renewable Natural Resources (1955), Marion County Public Schools, Fairmont, W.Va.

Education for Better Use of Our Resources (1952), Capitol Area School Development Association, State College, Albany, N.Y.

Suggested Material for Teaching Conservation in the Secondary School, Colorado State College of Education, Greeley, Colo.

A Curriculum Unit in Conservation of Natural Resources (1952), California School Supervisors Association, Northern Section, California State Education Department, Sacramento, Calif.

Using Resources Wisely (1956), New York State Education Department, Albany, N.Y.

An Outline for Teaching Conservation in High Schools (1955), U.S. Department of Agriculture, Soil Conservation Service (PA-201), Washington, D.C.

This brief list indicates that on various levels—a single school, city, county, state, and nation—materials for teaching conservation are being made available.

This handbook, *Teaching Science Through Conservation,* is designed to supplement existing materials. It is our hope that it may help teachers to develop their own individual way of teaching science through conservation.

PART 2

Conservation as a Study of Interrelationships between Living Things and Their Environment

3

Plants as Food Makers

This chapter concerns itself primarily with the green plant, the basic resource needed to sustain all forms of life. Someday, perhaps, man may learn to create food in test tubes from other raw materials. For the present, however, he owes his life to the food manufactured by green plants. He owes to them also many other important products: lumber, paper, pulp, textiles, chemicals.

A study of conservation can hardly begin without some knowledge of the food factories of plants and the way they operate. What are the basic raw materials needed? Where do they come from? How are they supplied? How utilized? What happens when there is a shortage of any of these raw materials or resources? What can be done about such a shortage?

These questions, and others like them, belong in any study of biology; properly they apply to conservation. As in all chapters, however, we have been selective and not all-inclusive. We have also taken the liberty of including comments from time to time on the relationship of the technique described and the concepts in conservation to which it applies.

FOOD MAKING IN GREEN PLANTS

3-1. Photosynthesis: A Chemical Reaction

The equation following is a *condensed version* of a most important chemical reaction, for upon it all living things depend.

$$6CO_2 + 6H_2O \xrightarrow[\text{Light energy}]{} C_6H_{12}O_6 + 6O_2 \quad (\text{Stored energy})$$

Research scientists all over the world are learning more and more about the many and intricate steps involved in the process of photosynthesis. Each month brings new discovery.

Perhaps your students will catch the excitement of watching the story unfold. When the answer is finally known, man may be able to set up his own photosynthetic factories for making carbohydrates and other foods, thus imitating the green plant's chemical laboratory.

You may want to begin the work by recounting the story of Van Helmont and the willow twig. Or, if possible, repeat the "experiment." Remember how he planted the twig, which weighed 5 pounds, in a barrel of soil weighing 200 pounds? The twig grew abundantly. After 5 years, Van Helmont weighed the plant. It had gained some 164 pounds in weight, while the soil had lost only a few ounces. Now, if the plant had not absorbed food from the soil, what was the source of the materials which the plant had converted into plant tissue? Van Helmont thought the tree had converted the water from the soil into plant material. What are the facts as we know them today?

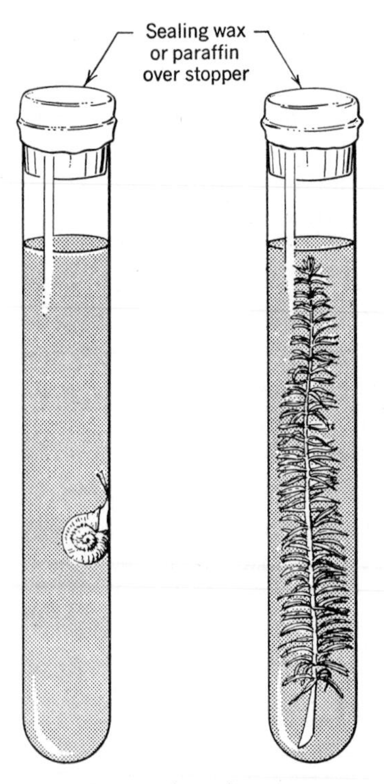

Fig. 3-1. What happens in each sealed test tube? (*a*) A snail in aquarium water; (*b*) elodea in aquarium water.

Or approach this fundamental work on food making in plants in this way. Seal a snail in a large-sized test tube of aquarium water (Fig. 3-1). How long will it live? In another test tube place a sprig of elodea (*Anacharis*). How long will this plant live in a sealed tube? Draw explanations from students. Lead into a discussion of how plants make their food. What conditions are needed for food making?

3-2. Starch: Evidence of Food Making

Have students select healthy plants such as geranium or other thin-leaved plants that have been in the light. Students may then test the leaves for the presence of starch. (Certain plants—the shoots of onion, for instance—do not store starch but store sugars instead).

Since storage of starch is an evidence of food making, students may test the leaves for starch by adding dilute iodine solution (Sec. 18-1*o*), but the chlorophyll must first be removed so that the green coloring does not obscure the results, as will happen when iodine solution is added to the fresh leaves. Be certain to have students use leaves of green plants that have been in sunlight for several hours. It may be necessary to use an electric lamp on cloudy days and set the plants about 2 feet from a 75-watt bulb for several hours.

First boil several of these leaves in water to soften them. Then transfer the leaves into warmed alcohol. When an electric hot plate is not available, take the precaution of setting a small beaker of alcohol into a larger Pyrex beaker of boiling water over a bunsen burner. Or use a long test tube in place of the smaller beaker so that the alcohol fumes are carried as far away from the bunsen flame as possible.

Call students' attention to the observation that the leaves have become blanched as the chlorophyll dissolves in the alcohol. The students should be sure to wash off the leaves in water and spread them out flat in a petri dish or other container into which a dilute iodine solution can be poured. After a few minutes, wash off the iodine and look for the bluish black color in the leaves. This is evidence of starch in the leaves. Compare this with the standard test for starch (Sec. 8-14).

You may want to develop the idea that the energy of the sun is transferred into many forms of energy (Fig. 15-1). For example, from where does the energy released in the burning of sugar or starch come? You might also want to develop the conditions needed by a plant for food making. Have students demonstrate what happens if any one of these conditions does not prevail (Secs. 3-6, 3-7, 3-9). Or you may prefer to show the color film *Gift of Green* (New York Botanical Garden) or *Photosynthesis* (United World Films).

Viewing Starch Grains. Starch grains are distinctive for specific kinds of plants. Students may examine grains of starch in the white potato. They may lightly scrape the cut surface of a raw potato and mount this material in a drop of water on a clean slide. After students locate these irregular oval grains, have them apply a drop of dilute Lugol's solution (Sec. 18-1*o*) to one edge of the cover slip as they remove the water from the opposite edge of the cover slip with filter paper.

Some students may want to make a comparative study of the different shapes that exist in starch grains. In fact, this has been a way of classifying plant types.

3-3. Other Food Compounds Produced by Plants

Most of your students will be satisfied to identify starch as the product of photosynthesis (Sec. 3-2). Other students, particularly those in your chemistry classes who have begun the study of organic chemistry, may be interested in reporting how the first product of photosynthesis, glucose, is converted not only into starch in some plants but into cane sugar in others. They may also want to discover what is known about the conversion of the glucose in plants into fats, oils, and proteins. Students will become aware that the complex protein molecules, in addition to containing hydrogen, oxygen, and carbon, also contain both nitrogen and sulfur and usually phosphorus. Where do plants obtain these elements? This might well lead into a discussion of and experiments in plant nutrients (Secs. 8-8 to 8-12).

One of your students might report on the short cut in the photosynthetic process made possible by photosynthetic sulfur bacteria. These bacteria, it has been discovered, can bypass the making of sugar and produce proteins directly through light energy.

Plants produce many organic compounds besides food, each species creating compounds peculiar to itself. Odors, flavors, colors are all due to organic compounds synthesized by plants. There is material here for special reports by students and for the beginnings of research.

3-4. Oxygen: A By-product of Food Making

1. Fasten a few sprigs of healthy elodea plants to a glass stirring rod with a rubber band. Add a pinch of sodium bicarbonate (a source of carbon dioxide) to a beaker of cooled aquarium water, which has been boiled to drive off the dissolved gases. Invert the elodea plants, so that the freshly cut stems are upward in the water. When sunlight or electric light shines on these plants, watch the different rates at which bubbles of oxygen-rich gas are given off when the plants are different distances from the light source.

2. Students may demonstrate that this gas is rich in oxygen. Remove the glass stirring rod, and insert these elodea plants into a glass funnel (Fig. 3-2). Collect the escaping gas in this way: Over the stem of the funnel invert a test tube filled with water. Leave the plants exposed to light for some hours. Students may observe how water in the test tube is displaced by the gas bubbling from the freshly cut stems. You may insert a glowing splint into a test tube of this gas to identify it as oxygen.

These demonstrations are rarely satisfactory, but you may have a student who would like to discover why the results are erratic. Probably the answer lies in many factors, e.g., the strength of sunlight, air spaces in the elodea, the carbon dioxide concentration, etc. Here are two suggestions that ought to help: When testing for oxygen, discard the first half inch of collected gas (mostly air) and start over. Instead of a pinch of sodium bicarbonate try using 2 cubic centimeters of 0.25 per cent solution of the bicarbonate for every 100 cubic centimeters of aquarium water.

A striking illustration of the evolution of oxygen during photosynthesis may be given in this manner: Place a potted plant and a mouse on a tray. Cover them both with a bell jar, making it airtight by sealing with petroleum jelly.

When the tray and its contents are in sunlight, the mouse will scamper about, but when in the dark, he will grow languid and almost lose

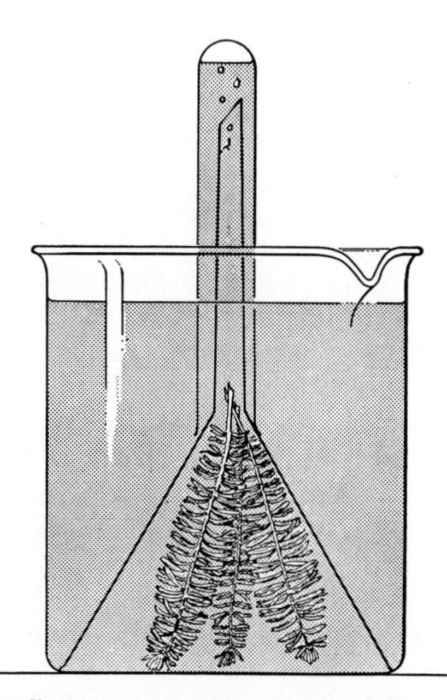

Fig. 3-2. Collecting oxygen liberated by elodea sprigs.

consciousness. As soon as sunny conditions are restored, the renewal of oxygen will cause the mouse to revive and scamper once more.

3-5. Chlorophyll in Food Making

Bring to class a green and white coleus plant or a silver-leaved geranium. Ask students how to demonstrate whether the chlorophyll is needed for starch making. Have a student repeat the demonstration in which the leaves are tested for starch with dilute iodine solution (Sec. 3-2). Of course the chlorophyll should first be removed from the leaves by heating in water and then in alcohol. Ask students to look along the streets, in the park or meadow for trees whose leaves are not green. Are there many? Do they make food? Students might bring a few leaves back to school to test.

You might want to follow this with another demonstration of the role of light in food making (Sec. 3-6), or elicit from students through reports a discussion of how nongreen plants get their food. For example, how do molds or mushrooms obtain food (Sec. 3-16)?

Green Plant Cells and Chloroplasts. Students may examine green leaves under the microscope to see what makes plants green. The water plant elodea is excellent for this purpose since its leaves are so thin. Mount a leaf in a drop of aquarium water on a clean slide and flatten the drop with a cover slip. Students should identify chloroplasts in the cells. In young leaves, you may find the cytoplasm streaming in the cells so that the chloroplasts are carried around the periphery of each cell.

You may want to have students compare these plant cells with some others that lack chloroplasts; for example, the thin membranes between the overlapping storage leaves in an onion bulb would show cells lacking chloroplasts.

Cell Arrangement: Cross Section of a Leaf. When students are studying some phase of photosynthesis there may be a need to examine a thin section of a leaf to see how the cells are arranged in layers.

Students may study prepared slides that have been purchased from a supply house (Sec. 18-3), or you may want youngsters to make freehand sections in this way: Cut a piece of a leaf, preferably a thick or succulent leaf to begin with, into half-inch pieces; drop these into a container of cold water. Then slit in half a fresh carrot that has been soaking in water, so that the carrot cells are turgid. Sandwich the piece of leaf between two halves of carrot and fasten with a rubber band. Or insert the piece of leaf between a slit made in elderberry pith, the pith of cornstalk, or balsa wood.

Now, with a sharp razor, cut thin, on-the-bias slices of the carrot or pith with the leaf between. Float the thin bits of leaves in cold water; transfer these by means of forceps into a drop of water on each of several slides, and apply cover slips. Under high power students may find a part of the section of a leaf thin enough to identify epidermal layers, palisade cells, and spongy tissue with air space interwoven between the cells. Which layers of cells are essential for food making?

3-6. Light and Food Making

Testing the role of sunlight in food making provides another chance for laboratory work to help students see how green plants are dependent on the sun's energy. Many kinds of thin-leaved plants may be used. Cover several leaves so that only a part of each leaf receives light. Use sheet cork cut into disks, carbon paper, or aluminum foil to cover part of each leaf (Fig. 3-3). Now place the plants in light (sunlight, or light from a 75-watt lamp placed about 2 feet away). Remind students that the plants should have been in the dark about two days previous to this experiment. Why?

Have students boil the leaves in water after the leaves have been in light for several hours. Then transfer them into warmed alcohol; wash the leaves in water. Next, immerse the leaves in dilute iodine solution (Sec. 18-1*o*). Students should be able to see the blackish areas where starch has been made since light penetrated the leaves and compare these with the light brown regions which were covered.

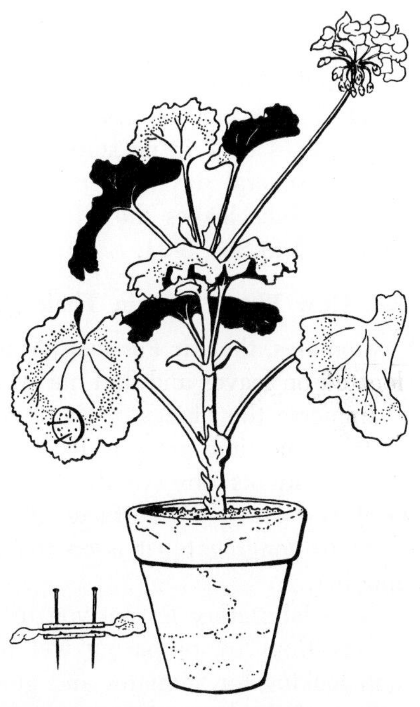

Fig. 3-3. Light is needed by green leaves to make starch. Apply a cork disk to both the top and the bottom of the leaf, and hold them together with pins.

3-7. Carbon Dioxide and Food Making

In Water Plants. When students learn the use of an indicator such as bromthymol blue, they can plan many effective demonstrations to show how plants absorb carbon dioxide in light or how both plants and animals give off carbon dioxide too (Sec. 3-13).

When bromthymol blue is acidified it turns from blue to yellow. Students may add 20 cubic centimeters of a 0.1 per cent stock solution of the indicator (Sec. 18-1*e*) to 50 cubic centimeters of the aquarium water in which elodea plants are growing. With a straw have students bubble exhaled air into the solution until the increase in carbon dioxide in the solution just turns it from blue to yellow. Now have students prepare several test tubes of this yellow solution. Into some add a sprig of elodea and let others stand without the plants. Students may also suggest that some test tubes containing the plants be covered over as additional controls.

Ask students to explain why the fluid in the test tubes in the light, containing elodea plants, turns back to blue.

Lack of Carbon Dioxide. You may want to show that a lack of carbon dioxide causes food making to be inhibited in green plants. Students may enclose under a bell jar a healthy geranium plant along with a beaker containing sticks or pellets of sodium or potassium hydroxide (handled with a forceps). Sodium hydroxide absorbs carbon dioxide (Sec. 7-8). Lubricate the bottom of the bell jar to make it airtight. Then set up a control in which the jar of sodium hydroxide is lacking. Students may figure out why both the control and the experimental plant should be in light for several hours. Students should also be reminded that the plants ought first to have been in the dark for several days so that their leaves contain no starch at the start of the demonstration.

After several days, when students test the leaves of both plants for starch, which leaves show less starch or no starch? Why? (Use the test described in Sec. 3-2).

3-8. How Plants Obtain Their Carbon Dioxide

Stomates, the Air Passages. Students may discover where stomates are located on leaves and find out what their role is.

Immerse the blades of the leaves to be examined in hot water while at the same time pressing the petioles of the leaves between the fingers. Have students observe the bubbles of gas that expand as a result of heat and leave the surfaces of the leaves. Note on which surface the bubbles congregate; it is on the surface where stomates are in greatest number.

As a laboratory lesson, you may want to have students confirm their observations by preparing wet mounts of the epidermis of the leaves and looking for stomates and guard cells.

Out of doors, students may examine the growth of some patches of grass. Why are they not found under trees? Where are the stomates of grass? Suggest that students take some blades back to the classroom for examination.

Stomates and Food Making. Select a geranium plant that has been in the dark for a 12-hour period and bring it to class. Have students apply a thin layer of petroleum jelly to the underside of each of several leaves.[1] (The stomates must be completely clogged to ensure success.) Then apply petroleum jelly to the upper layer of other leaves of the geranium plant. Place the plant in moderate sunlight for several hours. Later, when students have wiped off the petroleum jelly or dissolved it in ether or carbon tetrachloride, they may test the leaves for the presence of starch as in Sec. 3-2. Students should find that those parts of the leaves which had stomates clogged with petroleum jelly did not make starch, since carbon dioxide was lacking.

Role of Guard Cells. Strip off the lower epidermis of the leaf of a plant such as a geranium plant, *Bryophyllum*, *Asplenium*, or Boston fern that has been standing in bright sunlight for several hours. Mount the

[1] Red begonia, rubber plant, lily, nasturtium, and lilac are some typical examples of plants which, along with the geranium, have stomates in the lower epidermis.

thin strip in a drop of water and affix a cover slip. Locate the guard cells scattered throughout the epidermal cells. (Refer to a botany or biology textbook.) Under high power note the size of the stomate or opening between the two guard cells. Then have students place a drop of a 10 per cent glucose solution near the edge of the cover slip and draw off the water from the opposite side of the cover slip with filter paper. Look at the guard cells again. Can the students find that the stomates have closed as the guard cells lose their turgidity? Then some students may want to wet the tissue with tap water and watch for the change in turgor of the guard cells as they find the change in the size of the opening of the stomates.

3-9. Water and Food Making

This experiment might be performed with two healthy plants of the same kind in different flower pots. Conditions of light, soil, and temperature should be the same, but one plant should receive regular watering and the other none. What conclusion can be drawn about the necessity of water, not only for food making but for life itself?

WATER'S ROLE IN PLANT LIFE

3-10. How Plants Get Their Water

Some Physical Phenomena. To understand how plants obtain their moisture from the soil and how the soil holds its moisture, your students will need to know something about the forces of adhesion, cohesion, and capillary action.

Adhesion. Dip a pencil in water. Withdraw it. Ask students to notice the drops of water that cling to the pencil. Why doesn't all the water run off?

Cohesion. Students may note also that the liquid water sticks together in droplets.

Capillarity. Take a lump of sugar and dip one end of it in a colored liquid, or take a blotter and dip a corner of it in ink. In both cases the liquid rises above its original level by itself. Your students should become aware that this happens because of the adhesive attraction between molecules of the solid (sugar or blotter) and molecules of the liquid.

Take a narrow glass tube (a capillary tube if you have one) and dip it into colored water. Ask students to note how the water rises (adhesion of glass and water).

Capillary action plays a crucial part in plant life and, hence, in our own. First of all, water enriched with dissolved minerals in the moist soil several feet underground is raised by means of this action to the upper layers of the soil, where plants (once the water penetrates the root hairs) draw it up through ducts and thus receive nourishment. A porous soil is full of spaces which, if not broken up by cultivation, allow rapid evaporation of the soil water. Proper soil cultivation is an important conservation measure. Different kinds of soil have different water-holding capacities, the best ones holding water just long enough for the plants to obtain what they need.

How Much Water Do Plants Really Need to Reach Their Full Growth? Your students might write to Friends of the Land, 1368 North High St., Columbus, Ohio, for a reprint called *Why Grow a Jungle in Jersey?* In this article students will learn of the research on the amounts of water needed by plants for full growth conducted by Dr. C. Warren Thornthwaite, head of the Johns Hopkins University's Climatology Laboratory at Seabrook, New Jersey. The story of this research will no doubt suggest experiments that could be tried by your students.

Absorption of Water by Seeds (Imbibition). Stir a handful of dry seeds such as oats, peas, beans, or wheat into a paste made of plaster of paris. Pour the paste into a cardboard box about an inch in depth. When the plaster has set, peel off the cardboard and immerse the plaster block in water.

Students may watch how, because of capillarity, water is absorbed into spaces in the plaster and is thereby transported to the encased seeds. What happens when the seeds imbibe water? (The blocks should burst as the seeds swell.) This is called imbibition pressure.

You may show how much swelling occurs when seeds absorb quantities of water. Fill a glass containing water one-fourth full of dried peas or beans. Students may find after a few hours that the seeds almost fill the glass. How might this pressure of seeds aid in the formation of soil?

3-11. Rise of Water in Plant Ducts

Fibrovascular Bundles in Plants. In the spring or fall, you may want to go on a field trip to look for jewelweed (*Impatiens*) or similar clear-stemmed plants, which grow near water and swampy places. (Seeds or cultivated specimens may be purchased at many florist shops.) These plants may be studied in the field or students may collect specimens and preserve them in a solution made of equal parts of glycerin and 95 per cent alcohol.

Hold the stems up to the light and look for the bundles of conducting tubes, the fibrovascular bundles. Students may dissect out these ducts for examination.

You may want to have students place some of the fresh stems in a solution of red ink, or place a crisp piece of celery or a raw carrot or bean seedling in the same red solution. When students cut the stems or roots they should see the path where the red ink rose in the conducting tubes. Haven't the leaves turned a bit pink too? Cross sections made through a stem and leaf make it possible for students to examine the bundles themselves.

In addition, the seeds of jewelweed may be collected in the field, then subjected to freezing for two weeks in the freezing unit of a refrigerator. Then let the seeds dry out for two more weeks. Later the seeds may be planted in moist soil and the developing plants studied.

Using Radioactive Isotopes. Have you access to radioactive substances and a Geiger counter (Sec. 16-12)? Some school systems have made a start using radioisotopes in tracer studies with plants (including bacteria and molds) and goldfish. The valuable pamphlet of the Atomic Energy Commission, *Laboratory Experiments with Radioisotopes* (for high school science demonstrations) edited by Samuel Schenberg, 1953, will be particularly helpful. The pamphlet gives safety precautions in handling radioisotopes. Here are some examples of the kinds of work described in the booklet. Young tomato plants are tested with a Geiger counter. Then some are placed in jars of tap water; others are placed in jars of tap water to which 10 cubic centimeters of radioactive phosphorus 32 in the form of sodium phosphate, Na_3PO_4, has been added. These jars are shielded with lead foil. The leaves of the plants are tested every 10 minutes within the first hour for a trace of the isotope rising in the conducting tubes of the plants.

In another demonstration the rate at which radiophosphorus is removed from water by a goldfish is measured with a Geiger counter. The preparation of a radioautograph is also described using a fish skeleton, a leaf, and a colony of bacteria.

With this as a background, students may work out procedures for measuring the rate of absorption of minerals from fertilizers added to the soil. Furthermore, they might devise methods for tracing the path of food substances in the body. A study of the role of radioisotopes in medicine might follow. You may plan in advance to order some of these fine films: *The Atom and Biological Science* (Encyclopaedia Britannica Films), including a description of the role of tracers in studies of photosynthesis and in heredity; *Atoms and Agriculture* (Encyclopaedia Britannica Films), *The Atom and You, Atomic Greenhouse,* and several others describing peacetime uses of atomic energy (Atomic Energy Commission).

Lifting Power within the Plant. One way by which water rises in ducts to great heights in tall trees may be shown in this way. Cut off a healthy leaf shoot under water and insert it into rubber tubing. Into the open end of the rubber tubing, connect a piece of glass tubing, making an airtight connection. Now fill the glass tubing with water to the top, cover the end with one finger, and invert this into a container of mercury (Fig. 3-4). You may need to support the plant with a clamp and stand. Students should be able to see the rise of the mercury in the tube. What is the explanation? Compare this demonstration with the one to follow. (NOTE: Often this demonstration does not work, mainly because of the difficulty of making an airtight connection.)

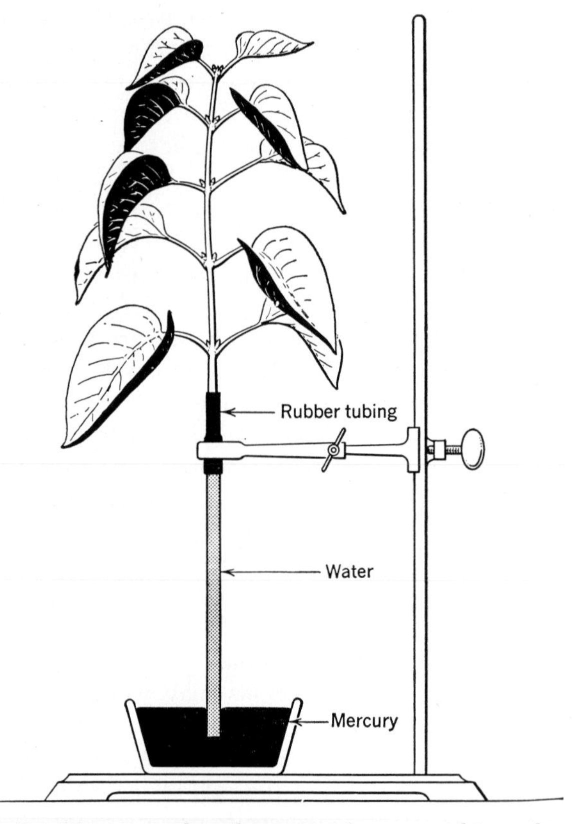

Fig. 3-4. Device used to show rise of water within a plant.

Effect of Root Pressure on Rise of Water. Another factor in the rise of water in stems may be shown in class or may be done out of doors. A section of glass tubing fitted to a short piece of rubber tubing is needed along with a ring stand and clamp. Several students can undertake the demonstration for the class. Have them cut off the stem of a plant close to the level of the soil. Quickly attach the rubber tubing to the rooted part of the stem. Clamp the glass tubing upright and pour a bit of water down the tubing so that the cut end of the stem is kept moist (Fig. 3-5). Within 15 minutes, students should see that water begins to rise in the glass tubing. A short section of rubber tubing is used so that after a short time the water may be seen through the glass tubing.

Study of Root Hairs. The increased surface for absorption of soil water afforded by root hairs may be studied by the class. Line a glass vial with wet blotting paper, and insert a few radish seeds between the glass and the blotter. Roots, root hairs, and shoots will be visible when the seeds germinate without removing the seeds or exposing them to air. Students may prepare vials for every member of the class so that each may study the fine root hairs with a hand lens.

Perhaps the class is ready to move ahead to a discussion of the diffusion of soluble materials through the root hair membranes.

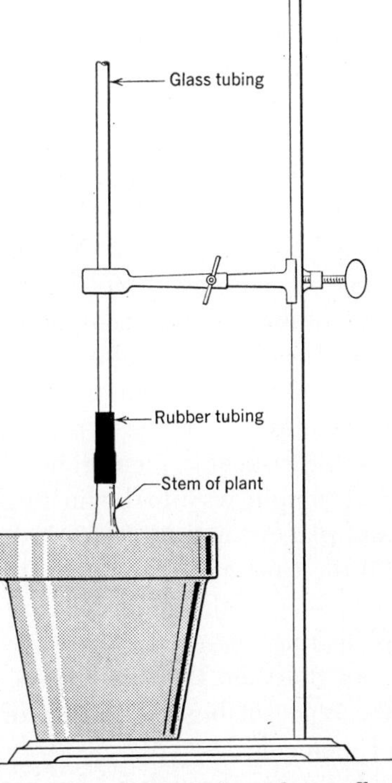

Fig. 3-5. Device used to show effect of root pressure in forcing the rise of water.

3-12. How Plants Get Their Mineral Nutrients

To understand diffusion of liquids, your students will need to learn something about solutions. How are valuable nutrients lost from the soil by leaching? What is the importance of solutions to animal life?

Solutions of Solids in Water. Do solids vary in their solubility in water? Ask students to place in separate test tubes exactly 1 gram each of very finely powdered (*a*) potassium chlorate, (*b*) hydrated copper sulfate, (*c*) barium sulfate, (*d*) calcium sulfate.

To each there is added 10 cubic centimeters of distilled water, and the test tubes well shaken. The mixtures are allowed to settle and the amount of undissolved solid noted. If in doubt whether any solid dissolves (as they will be in cases *c* and *d*), students may filter off 4 cubic centimeters of the liquid and evaporate this solution to dryness. What is the result? What is its significance? The solubilities of the four substances may be compared and the results checked with solubility charts and tables.

Students might also devise experiments to study the effects of temperature, fineness of powdering, and the amount of agitation or stirring.

You might also want to discuss diffusion as it relates to a solution.

The major reason why desert areas are not suitable for plant growth is, of course, lack of water. Plants receive their nourishment from minerals that go into solution in the water of the soil. A substance which does not dissolve cannot act as a nutrient.

"Dissolving" with Acids. Sometimes, of course, acid in the soil will do what water alone cannot do—dissolve an otherwise insoluble substance. Pour a little dilute acid onto a chip of marble or limestone in a test tube. Ask students to notice the effervescence. Allow the reaction to die down. Filter and evaporate the remaining liquid. Is there evidence that the acid "dissolved" some of the marble? What is the source of acid in the soil (Sec. 7-9)? You might want to discuss how in nature limestone is eaten away, forming caves, making the water hard, and supplying soluble calcium compounds to the soil.

Diffusion. How solutions get from the soil into the root hairs and roots of plants requires an understanding of diffusion—the motion of molecules from place to place, and particularly diffusion of water through a semipermeable membrane.

A simple way to begin might be to take a crystal of copper sulfate and place it in a large test tube or narrow bottle. Add water carefully to fill the tube and allow it to stand undisturbed for several days or longer. Notice how the blue coloring has spread upward. Ask students to explain this.

In diffusion there is always the greatest movement of molecules from the place of highest to that of the least concentration of the same kind of molecules.

Diffusion through a Membrane (color demonstration). When students ask questions about the movement of molecules from place to place you may want to show them this effective demonstration.

Fill a large-sized test tube with water and add about 5 cubic centimeters of phenolphthalein solution (Sec. 18-1*s*). This indicator is colorless but turns red when an alkali is added. Now spread a wet goldbeater's membrane or wet cellophane (not the kind that covers cigarette packs) across the mouth of the test tube and fasten this in place with a rubber band. Invert the test tube over a bottle of ammonium hydroxide.

Elicit from students an explanation of their observation of a swirl of red color rising within the test tube. You may want to correlate this observation with studies of diffusion of soluble materials through membranes of root hairs or membranes of villi in the intestine, or with the demonstrations described in the next paragraph.

That some kinds of molecules diffuse through membranes faster than others, building up pressures, can be shown in several ways. A small committee of students may try these two techniques which show how water is transported through membranes.

1. In the first technique, students may help each other in this way: Have one pour diluted molasses, glucose solution, honey, or corn sirup into the bowl of a thistle tube until the stem is filled, while the other student holds a finger to the bottom of the stem end of the thistle

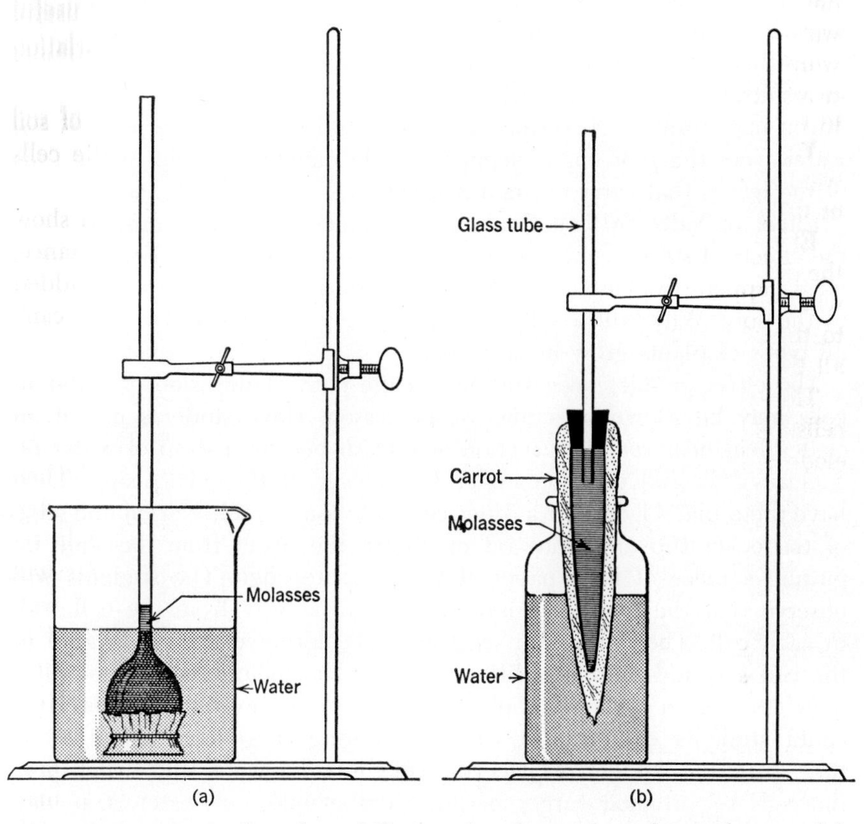

Fig. 3-6. Devices used to show diffusion of molasses through membranes. (*a*) Use of thistle tube covered with membrane; (*b*) use of scooped-out carrot.

tube. Then spread a wet membrane (goldbeater's or casing from a butcher) over the bowl and secure with a rubber band. After the bowl is immersed in a beaker of water (Fig. 3-6*a*), students should watch how long it takes for a column of molasses to rise in the stem. Mark the starting point with a wax pencil or a rubber band.

2. The second technique is a more ambitious one. Students may use an apple corer to remove a center section of a short, thick, fresh carrot.

This scooped-out part can then be filled with diluted molasses and a one-holed rubber stopper containing a length of glass tubing can be inserted into the carrot (Fig. 3-6*b*). This may need to be sealed with melted paraffin, as it should fit tightly. Here water enters cell membranes of the carrot tissue and must pass by diffusion from one cell to another until it passes into the "center" containing molasses. Students may watch how water rises in the tube. (Again, a caution: This may not work if the outer carrot "membrane" is not intact. But it may be useful to do this with several carrots and ask students to explain the variation in results.)

You may want to go further and have students trace the path of soil water from the root hairs (semipermeable membranes) up to the cells of the leaves that carry on food making.

Effect of Salts on Cell Contents. Sometimes you may want to show the effects of strong concentrations of salts on plant tissues. For instance, what happens to plants when high concentrations of fertilizers are added to the soil? Why will a salty soil destroy certain plants? Or, why can't all types of plants grow in salty soils?

The effect of salt concentrations on the path of diffusion of water in cells may be shown in a microscope lesson. Have students mount an elodea leaf or a very thin section of a fresh beet in a drop of water on a clean slide and examine under low power of the microscope. Then have them place 1 drop of a 5 per cent solution of table salt on one edge of the cover slip and draw off or absorb the water from the slide by putting a piece of filter paper at the opposite edge. The students will observe that the plasma membrane is drawn away from the cell wall in each cell. They may also see that the coloring matter is located in the cell sap and does not diffuse through the membrane as the water does. Ask for an explanation of the reason water leaves these cells. How could students demonstrate water reentering these cells? If there is time, have the students replace the cells in fresh water and watch how the cells regain their turgor because of the inflow of water. You may want to stress that the cell or plasma membrane, not the cell wall, controls diffusion of solutions into the cell.

In conservation practice, how does the effect of salt concentration of the soil affect the plants? How are radioisotopes used to find the answer (Sec. 3-11)? Why does a sprinkling of table salt in the soil around poison ivy plants destroy the plants?

3-13. Respiration in Plants

Oxidation of Living Cells. Your students will learn that respiration in plants, as well as in animals, consists of the oxidation of living cells.

Respiration is in one sense the opposite chemical reaction of photosynthesis (Sec. 3-1).

Where does the plant get the oxygen for respiration? Your students will recall that in the photosynthetic process oxygen is evolved, so that the plant gets some of its oxygen during the daylight hours in this way. From where does the plant get its oxygen supply at night?

You may want to discuss with your class the two phases in the metabolism of all organisms. In one phase, complex organic molecules are built up (as in photosynthesis). In the other, complex molecules are broken down (as in respiration).

Production of Carbon Dioxide by a Green Plant. To show that carbon dioxide is indeed a product of the respiration of plants, try these procedures:

This demonstration is the opposite of a technique used to show that water plants absorb carbon dioxide in photosynthesis (Sec. 3-7). Have several committees of students fill some test tubes with a 0.1 per cent solution of bromthymol blue (Sec. 18-1*e*), which has been added to aquarium water in the ratio of 2 to 5. Into each test tube insert a healthy sprig of elodea. Use other test tubes without plants as controls. Cover the test tubes with carbon paper or keep them in the dark for a few hours. Why does the indicator turn from blue to yellow? One student might exhale into a test tube of the indicator to show how exhaled air changes the indicator.

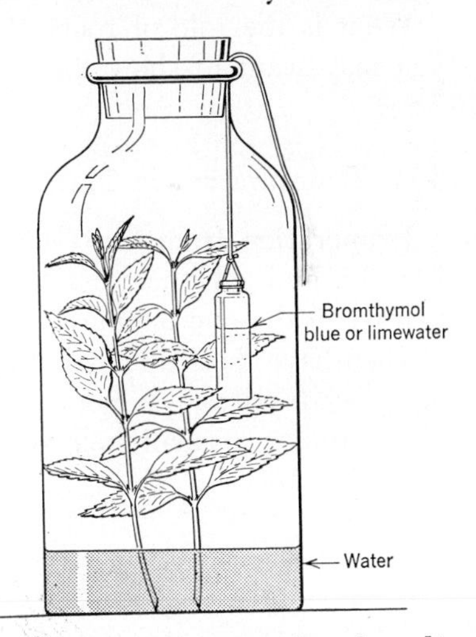

Fig. 3-7. Production of carbon dioxide by a green plant.

It may be possible to clarify the difference between photosynthesis and respiration in this way. Elicit from the class how it might be possible to get the yellow phase of the indicator changed back to blue again. The suggestion might be made that the test tubes need only to be kept in the light for a few hours. Then the carbon dioxide in the indicator would be absorbed by the green plants, changing the color from yellow back to blue again.

Here is another demonstration you might show to the class and ask them to explain (Fig. 3-7). Immerse the cut stalks of green plants in water in a jar or bottle large enough to hold these cuttings. In another jar have similar stalks but here remove the leaves from the cuttings.

Suspend a vial of bromthymol blue (Sec. 18-1*e*) or limewater (Sec. 18-1*n*) from the tightly fastened cork of the bottle. Keep the jars or bottles in the dark or cover them with a black cloth. Ask students why the bottles are in darkness. What process would go on faster in the light? Why is it so difficult to measure carbon dioxide production during the day? Students should recall that in photosynthesis large amounts of carbon dioxide are absorbed. In summary, have students describe the oxygen–carbon dioxide cycle in plants and animals.

Production of Carbon Dioxide by Roots. While this demonstration indicates that roots give off carbon dioxide, the significance of this small amount of carbonic acid in the process of soil formation might be stressed (Sec. 7-2).

Bromthymol blue may be used as an indicator here. When healthy growing plants are immersed by their roots in this solution the alkaline blue color of the indicator should soon change to yellow as the excretion of carbon dioxide continues. Your students might want to become acquainted with other indicators. Instead of bromthymol blue they might try blue litmus powder in solution (with just enough limewater added to make it a real blue), or phenolphthalein solution (Sec. 18-1*s*) (with a drop or two of sodium hydroxide solution added to change it from colorless to magenta).

What is the role of roots of plants in the formation of soil? Perhaps you may want to show the action of an acid on some limestone (Sec. 7-2).

3-14. Transpiration in Plants

Evaporation from the Leaves of Plants. Show the demonstration in Fig. 3-8 and ask the class to explain how drops of water got into the bell jar in the one demonstration and not in the control.

Then have the students repeat this for the next lesson. Place a handful of leaves from maple, geranium, *Sempervivum, Tradescantia,* or similar plants under a small bell jar. Let this stand in bright sunlight along

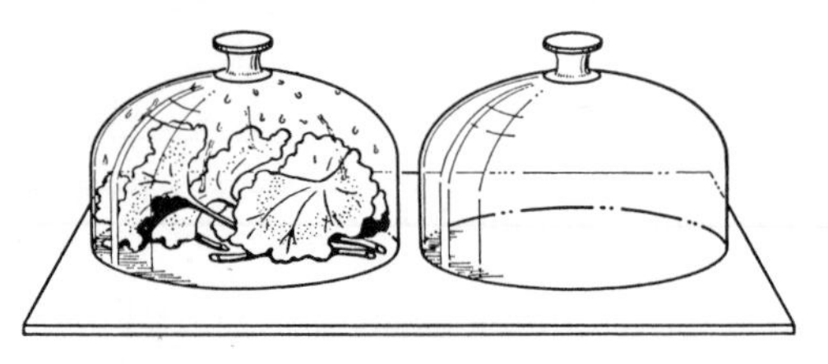

Fig. 3-8. Evaporation from leaves of plants. After a few hours under the jar, drops of moisture accumulate. The second bell jar serves as a control.

with a control consisting of a bell jar without plant cuttings or leaves. Students should see that within a half hour the inner surfaces of the bell jar will show a film of moisture as a result of the evaporation of water from leaves. This loss of excess water from the leaves is called transpiration.

You may prefer to use a whole plant enclosed within a bell jar. In this case, students should be reminded that the pot of soil should be wrapped in plastic or rubber sheeting or aluminum foil so that water may not evaporate from its surface. Under another bell jar students might place a wrapped pot containing soil only, as a control.

Transpiration from Upper and Lower Leaf Surfaces. Without detaching leaves from the plant, have students place a small square of blue cobalt chloride paper (Sec. 18-1*h*) on the upper and also on the lower surface of some leaves. Then fold a small strip of cellophane over the two surfaces of the leaves and hold in place with a paper clip (Fig. 3-9*a*). Have a student demonstrate how water applied to this indicator paper changes the color from blue to pink. Then heat the paper strip in a test tube. Notice how the paper turns blue again when moisture is removed. Students should be able to determine from their observations

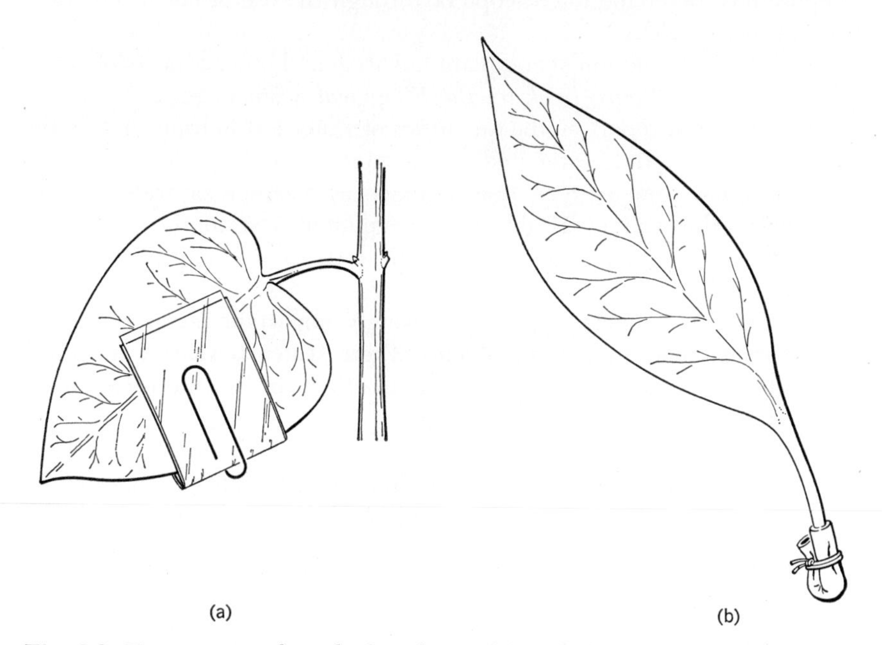

Fig. 3-9. Transpiration from leaf surfaces. (*a*) Cobalt chloride paper covered over with a sheet of cellophane on the upper and lower surfaces of the leaf; (*b*) preparation of leaf to determine its change of weight in transpiration.

which layer of the epidermis, the upper or the lower, releases more water in transpiration (through the stomates).

Loss of Weight during Transpiration. While students may know that water is lost from leaves in transpiration, you may want to make a quantitative study of this loss of water. For instance, students may give suggestions that lead into this kind of activity:

Take two leaves of some succulent plant—the rubber plant (*Ficus elastica*) is excellent for this purpose. These leaves should be about the same size. When the latex has stopped flowing, slip a 1-inch length of tight-fitting tubing over the stems and fasten with wire so that evaporation cannot take place from the petioles of the leaves (Fig. 3-9*b*).

Then students may weigh each leaf with its attached tubing and record their findings. Next, have them apply a thin coat of petroleum jelly to the upper surface of one leaf and to the lower surface of the other. After these leaves have been hanging in a dry room or out of doors for several hours, students may weigh both leaves again and compare the loss of weight due to transpired water. In the rubber plant the stomates are found on the lower epidermis; in other cases, a check may be made by examination of the upper and lower layers of epidermis under the microscope or through the use of cobalt chloride paper (Sec. 18-1*h*).

For still other experiments on plant nutrition and other aspects of plant physiology, see *A Sourcebook for the Biological Sciences* (Sec. 19-3*e*).

Students might report on the quantities of water lost in transpiration by particular plants. It is estimated, for instance, that a single corn plant may, on a hot summer day, lose as much as a gallon of water. What happens to this water? Might it be completely lost to the particular region where the plants grow? Do your students see why irrigation is considered a "consumptive" use of water?

Transpiration is becoming an increasingly important factor in watershed management. In certain regions where water is scarce, the type of vegetation planted has an appreciable effect on the preservation of the limited supply of water.

Students might be referred to studies being made by certain U.S. Forest Service experiment stations throughout the country. They might want to read *Vegetation and Watershed Management,* by E. A. Colman (The Ronald Press Company, New York, 1953), a research study sponsored by The Conservation Foundation.

RESPONSES OF PLANTS

3-15. Tropisms

When a plant grows, it responds to changes in environment and changes in moisture, light, etc. These responses often determine the plant's efficiency in its photosynthetic process.

An understanding of how different plants respond to stimuli of various sorts is indispensable to those interested in spurring the growth of plants and improving their quality. These are conservation measures of importance.

On a field trip (Sec. 18-5) planned around this study students may be asked to locate evidences of hydrotropism (response to water), or the growth of vines around trellises or other plants, revealing a thigmotropic response (response to touch).

Plants that may have fallen over, as corn plants often do, may show stems that have turned and grown upward again. Of course, the fact that roots are not found growing upward or stems growing into the soil is evidence of the responses to gravity: in roots, a positive response; in stems, a negative response. It may be that stems also respond positively to light.

Phototropism and Leaves. You may want to take a short field trip out of doors to see how leaves are arranged on the stems of plants in a mosaic. Have students observe examples of plants that show how each leaf is exposed to light. Notice that the leaves do not shade each other on a plant. Start a discussion as to the reasons why plants or seedlings do not grow well under a heavily shaded tree. What kind of underbrush is found in an evergreen woods? In a maple or oak forest?

This field trip may stimulate observations that can be verified by duplicating similar situations indoors, or follow this trip with a film such as *Reactions in Plants and Animals* (Encyclopaedia Britannica), or *Sensitivity of Plants* (Almanac).

In the classroom you may plan to set up examples of phototropism. Have students look for evidence of stems and leaves bending toward light.

Phototropism and Seedlings. Let a student sprinkle seedlings of radishes, oats, beans, or wheat on cheesecloth suspended over a tumbler of water. Allow some slack in the cheesecloth so that the roots of sprouting seedlings reach water before they dry out. Elicit from students a plan for checking the response of shoots to light.

You may already have on hand, for students to use, two small boxes, one of which has a slit to allow light to enter. Students should eventually observe in the experimental box how shoots grow toward light and how roots grow away from light (Fig. 3-10). Sometimes the shoots and roots grow at random in the control, the completely dark box.

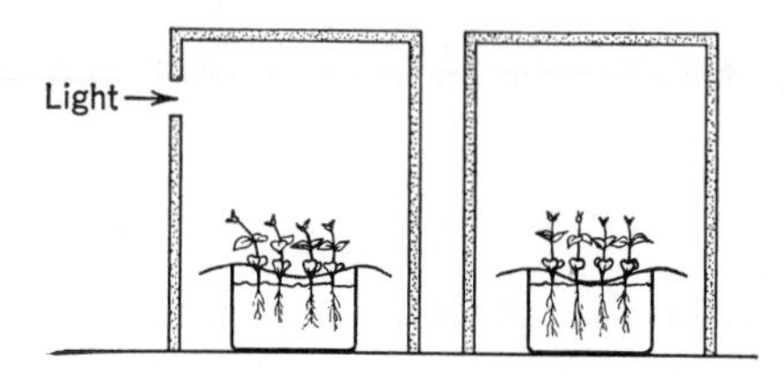

Fig. 3-10. A device used to show the response of shoots to light—phototropism.

You may want to refer to observations made on a field trip (Sec. 9-3) or to work on food making in plants (Sec. 3-1).

Geotropism and Stems. Bring to class the materials (test tubes, one-holed stoppers, clamps, and stand) to set up the demonstration in Fig. 3-11. *Tradescantia* responds rapidly and so, for example, does Begonia. You might use sprouting peas or beans, in which case you would have to fasten each seed to a one-holed stopper so that the root of each was immersed in water in the test tube. The growing shoots will respond quickly. Have students explain why the stems turn always upward.

Discuss with students the value to the plant of these responses. What survival value do they give the plants?

Geotropism and Roots. With germinating seeds such as those of radish or mustard, you may want to prepare a pocket garden. Place a sheet of moistened blotting paper upon a square of glass and arrange on it several sprouting seedlings so that their roots point in all directions. Then cover all this with another square of glass and hold these two squares together with rubber bands. Stand one side of the glass square in a container of water.

In a few days, when specific observations can be made, draw from students an explanation of the value of this positive response by roots to the stimulus of gravity. What happens if the "garden" is rotated to another position? Try it as a check.

Geotropism, Stems, and Roots. Soak some fast-growing seeds like radish or mustard for a period of 12 hours. (*Tradescantia* and Begonia are excellent for this demonstration, as they respond to light within an hour.) Line several test tubes with blotting paper and moisten the paper by pouring some water in and out of the tubes. Place several seeds between the glass and the moistened blotting paper so that their growth from day to day is visible to the class. Add a bit of water to the bottom of the test tubes from time to time to keep the blotters moist. You may want to seal the test tubes with melted paraffin so that the water will not drip out. Use wire or string to secure the test tubes to hooks or nails in class or laboratory. These will draw students' questions and give rise to an explanation of the survival value in the environment for plants that have these inherited patterns of responses.

Hydrotropism and Roots. Do roots of seeds grow at random or toward a source of water? Students may design a demonstration to show this example of hydrotropism. Have them prepare a pocket garden using two half-sections of blotting paper, for one must remain dry. Place soaked mustard or radish seeds in a row between the wet and dry

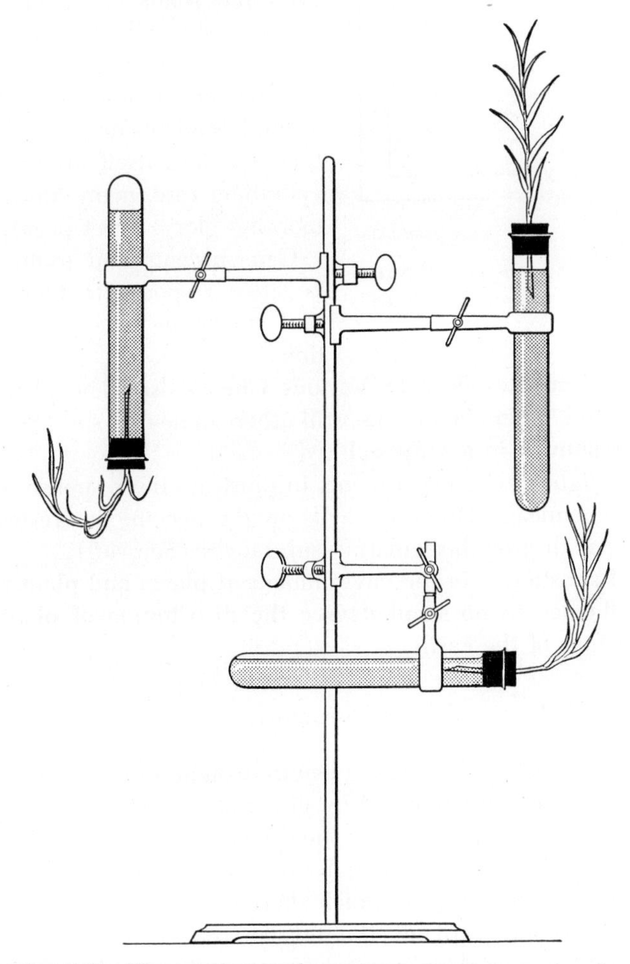
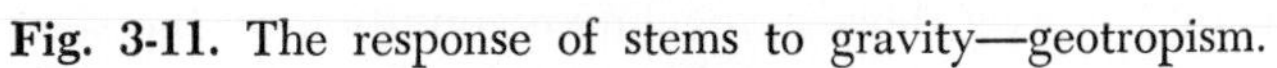

Fig. 3-11. The response of stems to gravity—geotropism.

blotters (Fig. 3-12). As the seeds grow, students should find that the roots turn and grow toward the blotter that has been kept moist.

Have another group of students sprinkle some of the same soaked radish seeds into a ball of wet sphagnum moss or a wet sponge. Hang this up somewhere in a darkened room or a dark container. In a short time students should see that shoots grow out but roots are not visible.

Why did the roots grow into the sponge or sphagnum? Students may ask why this was placed in the dark. Had it been left in the light, what stimulus might also have affected the growth of stems?

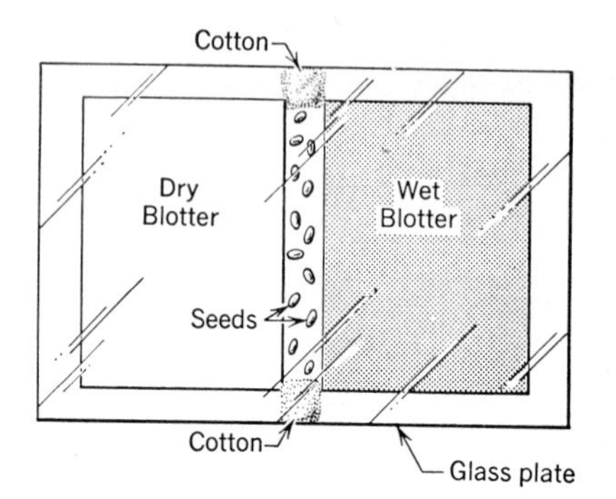

Fig. 3-12. A device to show the response of roots to water—hydrotropism.

Thigmotropism: Response of Tendrils and Roots to Touch. This response is shown by tendrils of climbing plants that grow toward an object they may touch and finally curve around. Students might study a plant that entwines itself around a trellis (climbing rose, many kinds of vine, morning glory, sweet peas).

Can students find examples of a negative response to touch? (Most root tips grow away from obstructions.

Chemotropism: Response to Various Chemicals. Some plants thrive well in acid soil, others in alkaline, still others in neutral soil (Sec. 7-9). A few species flourish in a salty soil.

Students might devise experiments to illustrate the responses of plants to various chemicals. Other students might become interested in experimenting with growth-regulating substances (Sec. 4-6).

Chemical substances in the environment of plants and plant reactions to them influence to no small degree the distribution of plant species over the surface of the earth.

3-16. Photoperiodism and Plant Structure

What is the effect of the relative length of light and darkness upon the character of the organs produced by growing plants?

In the Northern Hemisphere in June, when days are long and nights are short, many plants develop only vegetative structures (leaves and stems). Not until the days are much shorter are the reproductive structures formed. In other plants the reverse is true, reproduction being stimulated by the long days, a vegetative condition by the short.

Students might experiment with sets of plants in flower pots, exposing half of them to long illumination (either in sunlight or artificial light) while confining similar matched plants to short periods of light.

Typical "long day" plants (requiring a long day to flower) are hibiscus, red clover, timothy, and radish. Typical "short day" plants are cosmos, ragweed, bean, and tobacco. The length of the day seems to have little effect on some plants, such as the tomato.

4-2. What Happens When Seeds Germinate

How to Germinate Seeds. Students may want to know ways to germinate seeds for work with growth of seedlings (later in this section), for the study of hydroponics (Sec. 8-13), or for studies in respiration (Sec. 3-13). They may spread seeds over cheesecloth, which is stretched across a container of water. When a bit of slack is allowed in the cheesecloth, the material dips into the water and keeps the seeds moist. Students may find it suitable to impregnate the cheesecloth with paraffin so that the cloth does not sag so quickly. Many containers may be prepared in this way, or seeds may be germinated in excelsior, sawdust, sphagnum moss, moist sand, or blotting paper.

Some interesting experiments can be set up to show how to speed up the time of germination of seeds. Effects of soaking, freezing, soaking and freezing, etching the seed coat, etc., may be demonstrated.

Sterilizing Seed Surfaces. At times when seeds are prepared for germination, decay or luxuriant growths of molds overtake the seeds. This may be prevented (or reduced, at least) by sterilizing the surfaces of seeds, for they may be covered with spores. Students may immerse the seeds in a dilute formalin solution (Sec. 18-1*l*) for about 20 minutes. Similarly, a dilute solution of Clorox (1 part Clorox to 4 parts water) may be used. To what extent is the formation of mold on seeds a conservation problem? A student might bring in a report on "damping off," a constant detriment to forest seeding beds. Students might also experiment with the germination of moldy seeds in comparison with seeds that have had their surface sterilized.

Determination of the Quality of Seed. Obtain samples of a particular kind of crop seed. Students may examine these samples to determine how much foreign matter is present. They may also look for injured or substandard seeds. Next, students may run germination tests to determine the percentage of good seeds in a given sample.

Once these tests have been made and students are familiar with the purity and viability of the seeds they are investigating, it might be interesting to calculate the amount of seed that would be needed to plant an acre. (One would need to ascertain the established seeding practice.)

It would be possible to run these tests with seeds of different quality, to determine whether the least expensive seeds are really the cheapest, all factors considered.

Oxygen Consumption in Germinating Seeds. Here are two ways to show that air (more accurately oxygen) is used by germinating seeds.

Have students soak quantities of seeds, such as beans, oats, peas, or corn grains. Then pack a quantity of these seeds into a bottle and fill the remainder of the bottle with moist sand (Fig. 4-1); be sure to fill every crevice. Then they should seal the container with paraffin or petroleum jelly. Now they might set up another bottle in the same way, using the same number of seeds but filling the bottle full of moist, coarse sand so that there are air spaces. Leave this bottle open. Students may

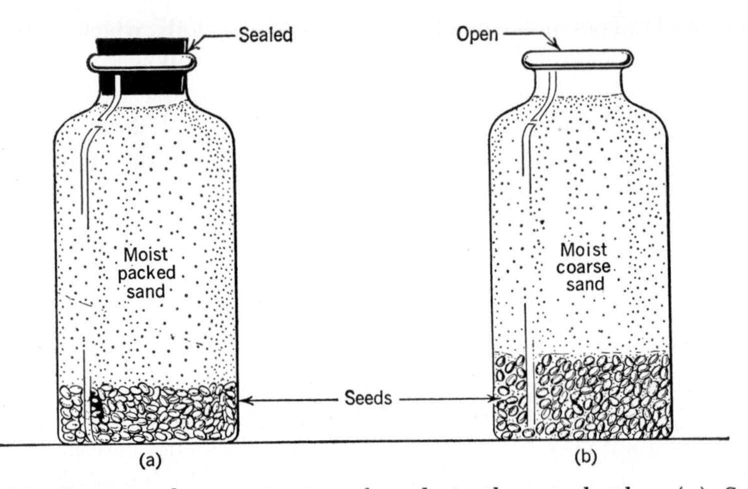

Fig. 4-1. Compare the germination of seeds in the two bottles. (*a*) Seeds packed in sand to top of sealed bottle; (*b*) same number of seeds packed loosely in coarse sand in open bottle.

compare the germination of seeds in both bottles after the bottles have been exposed to the same temperature conditions for a few days.

In a second method, students may test for the presence of oxygen in the bottle after a few days of growth of seedlings. Soak the seeds and fill several jars about one-third full of seeds. Close the jars and grease the surfaces. Include other bottles as controls in which killed seeds have been put. (Seeds may be killed by immersing them in 10 per cent formalin for a few hours.) After 24 hours, have students insert a glowing splint into each of the bottles. Does the glowing splint go out faster in any of the jars? Is there a difference in the amount of oxygen in the bottles containing living seeds when compared with the amount in the bottles of dead seeds?

What process is going on in germinating seeds for which oxygen is needed? In summary, for what purpose do both plants and animals need oxygen?

Production of Heat by Germinating Seeds. Students may devise a way to show that germinating seeds produce heat. For example, they may fill a pint-sized thermos bottle part full of germinating seeds such as beans, peas, corn grains, wheat, or oat seeds, letting them rest on a cushion of moist cotton. Then have the students insert a thermometer down into the mass of seeds by pushing it through a one-holed stopper. They may have to seal the thermometer in place with modeling clay and then tightly close the thermos bottle with this stopper (Fig. 4-2). Have students thought of preparing a control containing seedlings that have been killed in formalin?

Ask students to explain the rise in temperature. (There may be a slight increase in the temperature of the control also as a result of the generation of heat from bacterial decay.) What process is going on in these growing seedlings? What gas is used in the process? What gas is given off as waste?

When thermos bottles are not available, students may set up ordinary bottles in the same way. Then they may bury these bottles in a box of excelsior or sawdust. There may be a small loss of heat in this method, but effective differences should still prevail when the controls are compared with the experimental bottles.

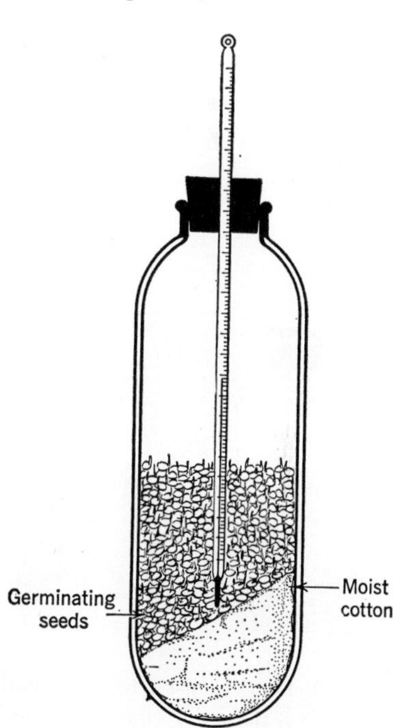

Fig. 4-2. Measuring heat produced by germinating seeds.

Production of Carbon Dioxide by Germinating Seeds. Prepare the apparatus shown in Fig. 4-3a. Have students explain the change in the color of the bromthymol blue from blue to yellow in the test tube, while another container with seeds killed in formalin is connected to a test tube containing indicator which has remained blue. (Limewater might be used instead of the bromthymol blue as an indicator. It turns milky in the presence of carbon dioxide.)

This technique might be tried instead: Wet cotton may be used to hold in place some germinating seeds that have been placed in the constricted end of a 100 cubic centimeter burette. When the burette is inverted into a large test tube of saturated potassium hydroxide solution (Fig. 4-3*b*), the level of the solution should be adjusted to the zero mark on the burette. (The solution is corrosive; handle with great care.) About 100 cubic centimeters of air should be trapped for contact with the seeds. The burette should be closed. Students may set up a control in which seeds are omitted or in which killed seeds are used. Have students watch the difference in the level of potassium hydroxide in the two burette tubes. This will be a crude measure of the carbon dioxide evolved in respiration, since potassium hydroxide absorbs the carbon dioxide in the tube.

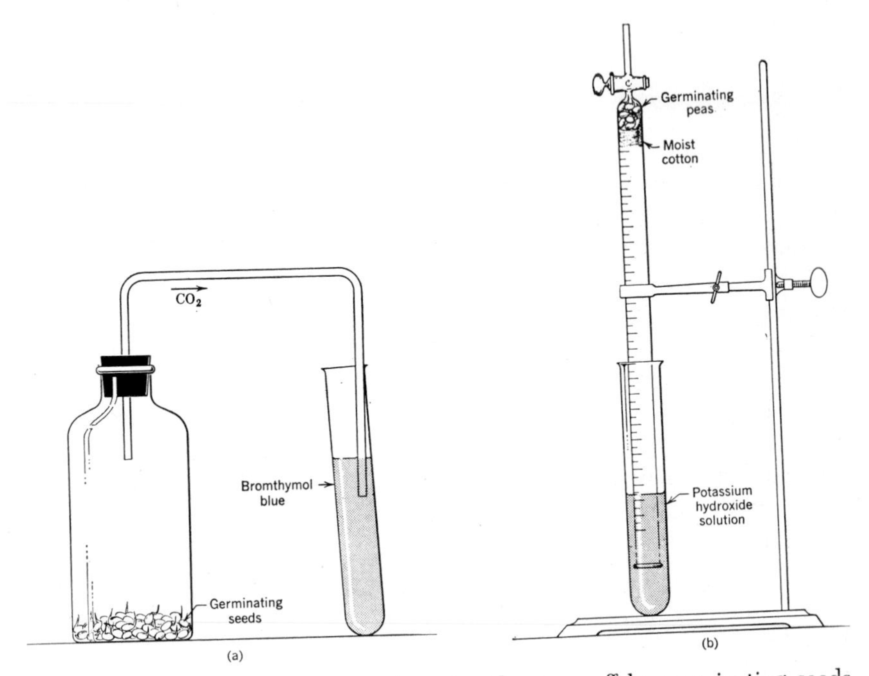

Fig. 4-3. Devices used to show carbon dioxide given off by germinating seeds. (*a*) Watch the color change in the liquid in the test tube; (*b*) watch the liquid level in the burette.

4-3. What Happens When Seeds Grow

Effect of Light on Growing Seedlings. Light seems necessary for the development of many of the supporting tissues as well as for photosynthesis. This may be shown in this way. Place several containers of germinating seedlings of beans or peas or oats in the light and keep other pots of seeds in the dark. After a week or more of this treatment, elicit from students an explanation of possible effects of light or lack of light on growth. How do they explain the yellowish, spindly plants and the long internodes? After a few days' exposure to light, what happens to the yellow, etiolated plants? Can students explain why there are few seedlings growing in the floor of a dense forest cover? How do spring flowers manage to survive in the woods? If you can arrange a field trip at this season students may note the adaptation of these delicate plants to their environment. Flowering and reproduction occur before the heavy shade of forest trees develops.

What is the advantage in survival value for a weed to germinate quickly? In germinating seeds, did students notice that some seedlings grew faster than others?

Perhaps this is also the time to show the film called *Plant Growth* (Encyclopaedia Britannica), or *Seeds and How They Grow* (William Cox Enterprises).

Antibiotics and the Growth of Seedlings. Although scientists have not yet found the explanation for the results, students might experiment with the use of penicillin or streptomycin on the rate of growth of seedlings. Controls would of course be needed.

Pattern of Growth. The pattern of growth in three dimensions may be traced in the growth of roots, leaves, and stems of germinating seedlings. As seeds germinate, groups of students may mark the roots of the seedlings with india ink. Blot each root dry and place a ruler alongside it; mark off ¼-inch lengths along the root with a toothpick dipped in the ink. You may want to show students how to make a graph of this growth. Then let the seeds continue to grow and have the students plot their findings on a graph.

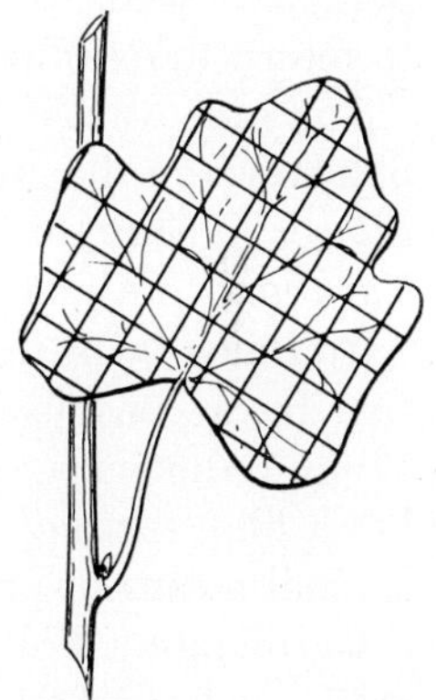

Fig. 4-4. Growth of a leaf. Notice the increase in size of the india-inked squares as the leaf grows. Is the growth uniform?

Another committee of students might mark the shoots of seedlings with india ink in a similar way. Oat seedlings are especially suitable for this work. Other committees of students may work with leaves, learning their growth pattern. Have them flatten a small leaf against a glass plate and mark off small rectangles with india ink (Fig. 4-4). Watch the change in the patterns of boxes each day. Other students might grow similar marked plants under different colored lights or different conditions of moisture or atmospheric pressure, to study environmental effects on growth of plants.

4-4. Propagation in Green Plants

The Flower, a Reproductive Organ. Where possible, students should learn the parts of flowers by studying living materials in the field. Plan a field trip around the school grounds, in a garden, meadow, or farm, and examine the parts of flowers belonging to different families of plants. In the spring students may examine forsythia, some cherry varieties, magnolia, dandelions, and possibly some flowering dogwood and maples. This may also develop into a lesson on evolutionary changes in plant families, from the primitive magnolia to the composite, the dandelion.

Students may learn that the colored parts of the dogwood are modified leaves. Look for the cluster of small flowers in the center.

Students may compare the number of stamens and pistils and count the petals. They may learn that flower parts occur in threes or fives or multiples of these numbers, and that this forms one way of classifying plants. Some students may try to key out some plants (Sec. 4-9).

Have students observe the pollen which rubs off on the finger; or with magnifying glasses examine the surface of the anthers and the stigmas. Use a few flowers to show the ovary and the ovules within the ovary.

Some students may try to germinate pollen grains; others may want to germinate seeds to show how any embryo plant develops (Sec. 4-2). Plan to return to examine these plants again when they have formed seeds.

You may want at this time to show a film that traces the development of a flower or the growth of a seed. Have you seen *Flowers at Work, From Flower to Fruit,* or *Seed Dispersal* (Encyclopaedia Britannica), or *Green Vagabonds* (Almanac)?

You may want to compare reproduction in seed plants with reproduction by a conspicuous alternation of generation as in ferns. The film, *Ferns* (Almanac), may be appropriate for this use. Indiana University has a film, *Asexual Reproduction,* that may be used for a comparison of asexual means of propagation with sexual means.

Germinating Pollen Grains. Some students may want to show pollen grains under the microscope for observation by the class. They may mount pollen grains of several different kinds of flowers in glycerin, water, or corn sirup, showing the different sculpturings that often are used in the identification of plants. A student may refer to R. P. Wodehouse, *Pollen Grains* (McGraw-Hill Book Company, Inc., 1935). The class should know that the motion they may see under the microscope is Brownian movement, a phenomenon in which molecules of the liquid bombard the light pollen grains.

Pollen grains of spermatophytes usually germinate in a sucrose (cane sugar) solution ranging in concentration between 2 and 10 per cent. Some students may try a technique described by D. A. Johansen in *Plant Microtechnique* (McGraw-Hill Book Company, Inc., 1940). Boil 0.5 grams of agar in 25 cubic centimeters of tap water. To this add 1 gram of sugar. After this solution cools to about 35°C, add 0.5 grams of powdered gelatin and stir until this is melted. Place the solution on a hot plate or in a water bath at 25°C to keep it fluid. Make a thin smear of the solution on a clean slide and sprinkle it with pollen grains. When several slides are made they should be kept in a moist chamber; then they do not need to be mounted with cover slips. Prepare a moist chamber by laying the slides across small Syracuse dishes containing water and cover these with a small bell jar. Students should experience some success when they use pollen grains of a tulip, sweet pea, lily, and daffodil.

Plastic "Flowers" for Bees. Interested students might get in touch with the USDA laboratory at Tucson, Arizona, to learn about the plastic "flowers" from which bees sip sirup (Fig. 4-5). Experiments are being conducted in the hope of solving such agricultural problems as the protection of bees against insecticides, the pollination of forage and fruit crops, and the finding of the correct location for beehives for honey production as well as pollination.

Fig. 4-5. Bee culture specialists at the Tucson, Arizona, laboratory of the Agricultural Research Service mark bees as they feed on sugar solution from this "artificial flower" so that they can determine how much of the sugar solution bees will take to the hive and how many trips they will make from hive to "flower" in any given period. (*USDA photo.*)

Artificial Pollination. As part of a study of heredity and reproduction, some students may try to pollinate begonia flowers or some similar plants. In this hybridization students might use a white-flowered begonia and cross it with a red-flowered one.

The flowers should be in the bud stage. Have students carefully open several flower buds and remove the unripe stamens with sharp scissors. Students should take care to wash the scissors in alcohol each time to avoid carrying foreign pollen to new flower buds. Next, cover these flower buds with small plastic bags until they are to be pollinated.

When the pollen is ripe, that is, when pollen grains can be seen on the anthers of those plants which are to contribute the pollen in this demonstration, remove the anthers and touch them to the surfaces of the stigmas on the flowers, which have been covered all this time. Quickly cover the flowers again and watch for the formation of seeds.

The seeds may be saved and planted in flats, and the hybrid plants should grow to produce the next generation. How do they compare in appearance with the parent plant?

Law of Segregation. Although the actual crossing of two plants, each hybrid for a trait such as height of plants, color of leaves in corn, or color of stems in sorghum, is usually not possible in class or even in a school greenhouse, students may grow the seeds resulting from such experimental crossings.

Seeds are available for purchase from many experimental agricultural stations, biological supply houses (Sec. 18-3), or college laboratories. After the seeds are soaked, they may be planted in paper cups of moist sand or soil, or in small flower pots. When students plant the seeds resulting from a cross of two hybrids, they should be able to count a 1:2:1 ratio or a 3:1 ratio when large numbers of seeds are planted. This ratio illustrates Mendel's law of segregation, which states that when two plants (hybrid for a trait) are crossed, this given inherited trait appears in the offspring in a double dose (pure) in 25 per cent of the cases; in 50 per cent of the offspring the trait is hybrid; in 25 per cent of the cases the recessive trait appears.

Hybrid Corn and Soil Conservation. The discovery of how to produce hybrid corn does not seem, at first glance, to have any particular relation to soil conservation. However, with an estimated increase in yield of 20 per cent for the United States as a result of the use of the hybrid variety, more corn can be produced on fewer acres, the poorer land can be retired to grass and tree crops, and more of the row crops can be rotated with grass and legumes. This would mean the better control of soil erosion and the increased fertility of the land. Acreage allotments and the soil bank were designed with these ends in view. Dr. D. F. Jones, the man who discovered how to produce the hybrid corn, has not usually been thought of as a conservationist, but actually he is one of first rank.

Vegetative Propagation. Students may recall from their experience the ways in which new plants may be grown without using seeds. In fact, they may bring examples of plants that illustrate the many kinds of vegetative propagation. In class or at home they may plant a leaf, a stem, or a root in a jar of water or moist sand. When some specimens are planted in the classroom students may watch their growth into new plants as the weeks go by. Since the genetic contents of the plants have not been changed, the new plants are similar, barring mutation, in color, quality, and other specific hereditary traits. Here are some examples of plants that students may prepare with success.

Tubers. Immerse a part of a white potato with two or three buds ("eyes") in water in a jar. Use toothpicks to prevent its slipping down farther into the water. Also try dahlia tubers.

Bulbs. Similarly, place an onion, daffodil, amaryllis or narcissus bulb in water or wet sand.

Fleshy Roots. Sweet potatoes, carrots, beets, or radishes may be prepared in water the same way. Watch how new shoots and young roots grow from the old storage root.

Rhizomes. Transplant Solomon's-seal, snake plants, Bermuda grass, or ferns in soil. Then have students look for new shoots arising from the underground storage stems.

Runners. Some aquarium plants such as *Vallisneria* may be used to show how horizontal stems touch the soil or sand and new shoots arise from the buried tip. These plants root easily and spread quickly in an aquarium tank. Spider plants (*Anthericum liliago*), or strawberry plants collected in season may be used also. Strawberry runners may be dried on cardboard, fastened with wire, and maintained for use throughout the year.

Stem Cuttings. Cuttings which include several nodes may be made of geranium, begonia, coleus, willow, pussy willow, tradescantia or forsythia. These should be put into water or moist sand until new roots grow. Then they may be planted in pots of light soil (three parts loam, one part sand, and one part humus).

Leaf Cuttings. Spread a leaf of a *Bryophyllum* plant upon moist sand and cover it with a square of glass so that the leaf touches the sand. Watch for the appearance of new plants in the notches of the leaves. Plant a 2-inch section of a *Sansevieria* leaf upright about an inch deep in moist sand. Also, try sedum and pepperonia.

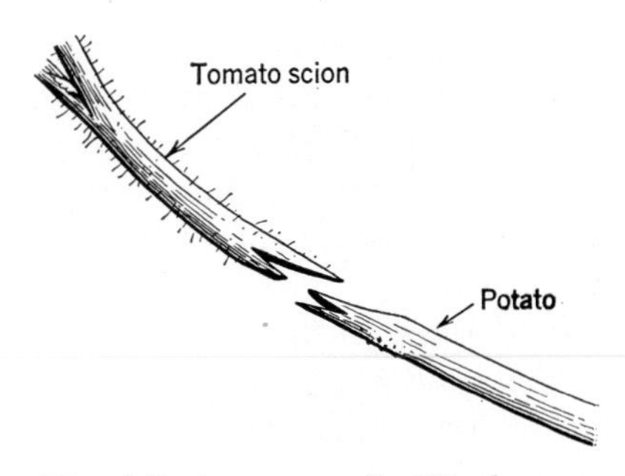

Fig. 4-6. A stem graft: Fit the cut scion to the rooted stock.

Grafting. Successful grafts may be made using two geranium plants, a potato plant and a tomato plant, or two cactus plants. White-flowering geranium scions may be grafted to red-flowering geranium stock. A thriving tomato plant may furnish healthy scions to graft onto a potato stock. Use only the simplest graft, a stem graft. Remove all leaves from the stock and the scion. Use a sharp, clean knife and place the two cut surfaces together so that the cambium layers grow together (Fig. 4-6). Bind with raffia or grafting tape and wax if needed. Some students may demonstrate how roses are grafted.

What is the advantage to the plant in reproduction by vegetative methods? What is the advantage to man? How does man propagate a new variation which seems favorable, such as a larger-sized fruit, or a seedless fruit? What would be the disadvantage to the plant if vegetative propagation were its only means of reproduction?

4-5. Propagation in Dependent Plants

Growing Bacteria. Students may start this experiment with three covered dishes partly filled with an agar gel (Sec. 18-1*a*). One dish may be opened and exposed to the air for several minutes before being closed. The second may be opened and a drop of water added before closing. To the third may be added a pinch of dust. All three dishes should be kept in a dark, warm place. Students may watch for colonies of bacteria. Students may report on the role of bacteria in the web of life.

Fungi and Conservation. Fungi are vitally connected with conservation. Man is continually fighting those that threaten him, his crops, his forests. On the other hand, certain fungi are essential to man's existence.

Spore Formation. What devices has a plant such as a fungus for effectively disseminating its spores? In general students are more familiar with seeds and their dispersal (Sec. 9-4). Students may bring to class specimens of bread molds (Sec. 3-16) or other molds growing on foods or leather, molds of wheat, rust, corn smut, or mushrooms and puffballs.

If your students can find a puffball, they may let it dry. Afterwards, the puffball may be squeezed and the clouds of countless spores observed.

Mount a bit of mold (or shake spores from a puffball into a drop of glycerin on a clean slide). After the spores have been examined under the microscope elicit from students the conditions needed for their growth. How do the fungi get their food (Sec. 3-17), since they cannot make their own? How do spores compare with seeds? What are the chances of variability among the offspring that develop from spores as compared with plants that grow from seeds (Sec. 4-9)? Students may report on the role of fungi in the decay of leaves in a forest. They may want to refer to *Soils and Men*, the USDA Yearbook (1938).

Making a Spore Print. Students may lay the umbrella-shaped cap of a mushroom right side up on a sheet of white paper. The cap should be covered for several hours with a bowl or glass tumbler to keep out the air. When the cover is removed and the mushroom cap lifted straight up, your students may note the pattern made by spores that have fallen from the mushroom. What does the pattern indicate?

Budding in Yeast Cells. How do plant cells which lack chlorophyll live and reproduce themselves? A demonstration of living, rapidly reproducing yeast cells may be examined under the microscope. This may be part of a class study of reproduction by asexual methods, or of fermentation, or a step in food chains and interrelationships among living things.

Students should prepare a culture by adding a bit of dried yeast to a small quantity of molasses which has been diluted with an equal volume of water. After the solution has been in a warm place for a few hours, mount a drop on a clean slide and examine it under the microscope. Under high power, students should find cells with buds, in fact, many cells clinging together forming a colony. A student might report on how yeast cells aid in wine making (Sec. 8-16, Alcohol from Sugar) or in breadmaking. Dough may be prepared from flour and water and placed in two containers. The dough in one container should have been mixed with yeast dissolved in water. Keep both containers in a warm place. What causes the increase in volume in one container of dough?

4-6. Controlling Plant Growth

Growth Regulators. There may be time for an extended study of the role of hormones in the life processes and growth of plants. Here are some experiments that might be tried.

Effect of Leaves on the Growth of Cuttings. Students may select some healthy cuttings of coleus, geranium, or other herbaceous plants. These should possess several internodes. Have students remove all the leaves from some cuttings; in other cuttings, remove only the lower leaves. Students might also try removing the terminal buds and growing tips in still other cuttings. Then plant all these cuttings in moist sand and keep them at the same temperature. Over the next few weeks what changes are evident? What may be the role of leaves in relation to growth of roots? Compare these regulators with hormones in the animal body.

How does a knowledge of these growth hormones explain the bending of leaves and stems toward light, i.e., phototropism (Sec. 3-15)? Some student might use a recent botany text for a report to the class about plant hormones.

Root-promoting Hormones. Students may try many experiments using growth-promoting hormones of plants. You may want to demonstrate this in class and ask for explanations later or have students carry on projects at home.

First, prepare flower pots in the following manner: Plug four small porous pots with corks and insert one each into larger flower pots that are filled with moist sand. The smaller pots, filled with water, will keep the sand in the larger pots moist.

Select four cuttings of begonia, coleus, geranium, or willow plants about 4 to 6 inches long. Dip the ends in water and then insert the wet ends of two of the plants into a powder containing a growth hormone. Hormodin, containing indolebutyric acid, Rootone, and Auxilin are only three among many trade products. Then shake the two twigs to remove the excess powder. Plant the four cuttings, the treated and untreated, in the separate, large flower pots of moist sand. Have students examine the cuttings after two or three weeks. They may also try cuttings of plants difficult to root such as yew, holly, and some kinds of privet.

Some students may look into the chapter, Plant Growth Regulators, in *Science in Farming*, the USDA Yearbook for 1943–1947 (pp. 256–266).

Jack-and-the-beanstalk Plants. Perhaps your students have read of the phenomenal growth of plants caused by the chemical, gibberellic acid (Fig. 4-7). Compounds containing this acid are now on the market and

Fig. 4-7. Both gloxinia plants were planted at the same time. The difference in growth is due to the plant growth stimulator called gibrel. Spray was applied to the plant on the left when the buds began to show. (*Merck & Company, Inc.*)

can be found in almost any store that sells garden supplies under such trade names as Plant-shoot, Miracell, Spurt, Plantstim, Boostaba, Tri-o-gen Gibrelin. If you have trouble finding any of these, you might write to Merck & Co., Inc. (Sec. 18-3), for their product gibrel, which is contained in the commercial growth stimulants.

Minute amounts of substances extracted from cocoanut milk, as well as from other nut milks, onions, and potatoes, also seem to have a stimulating effect on plant growth. Still other chemicals extracted from nut milks, as well as from onions and potatoes, serve as growth inhibitors. This is an area of research in which your students might participate.

REPRODUCTION AND GROWTH OF ANIMALS

4-7. Insects: A Study in Life Cycles

Insects have tremendous significance to conservation, both in the help they give and in the harm they do to other living things.

A statement like the above might start your students on a search for various kinds of beneficial insects (predators, scavengers, reducers of organic material, pollinators) and harmful ones (crop and tree destroyers, disease carriers, destroyers of grain and wood products, annoyers of man and animal).

In order to control insect pests, scientists need to study the life cycles of these insects.

Breeding Fruit Flies. The fruit fly is an excellent animal with which to study life cycles and heredity (Sec. 4-10), because many generations can be produced in a short time, each generation requiring only 10 to 14 days to develop.

Wild fruit flies can be collected, or they can be bought from some biological supply houses or from the Carnegie Institution, Washington, D.C.

Here is a simple technique for the breeding of fruit flies in small vials containing food:

Students may prepare a cornmeal-agar formula (Sec. 18-1*i*) or a banana mash. This should be streaked along the length of several clean slides and inserted into separate vials which can be covered with cotton after the flies have been introduced. These slides may be removed to examine eggs and larvae under the microscope, although a hand lens is adequate. Over a period of two weeks (at room temperature) the next generation of flies should appear.

If you wish to prepare regular stock cultures of *Drosophila*, this should be done in half-pint bottles (Fig. 4-8) containing food and agar.[1]

Life Cycle of a Fruit Fly: Complete Metamorphosis. Fruit flies produce eggs that can be examined by students for a study of the entire metamorphosis—egg, larva, pupa, and adult fly. These stages can be studied with the aid of hand lenses.

You may want to compare the development of a fruit fly showing complete metamorphosis with that of the praying mantis or grasshopper, which has an incomplete metamorphosis—egg, nymph, adult.

What advantage is there in knowing the stages in the life history of an insect? What are some ways man keeps insect pests in check? What are

[1] M. Demerec and B. P. Kaufmann, *Drosophila Guide*, 4th ed., Carnegie Institution, Washington, D.C., 1945.

checks and balances in nature? How does man often interfere with the balance of nature?

While many well-known texts or nature-study references deal with insect life, students may find the USDA Yearbook *Insects* (1952) a splendid reference describing all sorts of insects and their control.

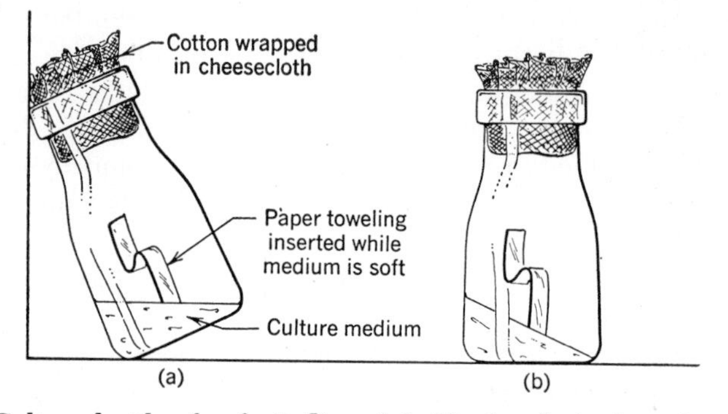

Fig. 4-8. Culture bottles for fruit flies. (*a*) The bottle is slanted to allow the soft medium to cool; (*b*) the medium has hardened and the bottle is ready for flies.

This is an admirable time for a film since the complete life history of an insect can be viewed all at one time. Have students seen *Bee City* (Almanac), *Your Enemy: Grasshopper* (available through state universities from the USDA), or *Life Cycle of the Mosquito* (Young America)?

4-8. A Study of Vertebrate Animals

Study of the vertebrates should increase the student's understanding of the interrelationships and interdependencies of all living things.

Frogs' Eggs and Sperms. To learn something of the vast number of sperms and eggs that a frog produces, students may dissect freshly killed frogs. In season they may collect these amphibians on field trips to nearby lakes or ponds. In the laboratory the frogs may be kept for short periods of time in a terrarium in which a pan of water is placed.

The frogs should be pithed in preparation for dissection, or they may be placed in a closed container with a wad of cotton soaked in chloroform (or ether).

Students may follow directions in a laboratory manual for dissecting animals. In general, the ventral surface of the animal is cut, exposing the underlying muscle layers, which must also be cut so that the internal organs become visible. In a female, the two ovaries often occupy most of the abdominal region, while in the male frog the testes are two small organs which lie near the kidneys.

Several students may prepare wet mounts of living sperm cells for all the students to examine under the microscope. In this way they may learn how small and how numerous sperm cells are in relation to the size and number of eggs produced by the female. This is a way to prepare such a wet mount:

In a small container such as a Syracuse dish, crush one testis of a freshly killed frog in physiological salt solution (Sec. 18-1*t*) or aquarium water. Use a scalpel and dissecting needles. Let this stand for a few minutes so that the sperm cells become active, for they are immobile in the testis. Use a medicine dropper to transfer a drop of this sperm suspension onto several clean slides and have students find the cells under the low and high power. Usually the cells need to be stained to see the tail or flagellum; this may be done by adding methylene blue stain (Sec. 18-1*p*); however, this stain kills the cells.

What material does a sperm cell contribute to the next generation? What does the egg contribute? What defenses do frogs have to avoid extinction in the web of life?

Frogs and Their Parasites. While the dissection of a freshly killed frog is an exciting experience in itself, the frog is excellent material to show some parasite-host relationships. The frog is host to many parasites that provide a wealth of living material for study. For instance, have students examine the lungs in strong light. Can they find small worms? They may mount lung tissue on a slide in a drop of physiological salt solution and tease it apart with dissecting needles. Then examine under low power of a microscope.

Have other students examine a part of the contents of the intestine. Mount bits of material from different regions, from the rectum up toward the stomach, in a drop of physiological salt solution. Perhaps students may find the large ciliated protozoan *Opalina*. *Nyctotherus*, another ciliate, may also be present in the rectum, but it does not seem to be parasitic since it also takes in solid particles.

As a special project, students may compare the parasitic forms in different species of frogs, or the parasites from frogs of different ecological backgrounds.

Developing Frogs' Eggs. On a class or small group field trip in the spring, students may come upon frogs' eggs or those of newts or toads. These may be kept in finger bowls or small aquariums where they may be studied over weeks as they develop and hatch into tadpoles.

When tadpoles are available, they should be fed chopped hard-boiled egg yolk once a week, along with pond weeds or aquarium plants in the water. Remove the egg yolk that is not consumed so that decay does not occur.

Which stage in the life history of an amphibian is the weakest, the most vulnerable stage? How have their eggs prevented amphibians from migrating great distances inland? What would happen to the amphibian population if their water supply evaporated? Would they be able to migrate, or would they die? What forms of life serve as food for amphibians? What forms of life hold amphibians in check?

Turtle Eggs. You may be able to find some turtle eggs near the shore of a lake or stream, even though the female turtle usually covers the eggs with sand or soft soil. Put three or four of the eggs in a box of moist sand and set them in the sunlight. Be sure to keep the sand moist so that the eggs will not dry out too much. As soon as the little turtles hatch, put them in a terrarium containing soil, water, and growing plants.

Living Chicken or Pigeon Embryos. You may wish to watch fertilized hen's or pigeon's eggs develop into chicks in the classroom. Buy a dozen

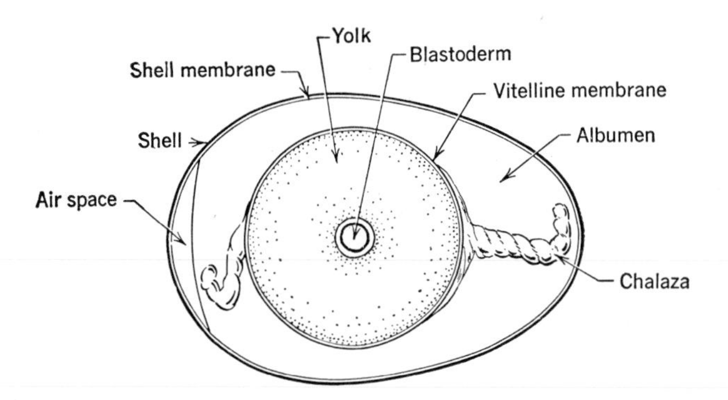

Fig. 4-9. Cross section of a fertilized chicken egg. (*By permission from J. W. Mavor, General Biology, 3d ed.* (*The Macmillan Company, New York, 1947.*)

fertilized eggs at a chicken farm. Eggs cannot be stored in the laboratory before incubation unless temperatures around 50°F (10 to 15°C) are obtainable.

Break an egg at the start of the experiment (Fig. 4-9). What is the function of the shell? Note the whitish spot on the yolk where the embryo will develop. What part do the yolk and the white play as the embryo develops?

Humidity and temperature must be rigidly controlled when the eggs are incubated. In an incubator a temperature of 100°F is needed. Students might calculate the degrees Centigrade (Sec. 18-2). Insert the bulb of a thermometer at the level of the eggs when you take a temperature reading, since there may be a difference of as much as 10 degrees in parts of the incubator. Pans of water should be included in the incubator so that the eggs do not dry out. Students should not wash the eggs since this would remove the protective film that reduces the chances of bacterial infection.

Students should be sure to turn the eggs each day to prevent the adhesion of membranes. There are two times you may expect a high mortality: when the embryos are 3 to 4 days old, and again just before hatching time.

Eggs that have been incubated for some 36 hours or more are the easiest to examine. Remove an egg from the incubator and hold it in one position for a few moments so that the heavier yolk sinks to the bottom and the developing embryo rotates to the surface. Now crack the egg on the edge of a finger bowl containing slightly warmed physiological salt solution (Sec. 18-1*t*). (Finger bowls of solution may be put in the incubator beforehand to reach just the right temperature.) The contents of the egg should be allowed to float into the saline solution so that the embryo is submerged by the liquid. Watch how the chick blastoderm, the beginning chick embryo, rotates to the top. When the embryos are older and more developed, you may have to pull the embryo portion around to the surface for examination.

With a hand lens or a binocular microscope students should be able to trace the development of the heart and blood vessels and the conspicuous brain formation. When the embryo is about 40 to 50 hours old the heartbeat may be seen; in fact, complete circulation of blood may be observed over the surface of the yolk. Watch the development of the embryo. On the twenty-first day the chick will peck its way out of the shell.

The chick need not be fed at once as it has enough food stored from the egg yolk to last for 48 hours. Keep it warm, and in 2 days it will be an active little chick, ready to feed itself.

Some students may want to compare development in the bird or amphibian with the development of the embryo of a mammal. Students may dissect a white rat, or the uterus of a pig may be purchased from a supply house (Sec. 18-3). In the uterus there are several embryos, and students may examine the arrangement of the placenta and the amnion.

Perhaps this is the opportunity to compare the relative number of eggs produced by all the vertebrate groups; for example, how do birds and mammals maintain their numbers in a given vicinity when they produce so few eggs? What are some of the reasons that fish and amphibians do not multiply beyond bounds but are kept in check?

Ecological questions like the above may help students to gain increasing awareness of the interrelationship binding all living things in a "web of life."

VARIATIONS IN LIVING THINGS

Emphasis may well be placed on the role played by variations in helping living things to adapt themselves and to flourish in a given environment.

4-9. Discovering Variations

Variations in Plant Growth. Along the edge of a lake or pond students might look for variations in the leaves of plants which are submerged compared with the leaves which grow above water. For example, the aquatic plant *Ranunculus fluitans* has broad leaves when growing on land but develops filamentous leaves when growing in water. Look for the deeply cleft leaves of the lower submerged parts of water marigold, *Bidens beckii,* while farther up on the stem portion, which is above water, the leaves are entire. Notice the arrow-shaped leaves of *Sagitarria sagittifolia* growing up in the air, while the submerged ones are thin, linear-shaped leaves. There are many transitional forms in the leaves too.

In fact, some of these variations, due to changes in some aspect of the environment, may be shown in class. Do students know how etiolated

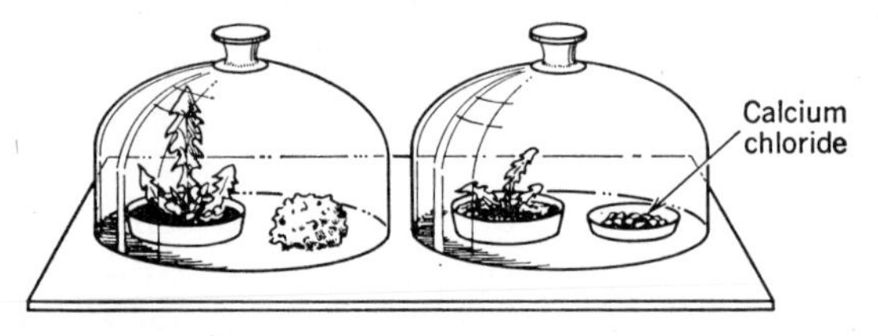

Fig. 4-10. Variations due to environment. (*a*) Plant grown in moist atmosphere; (*b*) plant grown in dry atmosphere.

seedlings look after growth in the dark (Sec. 3-15)? They may now examine the effect of the moisture-saturated atmosphere on the growth of herbaceous plants. Students may grow dandelion plants, *Sempervivum,* or similar plants in a moist terrarium (Sec. 9-5) or under a bell jar in which a wet sponge has been inserted. You may want to remind students to provide for controls with normal conditions of moisture and with dry conditions (Fig. 4-10). They may get a dry atmosphere by adding a dish of calcium chloride under the bell jar. Or they may add a container of concentrated sulfuric acid, but they should exercise more caution in this case.

After weeks of growth students may observe the long internodes and broad leaves of those plants grown in moisture, while in the dry condition the leaf blades should be smaller and the internodes shorter so that the plants are not so tall. At times you may find that dandelion leaves grown in moist conditions may be some 60 centimeters long while the "average" leaves under normal conditions may be about 15 centimeters long. Look for the thin cuticle on *Sempervivum* and its long, spindly appearance when grown in moist air.

Variations with a Species. While students may learn that similarities exist among different members of the same families of plants or between members of different phyla, they probably wonder about the differences too.

Are two peas in a pod alike? Are two snail shells? Students might collect large numbers of mollusk shells of one species at a beach at low tide. Can they find specimens of jingle shells, scallop shells, or oyster or mussel shells?

Other students might collect many leaves from one tree, or collect cones from one tree, or even bring a pound of pea pods to school. Some

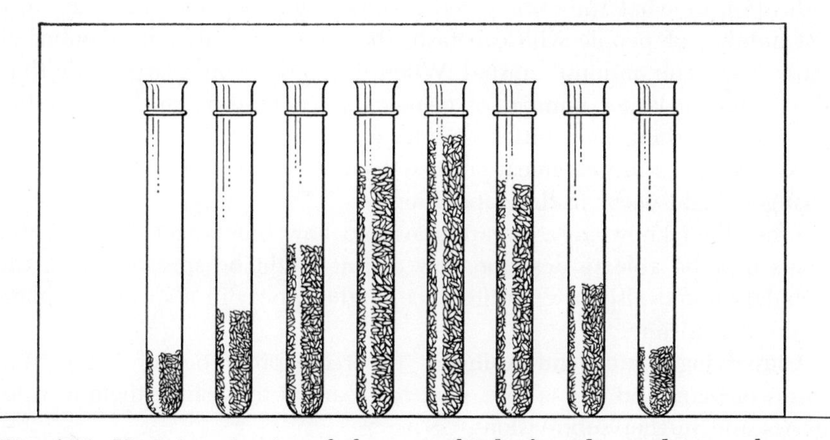

Fig. 4-11. Variations in size of the same kind of seed sorted into tubes according to length.

might examine a 6-inch square of clover and study variations in size and shape.

In each case described, students might measure the length of seeds, or the width of leaves, or the colorings of stripings of shells. Have students plan a display indicating the variations. They may prepare a chart of test tubes indicating different dimensions (Fig. 4-11), or use Riker mounts showing gradations in color of shells from light to dark, or no striations to many stripings. Have students explain these variations within members of the same species.

Variations among Human Beings (Quantitative). Suppose you ask the boys of a given age group to stand up in class. Have the rest of the class record as a graph the weight and height of the boys in that age group. Does the law of normal distribution hold for quantitative traits among boys and girls as well as for length of pine needles or mollusk shells?

Students may try to predict what the findings might be if they could plot on a graph the IQ of all the students in school or in their grade. Compare these quantitative variations with a qualitative variation such as ability to taste PTC paper, described in the next paragraph. At this time you may also want to show the film, *Heredity and Environment* (Coronet).

Variations among Human Beings (Qualitative). While many variations in human beings as well as in plants and animals differ in range and are called continuous or quantitative variations, there are some qualitative variations which students may investigate among themselves. Suppose they try this. Have schoolmates taste a small bit of PTC paper.[2] (To three out of ten persons it is tasteless.) It is better to give no preliminary indication of what the anticipated results might be. Students may tally the number of people who can taste the paper and also the number of those who taste nothing unusual. When this is done on a large scale they should find a larger number of tasters than nontasters since the ability to taste something sour, bitter, or salty is a dominant.

Now suppose this chemical possessed some kind of survival value, what changes might occur in the population?

From their knowledge of variations and how they affect changes, students may be able to describe how a trait might be spread among the population and also how a difference might appear in a species of plant or animal in time.

Classifying Plants and Animals. To create order out of the myriad forms of plant and animal life, man has learned to arrange them in categories and further subdivisions.

In discussing with students the need for order and the usefulness of classification, you may want to draw on their own experience. Perhaps there is a stamp collector in the group. He might explain how stamps are arranged by countries, years, special issues, etc.

Students might try to put certain plants or animals into broad categories and then into smaller groups.

Using a Key. Students, trying to sharpen their perception, might go out of doors to learn the nature and uses of a key in classifying and identifying plants or animals.

By beginning to pair off *single* obvious characteristics, students may go on to observe finer and finer differences. Thus they may begin to build their own simplified keys. Pocket field guides to trees, shrubs, wild flowers, insects, vertebrates, etc., are readily available and should become increasingly valuable as students learn to use them.

[2] This paper may be purchased from the American Genetic Association, 1507 M Street N.W., Washington, D.C. The chemical with which the paper has been impregnated is phenyl-thio-carbamide.

4-10. The Role of Heredity

An understanding of heredity is fundamental to propagating and breeding practices: Growing stronger and healthier plants and animals has an intimate bearing on conservation.

Genetics with Gumdrops. Genes may be represented with gumdrops. Toothpicks may be used to combine the genes into chromosomes (Fig. 4-12). These "gumdrop" chromosomes are useful in illustrating hybrids

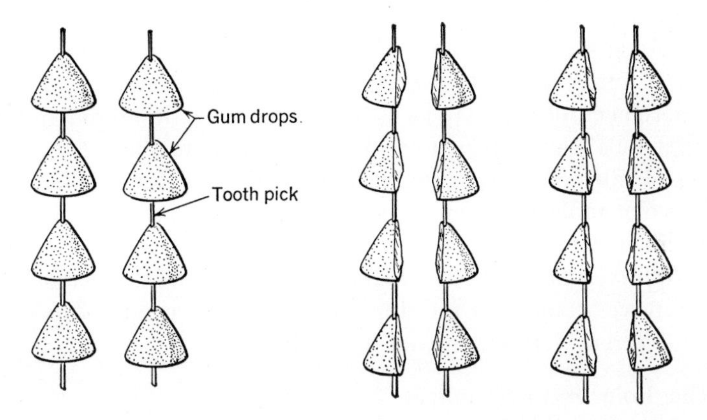

Fig. 4-12. Gumdrop genes and chromosomes. How chromosomes behave during mitosis and reduction division may be shown by splitting the gumdrops.

and pure strains. (Like-color gumdrops, pure; unlike, hybrid. Splitting the gumdrops is a mechanical means of splitting chromosomes. Emphasize that this is diagrammatic and is not essentially "accurate.")

Studying Genetics with Fruit Flies. Fruit flies, the standard "guinea pigs" of geneticists, have many easily discerned characteristics that students can observe from generation to generation. Mutations, too, can be easily developed through exposure to X rays or extreme temperatures. You will find material for a fine student project in the pamphlet, *Drosophila Guide*.[3]

Common Ancestry among Plants. The underlying pervasive objective in a study of interrelationships among plants and animals may be illustrated through a study of common ancestry. Families of plants share a pool of similar genes.

Have students soak seeds of several kinds of evergreens and plant these in moist sand or light soil. These seeds are slow to germinate, but the results are clear. For example, compare the first leaves of such seedlings

[3] Demerec and Kaufmann, *op. cit.*

as hemlock, spruce, pine, and arbor vitae. Ask the class why they are so similar. What does it mean when the differences appear later on?

The same work may be done with seeds that sprout faster. For instance, use seeds of monocotyledons such as corn, wheat, rye, oats, barley, and bluegrass. Observe the similarities in the first leaves. Or use dicot seeds, such as mustard, radish, lettuce, marigold, pepper, and tomato.

Common Ancestry among Animals. First show students how similar the development of members of one phylum is during the early stages. For example, students may study the developing egg masses of frogs, toads, and salamanders (Sec. 4-8). Why is the development so similar?

Then students might observe the development of many eggs: eggs of fish, eggs of birds, or some invertebrate eggs. These may be actual first-hand experiences, or this may be a time to trace full development through a film that tells a complete story. You may want to show *Life Cycle of the Frog* (United World), *Life Cycle of a Trout* (United World), *Sunfish* (Encyclopaedia Britannica), *Miracle of Life* (fertilization, cell division) (Almanac), *Development of the Chick* (United World), *Story of Human Reproduction* (McGraw-Hill), or *Human Development* (Bray).

How can we account for the similarities among the early stages of eggs of many different vertebrates and invertebrates?

4-11. The Role of Environment

Overproduction in Plants. Can you recall the number of seeds in the head of one sunflower? Or the number of seeds in a milkweed pod? Students might collect pine cones, pods of milkweeds, or clusters of seeds of *Ailanthus*, or pods of shepherd's purse. Each cone or pod might be put into an individual envelope. In class students may count the seeds as the cones or pods open.

In May count the seeds dropped from any seed tree like maple. Discuss the chances of survival. Also in May, look for new maple trees. They can be found growing in curbs where a little soil has collected, in broken street cracks, etc. Continue over a period to measure their rate of growth and note when they die. What makes them die?

What are the chances for each seed to survive? What devices to prevent overcrowding do many seeds have? Elicit from students a description of the role of variations among seedlings and plants (Sec. 4-9) in aiding them to establish themselves as fit, or adapted to a given environment.

Effects of Overcrowding of Seedlings. Knowing that plants and animals produce large numbers of seeds, of spores, of eggs and sperms, students may wonder what happens when many seeds, for example, fall in one area.

As a project at home or in school students may grow seedlings in many containers of the same size with this one difference. In one box plant ten seeds of the same kind, in another plant twenty seeds, in a third box plant thirty seeds, and so on. Also, have students plan to put ten seeds of mixed kinds such as beans, oats, radish, or corn grains into one box; in another box plant twenty seeds of different kinds together, and so on. All the boxes should be given the same conditions of temperature, water, light, and similar kinds of soil. Which seedlings germinate most rapidly? Within any one kind of seeds, are there seedlings that grow faster than others? Draw explanations from students as to which factors are due to heredity and which are probably due to environmental conditions. Which traits or factors have survival value for the individual plant? What devices do plants have for spreading their seeds? Students should be able to list several means of dispersal and collect specimens to show these devices.

At other times, you may want to vary this exercise by having students plant fifty seeds in each of several 2-inch flower pots and fifty seeds in each of several 4-inch flower pots. These demonstrations reveal variations in heredity and also the selective action of the environment.

Effects of Overcrowding in Flies. Students may plan a demonstration using fruit flies after they have discussed the results of the demonstrations with seedlings. Students may obtain culture bottles already prepared from a college laboratory or biological supply house, or they may prepare the culture medium described in *Drosophila Guide.*[4]

A simple demonstration involves the use of small vials and also half-pint bottles and quart-sized bottles containing the fruit-fly medium with a little yeast sprinkled over it. Into each of the containers introduce four pairs of wild-type flies. Students may count the number of flies in each sized container at the end of 2 weeks, 4 weeks, and 2 months. Flies need to be anesthetized if actual counts are to be made.

Overcrowding in Praying Mantes. If you can obtain an egg mass of praying mantes (they may be purchased, Sec. 18-3), place it in a small terrarium and keep it in a warm place. As the nymphs hatch out, provide a source of water by putting a small vial of water with a sponge inserted halfway down the vial into the tank. As nymphs grow, students may provide them with fruit flies.

Students may observe the daily decreases in the population of praying mantes as cannibalism and other effects of overcrowding occur. When the experiment is over, the mantes may be freed in a park or garden, for they are helpful insects.

Overproduction in Fish. Is it feasible to visit a fish hatchery? When such a field trip is planned, students may see how eggs are stripped from the female fish (Fig. 4-13) and fertilized. They may learn how these fertilized eggs are incubated. Why do these fish have a better chance for

[4] *Ibid.*

survival than those hatching out in a stream? What are some natural enemies of fish fry in a stream, which hold down the fish population? What would happen to the number of fish if their natural enemies were removed? Would this be beneficial to fish? To man? To the other plants and animals in the stream?

Fig. 4-13. Taking trout spawn at a fish trap. The spawn will be fertilized and taken to a fish cultural station at Yellowstone Park. (*Courtesy of E. P. Hadden, U.S. Fish and Wildlife Service.*)

In a fish hatchery, control of population is one of the most important management practices. This is because overcrowding produces stunted growth and loss of the fish crop.

Overcrowding of Human Beings. This might be the time to discuss with your class what happens when human beings must live and grow in overcrowded areas. Students will have plenty of examples of population pressures in our large and even in small cities—examples of schools "bursting at the seams," jammed traffic, poor living conditions. How about obtaining the film, *Baltimore Plan* (Encyclopaedia Britannica), to show what one community did to solve its slum problem?

You might also ask your students to project their thoughts to the end of the century, when it is estimated that the world population of

2½ billion will have doubled. Do we of today have any responsibility for the possible problems of the year 2000?

Population growth is a vital conservation problem and one that will seem real to students, particularly in crowded urban areas. Here is an opportunity to point up the effects of the pressure of an expanding population on our resource base. What kinds of solution might be sought?

Other Environmental Factors. You may want to discuss with your students other environmental factors such as lack of sunlight (Sec. 3-6), or lack of nutrients (Secs. 8-8 to 8-12), or change of habitat (Sec. 4-9). Students will gain a greater understanding of the role of environment as they become acquainted with the various kinds of biotic communities (Secs. 5-3 to 5-8).

As students learn the relations of migration, invasion, competition, and survival in the process of ecological succession, they may see that many conservation practices are based upon the applications of the principles of ecology.

4-12. Interaction of Heredity and Environment

In Green Plants. In advance of this lesson students might grow seeds in the dark. They should notice that chlorophyll does not develop in the dark. Remove some of the containers of seedlings into the light. What observations can students make within a few days?

Since the plants develop chlorophyll in light, they do have the ability genetically to produce green coloring matter. However, light is also needed; the appearance of chlorophyll is due to the interaction of genes operating in a specific environment.

How Have Adaptations Developed? Students may examine the protective coloration and mimicry among insects, the blending form and color patterns of birds, amphibia, fish, and mammals against the variety of environmental conditions. They may examine special adaptations of plants such as spines, thick cuticle, burred fruits, explosive fruits, and winged seeds. How may these adaptations have developed?

Students may want to describe the adaptations that special animals have in order to obtain their food, for example, the kinds of teeth in mammals, the beaks of birds, and the claws of many more animals, as well as examples of camouflage in color and shape. Have they seen the films called *Camouflage in Nature: Through Form and Color Matching* and *Through Pattern Matching* (Coronet)?

After a discussion of how traits are inherited and which characteristics are fortuitous yet play little part in survival, you may want to lead into the changes that have taken place in interrelationships in time as well as in geographic regions. As the environment has changed in time, how have plants and animals evolved so that they adapt to a given environment? What do we know of plants and animals in the past? If some plants had had a thicker cuticle, might they have developed some survival value if the environment became drier in time?

Upsetting the Balance. What happens when a given plant or animal species is transferred to a new region?

In a library lesson, groups of students may prepare reports to the class on the history of plant and animal pests such as the gypsy moth, English sparrow, tussock moth, Japanese beetle, Scotch thistle. These are only a few examples. How were they introduced into a new area? Why weren't these plants and animals considered pests in their former territory? Elicit the fact that the place where a plant or animal exists may not necessarily have the optimum conditions for growth and reproduction. What is a natural enemy? How has man upset the balance in each case described? In what other ways may the balance in nature be upset (Sec. 8-7)?

In another lesson, a second committee of students might report on their library research of ways in which man meddles with and upsets the balance in nature.

Have students report on the effects of these common practices of man: (*a*) cutting down trees indiscriminately; (*b*) overgrazing land; (*c*) overcultivating land; (*d*) offering bounties for killing off chicken hawks or other wildlife; (*e*) polluting rivers and streams with sewage or factory waste.

How can man correct the harm resulting from these practices and restore balanced interrelationships among plants and animals?

5

Water Masses and Living Things

When students understand what it is that makes a healthy community of living things, they will be on their way to a greater appreciation of the problems of maintaining a balance in the environment. This chapter is concerned with the relationship of some living things to their water habitats (aquariums, streams, ponds, lakes).

There is a section, too, on the sea—its teeming life, its mineral resources and the "mining" of them. As resources of the land begin to dwindle, scientists turn more and more to the vast, unexplored, undeveloped, and seemingly inexhaustible riches of the sea.

A STUDY OF BIOTIC COMMUNITIES

5-1. Ways to Begin

All living things, far from being independent entities, cannot exist without other living things. All living things, including man, depend on a variety of factors in the environment of which they are a part.

You may want to begin this study of biomes, or major communities of living things, with a field trip to a pond or lake (Sec. 5-2). At other times you may want to start with an aquarium in the classroom (Sec. 5-9).

If we expand the aquarium to represent a lake, or an ocean, can students describe food chains which probably exist in the lake or the ocean? What might happen if one kind of organism disappeared?

You may do the same with a terrarium (Sec. 9-5). It might be a swampy area, or a forest floor, or a desert area. What organisms might occupy each as a community or a biome?

What succession of living things might you expect to find in an area becoming wet or becoming exceedingly dry? Suppose it were a burned-over area of land, what kinds of living things would invade such a region?

What adaptations for survival in these areas must plants and animals have? What are some of their features which play no part at all in survival value?

This might be a time to show the films, *The Strand Grows* and *This Vital Earth,* produced by The Conservation Foundation, or *How Nature Protects Animals.* All these films are distributed by Encyclopaedia Britannica. The Soil Conservation Service and the Fish and Wildlife Service provide many free films that you may obtain for the price of postage (Sec. 19-10).

5-2. Field Trips

Field trips do not need to be long or distant to be meaningful. Sometimes the most successful are those of a few minutes' duration right on the school grounds, to seek the answer to a single question or to observe one object or phenomenon.

In planning any kind of a field trip these suggestions may prove helpful:

Advance Preparation for the Trip. Each trip should have a definite objective and it is wise for the teacher to pay a visit to the locale beforehand. Plans ought to be carefully formulated with the class in advance of the trip, so that students will not only understand the purpose of the trip but will know details of departure and return time, appropriate clothing, equipment needed, and safety precautions.

Conducting the Trip. Comments on observations should be simple and adapted to the group level. Questions are of course to be encouraged, and the answers "taught" rather than "told," by further exploration and discovery. Be sure that important points are often repeated or stressed in various ways. Be alert for the unexpected and make the most of it.

Conservation concepts will become apparent and may be discussed as students begin to see the interrelationships of the plants and animals in their environment.

Summary of the Trip. You may want to have students summarize the findings of the trip right on the spot, by an informal gathering. Otherwise the summary might be made soon after returning from the trip. For added field trip suggestions see Sec. 18-5.

5-3. A Pond or Lake

A Field Study. Students might go on a field trip to examine the physical features of a pond or lake and the kinds of plant and animal relationships that exist in such an ecological community. For example, they might draw in a notebook a contour map of the pond indicating its elevation in relation to the land, the depth of the water, and the area of the pond. Direct them to examine the type of bed (mud, hard clay, gravel, flat rock, etc.). Students should also record the temperature of the water, its turbidity or clarity. What is the source of the water supply—the possibilities of pollution? What kinds of plants are in the pond? Are they floating plants or submerged weeds?

Then have students diagram a cross section of the pond. Have them draw at the proper level in the pond the kinds of plants and animals that they find and label them; for example, under plants: floating or submerged, seed plants or algae. If the plants are algae, have the students try to identify them as microscopic kinds or free-floating types. Use such animal and plant guides as Ann Morgan's *Fieldbook of Ponds and Streams* (G. P. Putnam's Sons, New York, 1930), or James G. Needham and Paul R. Needham's *A Guide to the Study of Fresh Water Biology* (Cornell University Press, Ithaca, N.Y., 1953), or R. W. Pennak's *Fresh Water Invertebrates of the United States* (The Ronald Press Company, New York, 1953).

Have students indicate the kinds of animal forms and their abundance in the pond. Have them collect samples in a dip net. The net should have a strong wire frame 6 or 8 inches in diameter, strong netting of either bobbinet or nylon, and a handle about 3 feet long.

What are the kinds of animals—vertebrate or invertebrate? Are they free-swimming forms? Do any move on the surface or lie in the surface film? Which forms are found on the vegetation in the pond? Are they attached or tube dwellers? Which are bottom dwellers? Which of these burrow or form tubes?

What's on the Bottom?[1] To learn something about plants and animals dwelling on the bottom of a pond or stream, a simple dredge is helpful. Students might tie a burlap or lighter-weight bag to a rake as shown in Fig. 5-1. As the rake touches bottom and is drawn toward the operator, loosened plants and animals will enter the bag. Students might compare the differences in the living things found in a stream bottom and a pond bottom. What are the environmental factors that might be responsible for the differences?

Yearly Observations. As a long-term project some students may want to record yearly observations of the same pond. Over a period of five years what kinds of changes have occurred?

What would happen if the green plants in the water disappeared?

[1] We are indebted to *Conservation: A Handbook for Teachers* (Sec. 19-2*b*) for most of the techniques in this section and the next.

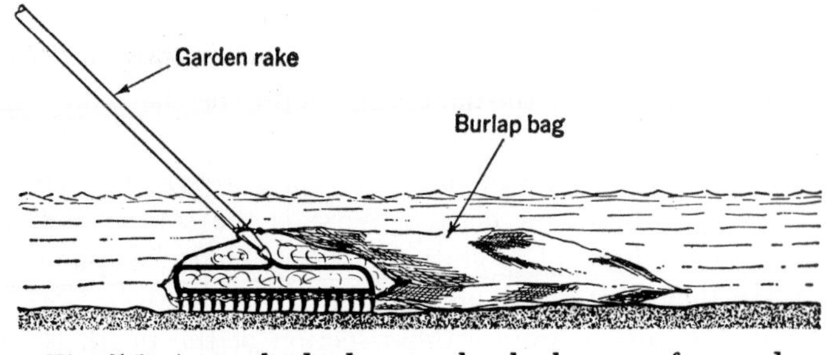

Fig. 5-1. A simple dredge to rake the bottom of a pond.

Or an animal form vanished? Would these changes affect the balance or web of life in the pond?

Under what conditions would the lake or pond become a swamp area? What succession of plants and animals would follow as swamps formed (Sec. 5-5)? Ultimately, what might happen to a swamp area? What kinds of plants and animals might invade this new bog area (Sec. 5-6)?

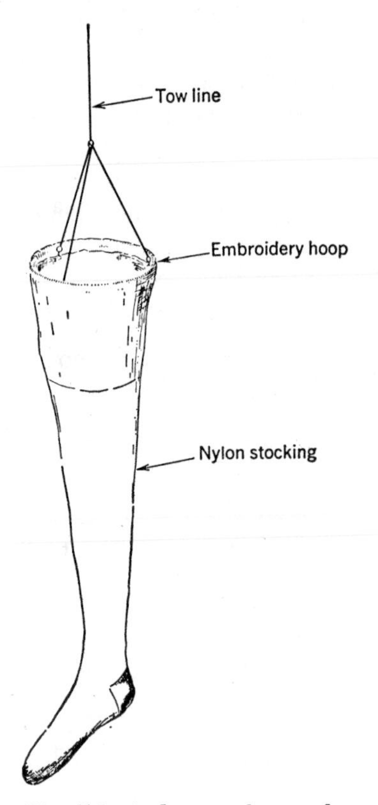

Fig. 5-2. A dip net for catching plankton.

A Geological Report. Some students may report on tremendous changes on the face of the earth throughout time, indicating how land areas now existing were once under water. They may explain how water builds new land and also wears away and transports soil to new areas.

Study of Plankton. Students may collect floating surface plankton, the minute plant and animal life from a lake, by using a dip net or a long-handled net, or they may make a special "net," for which they will need a wire hoop (an embroidery hoop or heavy wire), a discarded nylon stocking, and some string (Fig. 5-2). The hoop may have to be weighted in order to submerge the stocking. After the net is drawn through the water for a few minutes, it may be hauled in and the stocking turned inside out over a white enamel dish with a little water in it. Students may see the activity of such animals as crustacea (copepods, cladocerans, and so forth). Samples of water examined under a microscope should reveal a variety of protozoa, rotifers, and many eggs of animals. Among plant members these are likely to be found in plankton: algae of various types including desmids and diatoms.

Is the pond water clear or murky as samples are taken? Is any of the murkiness due to silt or clay, or is it due to millions of tiny plants and animals growing in the water? These latter form the first step in the complex food chains of aquatic animals.

5-4. A Stream

Life in a Stream. Students may use the pattern of directions given for the study of a pond (Sec. 5-3). In addition they might indicate the velocity of the water by measuring the rate of progress of a floating stick. The kinds of living things are quite different in slow-moving and in rapid streams. A fast-moving stream, for example, has a different oxygen supply, and therefore contains only certain plants and animals. Are they more active than those living in a slow-moving stream? Which organisms live in the stream's current and which abide on the banks or edges of the stream?

Students should use dip nets and white basins for examination of the materials they have collected (remembering also to turn over submerged rocks). Hand lenses as well as jars and vials in which to keep specimens will be needed. Students will probably be most successful in capturing organisms from slow-moving streams and transferring them to aquariums (Sec. 5-9) in the classroom.

A Sunny and Shady Stream. It might be interesting for students to collect plant and animal life from two sections of the same stream—a sunny and a shady portion. Are there differences in the number and kinds of living things in the two sections? How do the temperatures compare?

Water temperature is vital to fish habitats. One of the differences between warm and cold water is the variation in oxygen content (Sec. 6-1). Some kinds of fish cannot survive in warm streams with low oxygen content. Temperature condition is not, however, the sole determinant of oxygen content. Organic matter in polluted water, for instance, uses up much of the dissolved oxygen (Sec. 6-3).

A Closed Food Chain: Interdependence of a Parasite and Two Hosts. When your class is studying food chains in a stream, you might ask students to report on the closed food chain, which occurs among parasites and their hosts. For example, someone may describe the life cycle of the bass tapeworm. These tapeworms mature in the spring when bass reach their spawning grounds. Here small copepods (forms like cyclops) ingest the eggs of the tapeworms. These crustacea in turn serve as food for the game fish. The tapeworms live in the intestines and invade the liver and reproductive organs, therby lowering the fertility of the fish.

Some students may refer to textbooks in college zoology such as *College Zoology* by G. W. Hunter and G. W. Hunter, Jr. (W. B. Saunders Company, Philadelphia, 1949) or A. C. Chandler's *Introduction to Human Parasitology* (9th ed., John Wiley & Sons, Inc., New York, 1955). Ask them to describe the life cycle of certain liver flukes.

Students should be able to explain why parasites produce such large numbers of eggs. What would happen if the parasite destroyed its host?

5-5. A Swamp

Insectivorous Plants. In a swamp area students may find green plants with special adaptations for catching insects. These plants in some way receive nitrogenous substances for use in their metabolism.

Some of the plants that students may find are sundew, pitcher plant, and Venus's flytrap (Fig. 5-3). Students should observe how the leaves

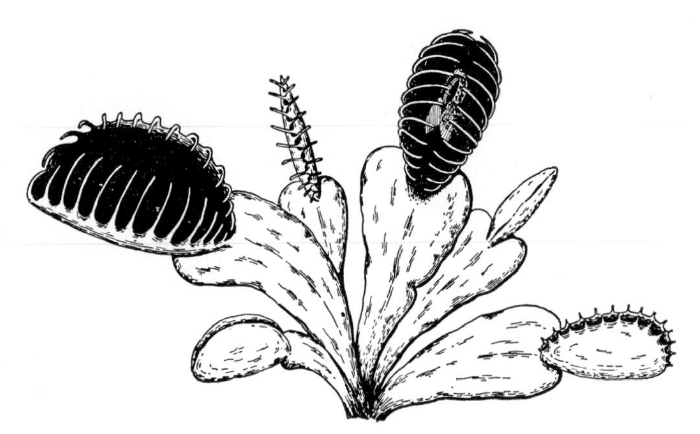

Fig. 5-3. Artist's sketch shows the Venus flytrap as it would look with an insect being caught in one of the traps. Notice the various traps on the plant. (*Adapted from a sketch by Karl Eric Haglund for Armstrong Associates, Insectivorous Plants, Basking Ridge, N.J.*)

have been modified for a specialized function. These plants may be cultured in class in a terrarium (Sec. 9-5), which is kept quite moist. Add a few bits of charcoal to absorb odors in the tank. On occasion introduce some fruit flies into the terrarium.

Lacking the living plants, you may plan to show a film such as *Plant Traps* (Encyclopaedia Britannica). Perhaps you might offer a text such as that by Edmund W. Sinnott and Katherine S. Wilson entitled *Botany* (McGraw-Hill Book Company, Inc., New York, 1955), or *Man and the*

Living World by Ernest E. Stanford (The MacMillan Company, New York, 1951). A report might then be forthcoming giving some details of how these plants catch the insects.

5-6. A Marsh or Bog

Similarly, students may examine the kinds of plants and animals in a flood-plain marsh, or in a bog. Test the acidity here (Sec. 7-8).

Students might describe the factors that exist in these biotic communities. What natural enemies hold the numbers of given plants and animals in check? What would happen if one kind of organism began to increase or decrease in number in one kind of biome?

5-7. A Beach

Hermit Crabs. On a field trip at low tide along a sheltered beach students may come upon hermit crabs scurrying about in shallow water. The small crab lives within an empty periwinkle or moonsnail's shell. Have students pull out the hermit crab from the shell to see how twisted and degenerated its abdomen has become. Notice how the body curves into the spiral of the shell.

At times you may find seaweeds or small sea anemones (relatives of jellyfish) attached to these or other kinds of snails' shells. These are examples of a symbiotic relationship. While the sea anemone is transported over some distance so that chances of getting food are increased, doesn't the camouflage help the snail or hermit crab?

Killer of the Seas. If your school is located close to the eastern seaboard, perhaps your students have noticed the film of oil left by tankers and other large vessels. Did they notice, too, that birds are often attracted by the shimmering of this oily water? How is this a menace to bird life? (Any sea bird alighting on oil-polluted water becomes oil-soaked; his feathers are soon matted together, which destroys their cold- and water-repelling properties. The bird then is unable to fly and unable to protect himself from the cold. Death from drowning, exposure, or starvation awaits him.)

This menace is not restricted to our own shores but is an international problem. A student might report on the agreement subscribed to by forty-two nations in London in 1954, designed to prevent ships from dumping their oily wastes in zones where birds or other creatures might be harmed. Has the problem now been solved?

5-8. Your Own "Back Yard"

Nonliving Factors as They Affect Life. Whether your school is in a city, a town, or a rural area, you and your students are members of a plant-animal community. Your students may find it interesting to collect specific information about some of the nonliving factors that affect living things in the region. These might include:

1. Temperature variations during a year
2. The date of the last killing frost in spring
3. The lengths of the longest and shortest days
4. The elevation above sea level
5. The annual rainfall
6. The average depth of the water table
7. The nature of the underlying rock, which partly determines the character of the soil

Students might be interested in gathering data on questions like these: What are the limits of temperature and pressure between which life for human beings is possible? How has science made it possible for man to thrive in climates where life would otherwise be difficult or impossible?

For much thought-provoking material on man in relation to the world in which he lives, your students might be referred to *Man's Nature and Nature's Man* by Lee Dice (University of Michigan Press, Ann Arbor, Mich., 1955).

PONDS, LAKES, AND SEA IN THE CLASSROOM

5-9. Aquariums and Marine Studies

Making an Aquarium. In preparing an aquarium students may use large battery jars, tall pickle or mayonnaise jars, or standard rectangular tanks. The most acceptable tanks are those which have iron or chromium frames and slate or glass bottoms (Fig. 5-4).

Tanks with a 4- to 5-gallon capacity prevent overcrowding of fish if not more than five to six pairs of fish (an inch or so in size) are introduced, together with plants and a few snails. Cover the tanks to prevent evaporation of water and avoid contamination.

At the start, a tank should be thoroughly washed with soap and warm water followed by prolonged rinsing in cool water. Then fill the tank half full of cold water and let it stand a few days. In this time, leaks may be detected and any soluble materials in the tank may be dissolved in the water. Now discard this water. The tank is ready for filling.

Cover the bottom of the tank with a half-inch layer of coarse sand that has been washed previously with boiling water. In this sand, bury a piece of chalk an inch long at each end of the 5-gallon tank. This should neutralize the acidity and provide calcium salts for the snails. Now add another half-inch layer of sand in which you may deposit a 2-inch square of copper stripping or a few copper coins to hold down the growth of algae. Next, place a sheet of paper over the sand and begin to fill with water. In this way the sand is not disturbed. Fill the tank to within a few inches of the top. Then let the new tank stand so that detrimental gases such as chlorine may evaporate from the water. Include a gallon or less of conditioned water from an established tank. Even better, add a gallon of water from an established *Daphnia* culture.

After a few days, add plants, both rooted and floating varieties. You may want to include *Anacharis, Vallisneria, Cabomba,* possibly the

Fig. 5-4. A fresh-water aquarium. (*General Biological Supply House, Chicago.*)

water fern *Salvinia;* when the tanks are conditioned add some algae such as *Nitella* or *Cladophora.* Place the plants in the background of the tank and include a few rocks to afford a hiding place for gravid female fish.

Place the tank in a northern or western exposure since strong sunlight causes an excessive growth of algae. This green water, incidentally, can be cleared to a large extent by the addition of *Daphnia.* Since these in turn will be eaten by the fish, it may be necessary to remove the fish temporarily so that *Daphnia* are not consumed before they clear the water. Remove excess growth of filamentous algae by adding more snails. Besides feeding the fish sparingly, remove dead plants and keep the level of water constant by adding small amounts of new water. Frequent changing of the tank should not be necessary once a tank is established. The average pH range (Sec. 7-9) should be between 6.8 and 7.2 in a conditioned aquarium.

What kinds of fish should be kept? Among native fish, the killifish or *Fundulus,* the stickleback, banded sunfish, red-bellied dace, and shiner are desirable animals for an aquarium. Small goldfish may be kept under the same conditions. They may be fed bits of boiled spinach in addition to other foods, and they feed upon the plants in the tank. For the beginner, guppies are desirable for they withstand low room temperatures and reproduce rapidly. The Japanese medaka (*Oryzias latipes*) requires live food such as *Daphnia,* or *Tubifex* for reproducing regularly.

Fish have many parasites, including the fungus *Saprolegnia.* Diseased fish should be isolated in a 10 per cent salt solution for about an hour. This usually removes the white patches on fins or scales. Then wash the fish in ordinary water and immerse it in an 0.5 per cent solution of potassium permanganate for 15 minutes. Keep the fish isolated and under observation for reappearance of the patches. The best advice may be to discard the infected fish, for it may infect other fish, and diseases among them are stubborn and resistant to treatment.

Developing Eggs of an Aquarium Snail (*Physa*). When students want to learn how an animal's egg develops (see also Sec. 4-8), they may use snail's eggs, which are available all year round from the classroom aquarium, or they may bring snails from their own tanks at home.

In class they may dissect a snail to remove the multiple-lobed ovotestis which lies in the uppermost part of the spiral of the snail. This should be macerated slightly in a drop of aquarium water on a clean slide. Under high power the student may see sperm cells as well as the spherical eggs. In fact, he may see fertilization take place. Then the fertilized eggs should be segregated into small finger bowls and their development followed for the next few days with a hand lens or a binocular microscope.

Reproduction in Fish (Medaka, *Oryzias latipes*). The early development of the eggs of certain fish may be studied regularly in the classroom. When the fresh-water fish, medaka, are given proper conditions of light and temperature and are fed *Tubifex* or *Enchytrea* worms or mixed dry food, the females produce eggs daily, usually just before dawn. The eggs, which are fertilized externally, remain attached to the female for several hours.

Students may isolate these fertilized eggs in small containers of aquarium water and over the next 6 days they may follow the development and hatching. With a hand lens, students may look for the first cleavage, which occurs about an hour after fertilization, then the second cleavage stage about an hour and a half later. The third cleavage stage, which occurs about two hours after the second, results in a mass of eight cells.

A Marine Aquarium. An especially fascinating class study for students in inland cities is focused around life among marine invertebrates such as small starfish, clams, small oysters, and sea anemones. These tanks (Fig. 5-5) need more care, for sea plants are not good oxygenators. Therefore, an aerator and a pump are needed. Synthetic sea water along with small invertebrates and seaweeds may be purchased as a kit from many supply houses (Sec. 18-3).

The specific gravity of the salt solution should be between 1.017 and

Fig. 5-5. A marine aquarium. (*General Biological Supply House, Chicago.*)

1.022. A hydrometer will give the reading. To replenish salt used by the organisms add a teaspoonful composed of 1 part Epsom salts to 3 parts rock salt to a 20-gallon tank once a month. A small piece of plaster of paris may be added every five months. Avoid the contact of metals such as zinc or copper with sea water. Why?

Students may watch the movement of starfish and of mollusks. Feed the animals bits of worms in small containers so that the large tank does not become contaminated.

Have students trace the food chain in the sea and compare this with the interrelationships in fresh water and on land. In each biome what are the natural enemies that check the number of individual plants and animals?

Eggs of Brine Shrimp: *Artemia.* Eggs in a dried state may be purchased from aquarium supply houses so that live material can be available for study at any time in the classroom.

Larvae hatch out of the eggs in 1 or 2 days after the dried eggs are put into a salt solution. The developing stages may be observed under a microscope in depression slides.

This is a procedure which has been successful: Add 4 tablespoons of rock salt to a gallon of tap water. Keep this in a flat pan or aquarium. Place a half teaspoon of dried eggs in a feeding ring in the salt solution and cover the pan to keep out the light. Within a few days almost all the eggs should hatch. If you remove the cover from part of the pan you should find that the larvae congregate in the light region of the pan. Then you may collect them to put into fresh salt solution or transfer them to depression slides for students to observe over several hours. These slides may be circled with petroleum jelly and the cover slip pressed into it, thereby sealing the slide so the material can be studied for several hours without drying. The slides may be placed in a moist chamber such as that used for germinating pollen grains (Sec. 4-4).

What place do forms like *Artemia* occupy in a study of food niches in a food chain?

Fig. 5-6. A sealed microaquarium. What will happen inside?

A Microaquarium. How are plants and animals related in a balance in nature? Students may have studied the web of life in a pond or lake field trip (Sec. 5-3), or even in a balanced aquarium that they have made (Sec. 5-9). Yet at some other time it may be useful to make a completely sealed microaquarium. In the sealed soft glass tube shown in Fig. 5-6 is a snail and a good oxygenator such as *Anacharis* or *Cabomba* in aquarium water. Since this sealed tube might represent a relationship among living things in terms of balance, dependency, or, in broad terms, aspects of conservation, what would happen if the plants died out? What gases are interchanged within the tube?

Students would enjoy watching you pull out a large-sized soft glass test tube over a bunsen flame. Rotate the ends of the test tube slowly to distribute the heat evenly. As the center of the test tube takes on a red glow and becomes soft (Fig. 5-7*a*), remove it from the flame and pull out the tube so that an inch in the center is elongated.

Since the tube is hot, it cannot be filled immediately. It would be advisable to prepare some pulled tubes before the class meets so that cold tubes are available. Then students can watch the entire procedure and possibly try to make these microaquariums too. Pour an inch of aquarium water into the bottom half of the cold tube. You may want to add bromthymol blue indicator (Sec. 18-1*e*), so that students can watch the changes in the concentrations of carbon dioxide in the water during light and in the dark (Sec. 3-6). Insert an elodea plant and a snail

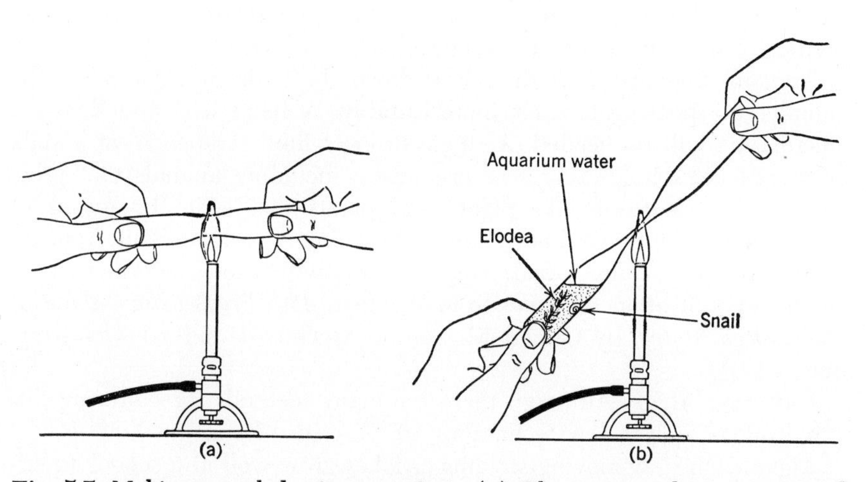

Fig. 5-7. Making a sealed microaquarium. (*a*) The empty tube is constricted by heating and pulling; (*b*) the constriction is made very narrow when the materials are in the tube; when the tube has cooled a bit it is completely sealed.

down the pulled part of the tube into the bottom of the test tube. Gently heat the elongated part by slightly tilting the test tube over the flame, but avoid heating the water (Fig. 5-7*b*). Now pull the center constriction into a narrower bore by pulling on the upper end of the test tube, but don't seal the glass completely since the sudden sealing while warm would cause the glass to crack. After the narrow bore has cooled, then completely seal the tube in the flame.

These sealed aquariums containing a green plant and a snail survive for many months when kept in moderate but not direct sunlight.

Plastic bags, available at pet shops and department stores, might be substituted for the test tubes. Your students might be interested in using a large sealed bottle to set up a marine microcosm and to study its changing balance. They will find helpful suggestions in the April, 1958, issue of the magazine, *The Science Teacher,* published by the National Science Teachers Association.

A STUDY OF MICROSCOPIC LIFE

5-10. Thallophytes

Collecting Algae. A common variety of rockweed might be used to introduce your students to the thallophytes, the grand division of the plant kingdom occupied by the algae.

To make specimen preparations of the big ones, float them in whole or in part onto a sheet of paper and let them dry. The leaflike parts of many consist of only two layers of cells coated with a clear pectinous substance. They dry on the paper without apparent thickness, like ink, forming beautiful "abstract" designs.

As your students work their way down the scale of algae sizes, the number of species increases immeasurably. A hand lens and finally a microscope will be needed. A single drop of fluid scraped from a stalk of marsh grass holds scores of organisms, including animals that grow in branching patterns like plants and plants that swim by means of whiplike tails and eat like animals. Learning to tell a plant from an animal becomes quite a feat. Your students will receive enormous help in the identification of algae from the text, *The Fresh-water Algae of the United States,* by Gilbert M. Smith (McGraw-Hill Book Company, Inc., 1950).

Culturing Algae. Although there are many methods for culturing different algae, only a few techniques are described here.

Algae from slow-moving streams or lakes grow well in a school aquarium (Sec. 5-9). *Euglena* may be found in sunny shallow pools. Look for *Chlamydomonas* in the same places. In the greenish mud along the edge of a lake you should find desmids. Slippery, fine threads of *Spirogyra* may be floating in sunny areas along with *Volvox.* A fascinating sidelight on *Volvox* may be found in *The Great Chain of Life,* by Joseph Wood Krutch (Houghton Mifflin Company, Boston, 1956). The theme of the chapter called The Machinery of Evolution is that with *Volvox* sex and death made their first appearance on earth.

Also, collect the green felt covering on rocks and flower pots, for this probably is *Vaucheria* or *Protococcus.*

Culture the aquatic algae by placing small amounts in an aquarium that has been established at least two months. Or prepare a nutrient culture solution as described in Sec. 18-1. Growth is often enhanced by adding some soil from the pond or lake, or a good garden soil. First, however, add distilled water to the soil and bring to a boil. This will destroy any algae already present, which may contaminate the culture you want to grow.

You may add *Spirogyra* to a thriving culture of *Daphnia.* (Many other algae also thrive well in this culture.) Keep the culture in medium light or at a north window at a temperature between 19° and 25°C. You may add to the culture each week a pinch of fresh hard-boiled egg yolk pulverized between the fingers. Also keep a few snails in the culture.

Other successful methods of culturing algae are described in *A Sourcebook for the Biological Sciences* (Sec. 19-3*e*).

Algae for Food. Your students will find an excellent report on the one-celled water plant *Chlorella,* with an account of the first promising attempts to grow it economically on a mass scale, in the October, 1953, issue of *Scientific American.*

Your students may also be interested in the work being done by Professor Harold B. Gotaas of the University of California, Berkeley, in growing algae in sewage ponds, then harvesting and drying the product.

Algae will no doubt find use as a filler for animal foods, as is the case with soya and alfalfa meal. What do your students think about algae as a dinner dish for themselves? Their reactions may bring home to them that the evolution of human tastes is somehow involved. What are other factors?

5-11. Protozoa

Culturing Some Protozoa. Students may prepare cultures of protozoa such as *Paramecia* or other forms by the following procedures that have been successful in the classroom:

1. A generalized simple method for culturing many protozoa is this one: Boil a liter of pond water or spring water, then add a small handful of timothy hay (or finely shredded lettuce leaves) and boil another 10 minutes. Allow this to cool, then add about six uncooked rice grains. After 2 days, inoculate this fluid with a few pipettefuls of the protozoa culture you want to maintain.

2. A more time-consuming technique involves the preparation of a synthetic pond water. Some twenty different kinds of protozoa, including amoebae, may be cultivated in this solution. Prepare a stock solution first by weighing out these salts into 1 liter of distilled water:

Sodium chloride, 1.20 grams
Potassium chloride, 0.03 grams
Calcium chloride, 0.04 grams
Sodium bicarbonate, 0.02 grams
Phosphate buffer (pH 9.9 to 7.0), 50 cubic centimeters

This stock solution should be diluted one part to ten parts of distilled water in making culture solutions, i.e., for each cubic centimeter of stock solution, add 10 cubic centimeters of distilled water. Add a few uncooked rice grains to the fluid in a finger bowl, then inoculate with the desired protozoa.

Fission in Protozoa. Your protozoa cultures may be used in demonstrations under a microscope to show how microscopic forms of life reproduce themselves. Students may find transverse fission in paramecia; in other protozoa they may witness lengthwise fission too. Mount a drop of thick culture on a clean slide, then add a drop of methyl cellulose or gum tragacanth to the same drop in order to slow down the protozoa. Or prepare the slides in advance so that the weight of the cover slip slows down the movement of ciliated forms. Examine the slides under both low and high power.

Other Lessons in a Culture Dish. Some students may want to study succession among the microscopic forms of life in a culture jar. What do protozoa use as food? What factors affect the life cycle of protozoa?

Or students may want to make a study of food niches in a culture dish. Guide them to see how bacteria and small flagellated forms multiply rapidly, particularly around the rice grains. As weeks go by, students might keep a record of the kinds of protozoa which rise to dominance in the culture. Finally, they may notice how rotifers, many-celled organisms, take over an old culture. Students may also report to the class on the ways that protozoa ingest their food. Any text in college zoology or protozoology will give this information.

"THE SEA AROUND US"

5-12. "Water, Water Everywhere . . ."

Ask your class, "What is the most valuable thing in the sea?" (Fig. 5-8). They may at first be unaware that the chief resource of the sea is not fish, not salts, not magnesium or bromine or any of the other valuable materials that can be extracted from it; the greatest resource of the sea is *water*. Again we are back to the all-important hydrologic cycle—the interaction of air and sea and the energy of the sun that makes this water available to us. This interaction of air and sea is so intimate that your students must understand both in order to understand either.

Ask them what would be the new outlook if we could learn to control our climate (involving as it does all phases of the earth's water, temperature, and winds). Their suggestions might include taking the weather problem out of farming; making present "waste" lands available for farming; making areas now inundated suitable for the raising and harvesting of foodstuffs.

Your students would gradually become aware that there is indeed water enough to go around, if only it were suitably distributed in time and space.

Institutions with which your class may want to become acquainted are, for example, the Oceanographic Institution at Woods Hole, Massachusetts, the Scripps Oceanographic Institute at La Jolla, California, the Lamont Geological Observatory at Columbia University, the Marine Laboratory of the University of Miami, the Bingham Oceanographic Laboratory at Yale. At these places scientists in many different fields are devoting their combined efforts to the problems of observing and understanding the ocean and the atmosphere. Here is a vast area of scientific exploration for the future. Perhaps one of your students will be caught up in its adventure.

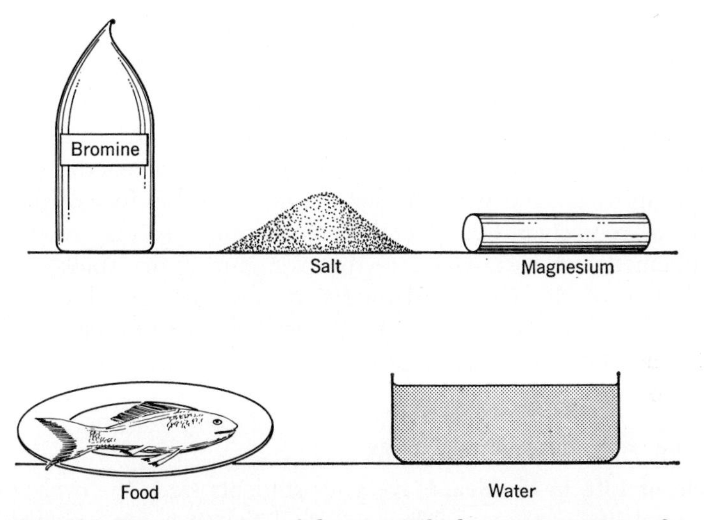

Fig. 5.8. Some resources of the sea. Which is most important?

It is evident that for this great exploration a team approach is needed. Have your students suggest the membership of such a team—fishery biologists, oceanographers, meteorologists, engineers, geographers.

Scientific Teamwork: An Example.[2] The following would make an interesting class report:

An example of excellent cooperation between engineers and biologists was offered by the Delaware diversion problem, when New York City proposed a reservoir in an upper branch of the Delaware River. Some 200 miles downstream from the dam, where the river meets the sea, are extensive oyster beds and fishing grounds. What effect would the impounding of the river water have on this important food resource?

[2] From Bostwick H. Ketchum, "The Engineer and the Biologist," *Oceanus,* vol. III, no. 4, Woods Hole Oceanographic Institution, 1955.

Engineers asked this question and together with marine biologists worked out a solution.

The oyster lives midway between river and sea and if the water surrounding becomes either too salty or too fresh it dies. The oyster's natural enemies (starfish, for example) cannot stand as much fresh water as the oyster, so that they are held back on the sea side, leaving a part of the estuary where the oyster can thrive.

How would the new reservoir affect the oyster and its enemies? The water restrained by the dam during the high river flow would benefit the oyster population since this would prevent the arrival of too much fresh water, but if too much river water were removed the sea would advance upstream and with the salt would come the foes of the oyster. Periods of low river flow are dangerous times, so the reservoir has been planned to release water to the river during dry spells, when the natural flow of the river is dangerously low and would threaten the oyster with an invasion of its natural enemies from the sea. Thus man's engineering skill has been employed to provide an important resource with an even better habitat.

5-13. The Sea and Living Things

Cycle of Life in the Sea. Have your students trace the cycle of plant and animal life in the sea. They will find that it is not vastly different from what it is on land. Plants live and grow, carrying on the process of photosynthesis, absorbing from their surroundings nutrient substances such as phosphates and nitrates; small sea animals "graze" on the vegetation and are in turn consumed by the larger animals. When organisms finally die, all of them, large and small, decay and are decomposed by bacteria, the remains dissolving in the water in the form of carbon dioxide, nitrate, phosphate, etc.

If you wish, let your students trace the nitrogen cycle of the sea. Bacteria, similar to those on land, act on the ammonia resulting from protein decay, oxidizing it to nitrites and then to nitrates.

Students should recall that all forms of life need oxygen to live. From where does ocean life obtain this oxygen?

If you are near the sea, allow a glass of ocean water to stand for several hours. Notice the bubbles of air that collect on the sides of the glass. This is another example of the interchange constantly taking place between air and ocean. Your students will realize that marine life is dependent on the air as well as the sea, just as life on land needs the sea as well as the air.

Food from the Sea. Ask your students to find out how rich a food we have in fish. Why is fish (Fig. 5-9) not being used at present as

Fig. 5-9. Unloading salmon in Alaska. Why is the abundant food from the sea not so widely used as it might be? (*Courtesy of V. B. Scheffer, U.S. Fish and Wildlife Service.*)

widely as it might be? This will lead to consideration of the fact that although fish are abundant, they are widely scattered, difficult to find and catch, and often far from the market. How would better ways of freezing and refrigerating help?

What about food from the sea in the form of algae (Sec. 5-10)?

Prospecting for Fish. As students investigate this subject they may be surprised to learn that airplanes, television, and sonic devices are all used to locate schools of fish. This is a fascinating story that may be found in *The Sun, the Sea and Tomorrow* (Sec. 19-7*i*).

5-14. Mining of the Sea

Dissolved Solids. If your students are near the ocean, they might get a sample of sea water, weigh it, and then evaporate it. Then they might weigh the residue and calculate the per cent of solid in their sample.

If boiled away, 100 pounds of sea water will leave behind close to 3.5 pounds of solid matter, most of which is common salt.

Students might weigh a given volume of sea water and weigh an equal volume of pure water. Next, they might calculate the specific gravity of the former. (The specific gravity of sea water is 1.03.)

Have your students compile a list of the dissolved minerals in sea water and the estimated quantity of each per unit of volume.

Land Resources Flow to the Sea. Your students might try to find out how many millions of tons of minerals and undissolved solids are carried to the oceans each year by the rivers of the earth. How is this dissolved and suspended matter removed from the land? What are the effects of this withdrawal on the soil? What is the name given to this washing away of the soil?

Salt from the Sea. Students may set a dish of salt water in the freezing unit of a refrigerator. They will notice that the water freezes and rises, leaving the salt, or a concentrated solution of it, behind. In what regions might this be a useful process? Just how is it done on a large scale?

Ask students to take a shallow dish of salt water and set it in the sun. As the water evaporates the salt is left behind. In what kind of climate would this be a good way to get salt from the sea? What are the details of the process?

Have a student report on the way salt is mined from wells. How is the salt brine brought to the surface? Where in the United States are salt wells located? How do scientists believe they were formed?

Your students will realize that to crystallize the salt from brine the water will need to be evaporated by heat. In hot countries the sun is used to bring this about. In cool countries to boil off the water would involve a costly fuel bill. Is there any way of increasing the rate of evaporation and using less heat?

To show your students how reduced pressure increases rate of evaporation and even causes a liquid to boil at a lower temperature, the following experiment may be performed:

Let a Pyrex flask, half full of water which is boiling vigorously, be removed from the flame and instantly corked airtight with a rubber stopper. Use caution in this experiment since the flask might collapse. You might use a wire screen to cover the flask. Invert the flask as shown in Fig. 5-10 and cool the top by pouring on cold water. The water in the flask immediately begins to boil again. Elicit from your students that this is because the steam in the top of the flask is condensed and so the pressure on the surface of the liquid is much reduced. Lowered pressure on the water causes it to boil at a lower temperature.

A student might report on the details of the commercial method of crystallizing salt by evaporation under reduced pressure.

Your students will probably be familiar with the importance of salt to life and of its various ordinary uses. They may be less familiar with salt as a raw material from which a great many other important products are made.

You might like to try this technique when studying this topic with your chemistry students: Ask each member of the class to select different chemicals that are made from salt—such as lye, baking soda, washing

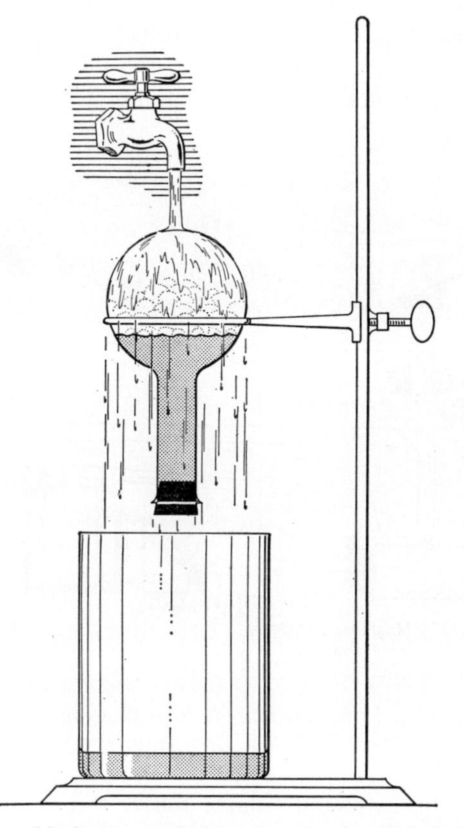

Fig. 5-10. A cold shower and the water in the flask boils. Why?

soda, hydrochloric acid, sodium sulfate, trisodium phosphate, sodium chloride, sodium bromide and iodide. The processes, chemical reactions, uses of the product, and simple demonstrations could then be prepared for sharing with the whole group.

Magnesium from the Sea. Ignite a piece of magnesium ribbon, held in a forceps in the bunsen flame. Students should shield their eyes from the brilliance of the burning. This will suggest to students why magnesium is used for flares, fireworks, photoflash bulbs, and flashlight powders.

Have students collect and display samples of magnesium alloys. Because it makes light, strong alloys, magnesium has found increasing usefulness in aircraft, etc.

What happens when there is a new and great demand for a material? A search for a new and greater supply is stimulated.

Have your students look up the abundance of magnesium and how and where it was previously mined. When these sources became insufficient scientists turned to the sea with its 9 million tons of magnesium ions per cubic mile of water. Here was indeed a treasure trove of the valuable metal! It sounds easy but actually less than 2½ pounds of

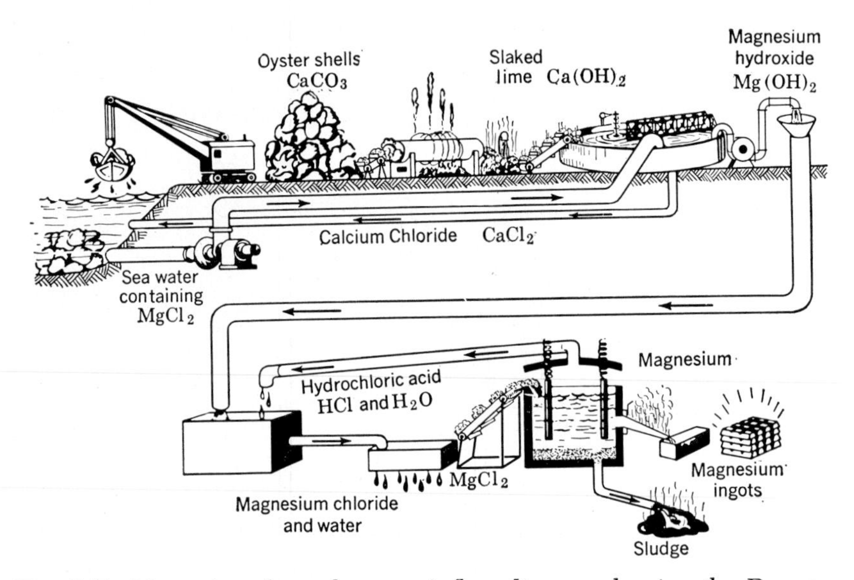

Fig. 5-11. Magnesium from the sea: A flow diagram showing the Dow sea-water process. (*The Dow Chemical Company, Inc.*)

magnesium can be extracted from a ton of sea water. However, huge plants set up along the Gulf of Mexico and on the Pacific Coast are today producing all the magnesium used in the United States.

One of your chemistry students might be interested in bringing to class a flow diagram showing the main steps in the extraction of magnesium from sea water (Fig. 5-11).

Here is how it can be done in the laboratory: The method consists in the electrolysis of fused magnesium chloride. In order to make the magnesium salt melt at a low temperature, use 10 grams of magnesium chloride, 4 grams of potassium chloride, and 2 grams of ammonium chloride. Dissolve these in 50 milliliters of water in an evaporating dish and evaporate to dryness, so that there is a single fused mass. Break this mass up and place it in a clay crucible on a ring stand,

A carbon rod, suspended above the crucible, serves as anode and a thick iron nail as cathode. Now melt the salt mixture and connect anode and cathode to a source of direct current. The voltage should be approximately 10 and the amperage between 8 and 10. The electrolysis should continue for 15 or 20 minutes. At which electrode does the magnesium collect? Can your students identify by its odor the gas produced at the other electrode?

Bromine from the Sea. Make some bromine so that your students may become familiar with it. This may be done as follows: Put in a test

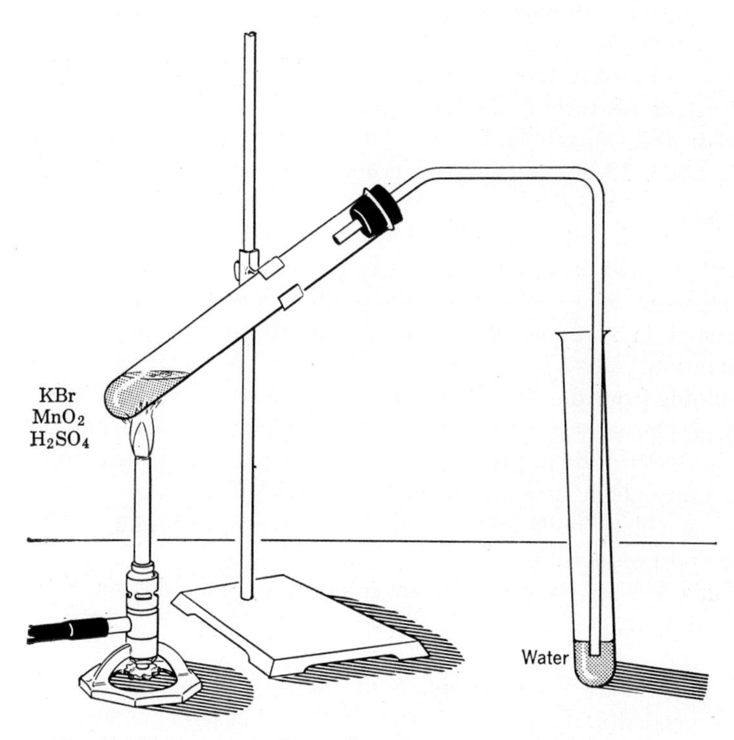

Fig. 5-12. Apparatus for making bromine in the laboratory.

tube generator 2 grams of potassium (or sodium) bromide and 3 grams of powdered manganese dioxide. Add 5 cubic centimeters of concentrated sulfuric acid. Pass the generator tube into another test tube containing 4 cubic centimeters of water (Fig. 5-12).

Heat the generator tube in a hood. (The vapor is poisonous.) Bromine forms, passes over, and dissolves or condenses in the water of the second test tube. Distill the bromine over until the solution is red and saturated and, if possible, a little drop of dark red liquid bromine appears at the bottom of the test tube.

Add 1 cubic centimeter of carbon disulfide (or carbon tetrachloride) to 5 cubic centimeters of bromine water. Shake. Two layers form, with the water on top and the carbon disulfide on the bottom. The bromine, being far more soluble in the latter, turns it red or reddish-orange in color. This is a test for free bromine.

Students will discover that by far the largest use of bromine is in the preparation of the compounds that go into "leaded gasoline." So enormous became the demand for bromine that scientists turned to the sea, where bromine is found in less than 70 parts to the million. The result of research and experimenting culminated in a success that is a masterpiece of technical skill.

To 5 cubic centimeters of potassium bromide solution add 2 cubic centimeters of carbon disulfide. Shake. The carbon disulfide remains colorless as it sinks to the bottom. Add a few cubic centimeters of chlorine water (Sec. 18-1g). Shake and note the color of the carbon disulfide, which is now reddish-orange due to the liberation of bromine.

This experiment illustrates the way bromine is prepared from sea water. Bromine is found in the sea in the form of bromides. To extract the bromine, sea water is treated with chlorine. A student might be interested in studying and reporting on the details of its commercial preparation.

Colloids from the Sea. Red sea plants, known more familiarly as Irish moss, are processed to yield extractives which are used particularly in gelling and thickening foods. These colloids of the sea are contributing important advantages to over a hundred different products, ranging from chocolate milk and ice cream to toothpaste and a number of industrial products.

Your students may obtain an interesting pamphlet on this subject by writing to Seaplant Chemical Corporation, 63 David St., New Bedford, Mass.

Living Things Mine the Sea. Some things that our scientists have not yet succeeded in doing have been done by other living creatures. Oysters, for instance, concentrate copper from sea water in their tissues, while seaweeds concentrate iodine, even though the iodine occurs in concentrations of only 2 parts per million. How is iodine extracted from the giant kelps of the Pacific Ocean?

5-15. Sea Resources and the Future

Here are some questions for class discussion:

What are the advantages of land mining over the mining of the sea for minerals? Why does industry prefer the former? (It is, in general, cheaper to extract metals from the more concentrated ores.)

Is more energy needed to extract metals from dilute concentrations of ore? What are possible new sources of low-cost energy (Chap. 16)?

Many oceanographers feel that the wealth latent in the seas will remain only potential unless we can increase materially the research and technological skill now being devoted to the development of our oceanic resources.

Your class could study reports of the International Oceanographic Congress held at United Nations headquarters in New York during September, 1959. At that time, 800 oceanographers from thirty-eight countries compared notes on their progress in the study of the sea. This was the first international effort to bring together and to pool the knowledge of the oceanographers of the world.

6

Water and Man

Water is indispensable. Life cannot exist without it. Although scientists are finding substitutes for other resources by learning to use more plentiful substances for less plentiful ones, a substitute for water does not yet exist, if it ever will.

This chapter deals with water as it is found in nature and as it is detoured by man for his various needs. How to make more effective use of the hydrologic cycle is one of our most pressing conservation problems.

WATER AS MAN FINDS IT

6-1. What besides Water Is There in Natural Water?

Living Organisms. Students may examine a drop of pond water under a microscope. You may want to conduct a field trip to a pond or stream (Sec. 5-3 or 5-4). In planning for the trip, students will find it wise to prepare containers and aquariums for the animals and plants they will collect (Sec. 5-9).

Dissolved Gases. Warm a test tube of pond water very gently. Bubbles may be observed forming on the sides of the tube, long before the boiling point is reached.

Leave a glass of ice-cold water standing in a warm room. Air bubbles, many of them, will presently be noticed on the inside walls of the glass, as dissolved air is forced from the liquid as it warms.

Use one beaker of warm water and another of cold. Put them under a bell jar and attach a vacuum pump. The difference in the amount of air coming out of solution is made strikingly visible.

Students may look up the solubility of the two most important components of air (oxygen and nitrogen). What happens to the solubility of these gases as the water is chilled?

Your students might make a determination of the dissolved oxygen (DO) in water by using the Winkler method. This is described in detail in the April, 1958, issue of *The Science Teacher.* There are also a number of suggested applications of the DO determination.

Could aquatic life exist without the oxygen dissolved in water? Cool some freshly boiled water (allowing no air to get at it) and immerse a goldfish in it. Observe what happens. (Be ready to rescue the fish quickly!)

Now you may want to discuss with your class the importance of oxygen to the cycle of life (fish, insects, plants, bacteria) living, dying, and living again in a body of water. Much is already known in this area but discussion might emphasize the need for further research in the field of ecology in order that we may understand even more fully how natural water, with its teeming life, is self-purifying if given half a chance.

Miscible and Immiscible Liquids. Students may test the solubility of 1 cubic centimeter of each of the following in 5 cubic centimeters of distilled water: kerosene, salad oil, glycerin, alcohol. (Note the variation from the insoluble to the extremely soluble.) In discussing this experiment, you may want to elicit from students that liquids both miscible and immiscible with water can cause serious pollution problems. For example, the oily scum so often visible on the surface of lakes, aside from polluting the water and spoiling its beauty, may actually be a fire hazard and may menace the life of marine birds (Sec. 5-7). Soluble liquids, too, may cause trouble by being toxic to certain water animals. If the soluble liquid happens to be organic and oxidizes, it may seriously lower the oxygen content of the water.

Dissolved and Suspended Solids. Collect a sample of pond or river water (Fig. 6-1). Hold it to the light. Is it murky or cloudy? Filter it and see if there is any residue on the filter paper. Discuss with your students how undissolved solids, such as silt, may constitute a serious form of physical pollution in water.

Take a 10 cubic centimeter sample of the filtered water and heat it to dryness in a porcelain dish. Is there a residue? Elicit from students that this residue represents the dissolved solids. Which of these solids are helpful to life? Which may be harmful? Without certain dissolved solids plants would not obtain their mineral nutrients. Some dissolved solids, on the other hand, are pollutants, highly toxic to living things.

Hardness. Students may dip their fingers into rain water or distilled water, rub them together and note the "feel." This is soft water. Students might do the same with hard water from a well or other source, or they might use a solution of calcium or magnesium sulfate (Epsom salts) as a substitute. The difference in the "feel" of the two samples should be noticeable.

Students might try soaping their hands with hard water and soft water. In which kind of water is the greater amount of soap suds produced?

Fill one test tube one-third full of rain or distilled water and another test tube with hard water. Using a medicine dropper, allow 5 drops of liquid soap to fall into each test tube. Shake it to form suds. In which

Fig. 6-1. Students collecting a sample of silt-laden water from the Milwaukee River. (*U.S. Soil Conservation Service photo.*)

kind of water are the most suds produced? The fact might be stressed that commercial users of hard water have larger soap bills.

Place on watch glasses over beakers of boiling water 7 cubic centimeters each of tap water, rain water, and hard water. Evaporate to dryness. Compare residues and help students to draw conclusions about the purity of rain water as compared with the others.

To determine how hard water is formed in nature: Ask a student to breathe carefully through a straw into a test tube of limewater. The carbon dioxide of his breath reacts with the limewater to form particles of solid calcium carbonate, really a form of limestone, which is commonly found as rock in nature. If more carbon dioxide from soda water is bubbled through, the milkiness will disappear, because the excess of carbon dioxide, reacting with the calcium carbonate, forms the soluble compound calcium bicarbonate. This is one kind of hard water.

Your students may imagine how, during countless ages, underground water bearing carbon dioxide has dissolved the limestone far below the earth's surface, leaving holes or caves. The water itself has become hard.

Instead of blowing through limewater your students may set up a carbon dioxide generator (Fig. 6-2). The gas may be bubbled through the limewater until the precipitate first formed disappears. The test tube is then put in a flame and its contents boiled. The precipitate will reappear as the insoluble calcium carbonate once more precipitates and carbon dioxide leaves the solution. You may now want to discuss the formation of stalactites and stalagmites in limestone caves.

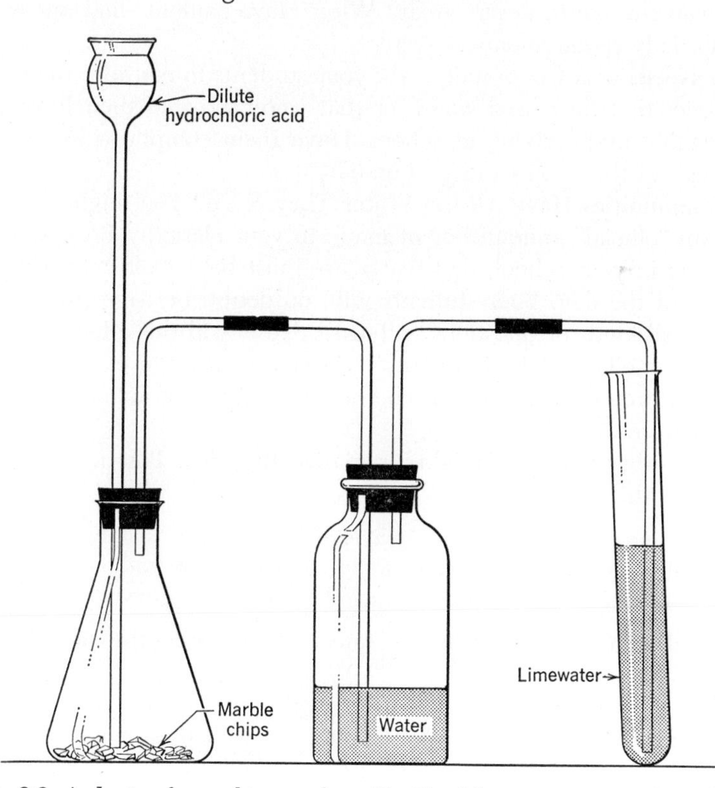

Fig. 6-2. A device for making carbon dioxide. The gas, generated in the flask, is washed in the bottle and bubbled through limewater.

Ask students to discover the difference between *temporary* and *permanent* hardness. They might illustrate the difference by boiling a sample of each in separate test tubes. (The temporary hardness precipitates on boiling, while the permanent hardness remains in solution.) Students may apply the soap suds test (Sec. 6-4) before and after boiling in each case.

6-2. The Importance of Water

Water in Living Things. Weigh a fresh apple. Place it in a drying oven overnight and weigh once more. What is the percentage of water in an apple? Some of your students could vary this experiment by using other fruits or vegetables.

How much water is there in human beings? Have your students find out. They might be interested in calculating the pounds of water in their own weight. You might want to discuss the function of water in the living body.

Living Things Need Water to Survive. Ask students to recall what happens when they neglect to water plants. What kinds of plants and animals can survive in desert areas? Why? Have students find out what are man's daily requirements of water.

Water Needs of a Community. Ask your students to consider the number of times that they used water, or that water affected their lives, between waking and arriving at school. Have them compile a list of the water needs of their community (Fig. 6-3).

Do Communities Have All the Water They Need? You might arrange to have an "official" announcement made to your class, by PA system if there is one in your school, that water use must be cut off between certain hours of the day. Your students will, no doubt, be eager to discuss this news. All kinds of questions will arise. "How will this affect us? Our families? Our city and its industries?" After assuring the class that this is a feigned broadcast, ask them whether this might not actually happen during a severe drought.

Here's another way you might dramatize the idea. Post a real news clipping like this one:

> Water: Averaging 5¢ a ton "delivered," city water is a bargain—but costs may go up as supplies dwindle—about 40% of leading U.S. cities are already in tight supply, limiting their industrial growth.

One might immediately pose the question, "What is the situation in *our* community?"

Still another approach might be to present your students with a statement like this: "The Department of Commerce in 1956 estimated that the nation will come close to doubling its use of water by 1975. A Department report said the nation now uses 262 billion gallons of water a day."

What are some of the factors that cause experts to predict such an enormous rise in water use? Discussion should emphasize that estimated growth in population foreshadows huge industrial expansion.

One of your students might write for the free USDA pamphlet, *Water Facts* (1957). In it are to be found estimates such as this: "Average daily

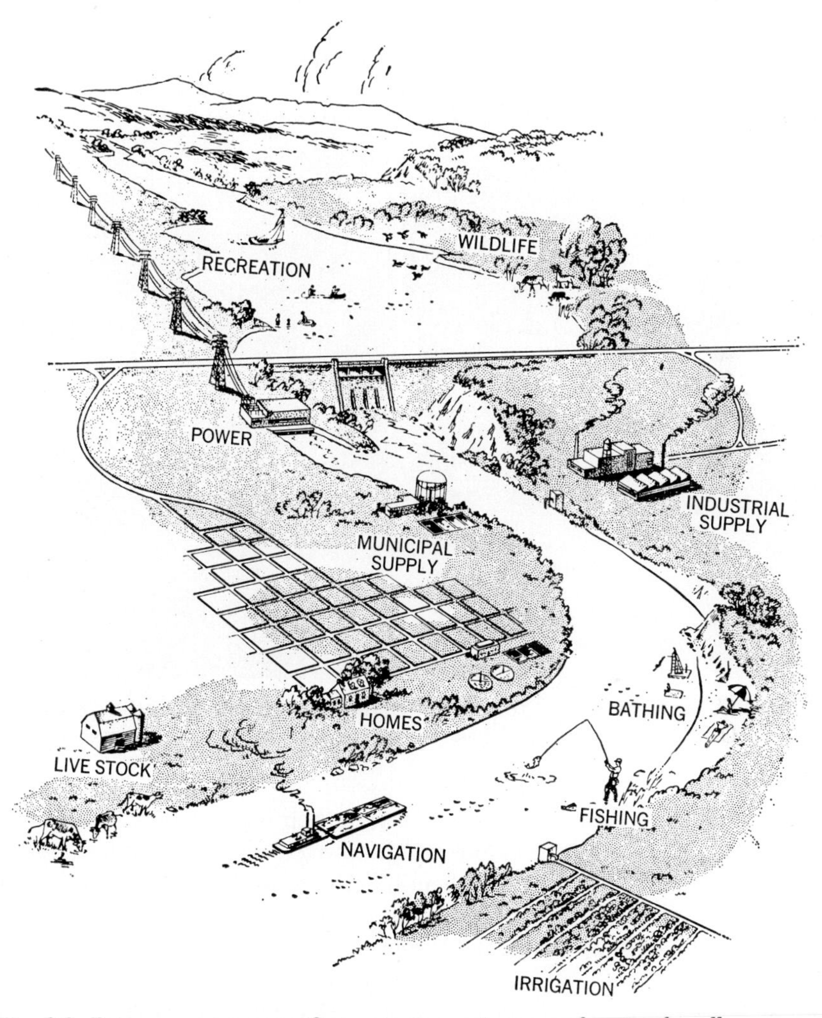

Fig. 6-3. Primary water uses. Our ever-increasing use of water for all purposes places a tremendous burden on our water resources. (*U.S. Public Health Service Publication no. 631.*)

use for all purposes increased from 600 gallons per capita in 1900 to 1,100 gallons in 1950 to 1,300 in 1955. By 1975 the country will be using 1,800 gallons of water a day for every man, woman and child." These figures and others similar to them are staggering. The ingenious teacher and student will think of ways of dramatizing them so that they may become meaningful. Here is one possible way: It has been estimated that the per capita daily consumption of water for irrigation alone (Fig. 6-4) is 500 gallons. How can students "visualize" this statistic? Suppose you ask

Fig. 6-4. A farmer irrigates 16 acres of netted gem potatoes on the Deschutes Project, Oregon. Notice desert country in background. (*U.S. Bureau of Reclamation.*)

students to figure the ratio of 500 gallons to their own weights.[1] (This will also afford an opportunity to look up the conversion factors in Sec. 18-2.) If a student weighs 100 pounds, then something like forty times his weight is used in our country every day to help grow the food he alone eats.

Water: Competing Demands. When your students have noted all the water needs of their community, they might evaluate those which are of prime importance and those which might have to give way in case of

[1] 1 gal = 231 cu in.
1 cu ft contains 12 × 12 × 12 in. = 1,728 cu in.

$\therefore$ 1 gal is equivalent to $\frac{231}{1{,}728} = 0.134$ cu ft

1 cu ft of water weighs 62.4 lb
$\therefore$ 1 gal of water weighs 62.4 × 0.134 = 8.36 lb
500 gal of water weighs 8.36 × 500 = 4,180 lb

emergency. (Air conditioning, for instance, might not be as important as irrigation.) If water is in short supply, can your students suggest ways of improving the situation? Ask them whether it is possible to limit plans for adequate water supply to individual communities. How do the county, state, region, and nation fit into the picture? Where does one begin?

Do We Now Use All the Water Available in the Hydrologic Cycle? This is a question about which thoughtful students are apt to wonder. Here are some of the statistics that will help them find an answer:

The U.S. Weather Bureau tells us that the average annual precipitation in the United States is 30 inches. The U.S. Geological Survey gives 21.5 inches as the figure that approximately represents the amount of rainfall that annually returns to the atmosphere through evaporation and use by vegetation.

It is estimated that 8.5 inches of rainfall runs off the surface of the earth through the ground or directly into streams and hence into the ocean. It is estimated also that only about ¾ inch of water is actually intercepted annually and used directly by man.

Nationwide averages, of course, do not tell the story for a particular region. Thus, the New York City watershed, located in the Catskill Mountains, has an average precipitation of 48 inches, of which slightly more than 50 per cent is yielded as runoff.

Whether these figures are completely accurate or not, they do indicate that we are far from reaching the limit of our water resources. What, then, are the conservationists concerned about? (Now your students are face to face with a challenge which will require a careful compiling of facts and figures and thoughtful consideration of their significance.)

Some Projects Relating to Water Use. Students might investigate and report on topics like these: The part water has played in the development of their home town; the number of days water would be available if the source were cut off; the area of the watershed for the town's water supply and its adequacy for present and future needs. Students might distinguish between ground and surface water sources and might also discuss the value of impoundments as an additional source. The project might include the construction of a model of their community water supply system.

WATER AS MAN USES IT

6-3. Water Pollution

Here are several ways to start the study of water pollution:

Bring to class 2 gallons of contaminated water and ask the students to purify it. This will immediately lead to a discussion of what are the impurities to be found in this water. For what purpose will the water be needed? How are the various impurities removed? Is it necessary to remove them all?

Another technique you might use is to prepare in advance five labeled glasses of water. No. 1 contains water with suspended soil; no. 2 is clear but colored with ink; no. 3 contains table salt; no. 4 contains ammonia; and no. 5 is tap water. "Why," you might ask, "is no. 5 the only glass of water you would choose for safe drinking?" Your class might want to begin to list jobs for investigation: What is the source of our community's drinking water? What are the impurities found in it before treatment? How may impurities in water affect us? How is water made fit to drink?

The Problem. An inventory of the harm and danger of polluted water can be made by your class. They will, no doubt, be quite aware of the general problem of water-borne diseases. Your students will surely have some experiences relating to curtailed recreational facilities, to swimming holes that are no longer safe, to boating that is not pleasant any more, to fishing that does not yield even one nibble.

Perhaps they have given less thought to the fact that polluted water may threaten agriculture and that it can and does hamper the growth of cities, scaring away industry and undermining property values.

In discussing pollution it is important to bear in mind that water is the inevitable vehicle for disposing of waste matter. It is the means of ultimate and proper oxidation and dilution when solid waste is removed or when the liquid form of sewage is properly treated before its journey to the sea.

Natural waters are self-purifying and it is also possible for a stream to handle a certain amount of man-made pollution, if it can still maintain enough dissolved oxygen to support its underwater life. Bacteria multiply, attack the intruding waste, and are themselves consumed. Thus, given half a chance, a stream will in course of time restore the natural balance. But there is a limit beyond which nature cannot go. When man exceeds that limit by dumping too much sewage and industrial waste into the water, he poisons the stream so thoroughly that it can no longer recover from its disease (Fig. 6-5).

With our skyrocketing population and the rapid growth of our cities, few streams have a chance to be self-purifying. This means that there is increasing need for pollution abatement and for sewage disposal systems.

To keep pollution down to levels that will yield to proper treatment is the nub of the problem. It will, of course, cost money. Dr. Paul Sears, in the December 10, 1954, issue of *Science,* makes an important point when he writes "all the sound and fury over water pollution accomplished little until organized business, labor and sport sensed a common threat and began to join forces on the problem. The task still remains of awakening some thousands of municipalities to their responsibility."

Fig. 6-5. Thousands of dead shad from the Anacostia River, Washington, D.C., are the victims of hot weather and river pollution. The oxygen content of the water was decreased so much that the fish could not exist. (*Charles del Vecchio, Washington, D.C., Post Times-Herald.*)

Detecting Organic Matter in Water. You may want to show the presence of organic matter in water by testing for a nitrite. (This compound is formed from the ammonia given off by the decomposition of organic or animal matter.)

Take 10 cubic centimeters of a dilute solution of sodium nitrite. Add a few cubic centimeters of freshly prepared concentrated ferrous sulfate solution. Add acetic acid. A brown coloration indicates the presence of a nitrite. Having tried this test on a known nitrite, run the test on tap water and contaminated water.

Or, if you can obtain the chemicals needed, try this test: Fill a large cylinder nearly to the top with water containing a little dissolved sodium nitrite. Add 1 milliliter of sulfanilic acid solution and 3 drops of hydrochloric acid. Now add 2 milliliters of alpha-naphthylamine acetate solution and stir. A faint pink color which can be seen against a white background indicates the presence of nitrites.

Do Problems in Pollution Vary with the Season? Your students might think about these questions: Does the amount of water in our streams vary with the seasons? How about the amount of dissolved oxygen? Your class may figure out that the lowered oxygen content in summer usually makes pollution problems far more severe in hot weather.

A student, returning to school from a summer trip, made this report to the class:

> It was interesting to note, on a visit to a paper mill in the far West, that wastes were being chemically treated and salvaged in the summer but were being dumped into the river in winter when there was more water and also considerably more oxygen, due to its greater solubility in cold water. It had not yet become economically feasible for the company to salvage its waste for the entire year, nor had the winter pollution of the stream reached a dangerous enough level for a law violation. The company, however, was ready with the "know how," and was constantly doing research trying to discover commercial uses for its salvaged waste.

Have your students bring in clippings from current newspapers and periodicals showing the latest news of conservation "hot from the griddle." This material may form the basis for fruitful class discussion. For instance, here is a short report a student gave on Recent Advances in Conservation.[2]

> Though there is an increasing supply of oxygen in the cold waters of winter, due to more rapid flow and greater solubility of the gas, a team of scientists in Ohio in the winter of '55 discovered that pollution from sewage affects a much wider area in the cold months than during summer in their experimental stream. It seems that the organic wastes in winter formed a life-killing blanket over the stream bottom in downstream areas that were clean and pollution-free in summer.

Here we have an example of the kind of new evidence that is constantly being turned up by the patience and skill of research scientists. What effect will such work have on the theory and practice of tomorrow?

Sewage Pollution. How does your community take care of its sewage disposal? Discuss how the growth of our population and the crowding of our cities have affected the problem. Is there a sewage disposal plant that your class might visit (Sec. 6-4)?

Industrial Waste. If there is an industrial concern in your neighborhood, might a field trip be arranged? Have students learn why the industry needs so much water for its processing and waste removal.

(Many organic wastes from such industries as slaughter houses, canneries, creameries, paper mills, or tanneries require oxidation. This oxygen must come from that dissolved in water. But sewage requires this oxygen, too, not to mention aquatic life, which cannot survive when

[2] *Science Newsletter*, Oct. 29, 1955.

oxygen is withdrawn.) Now your class will be ready for the idea that unless a stream can take the wastes dumped into it during the warmest months of lowest oxygen content, the "oxygen balance" control will not be satisfactory.

Your students might now consider that industrial production rose 700 per cent between 1900 and 1950 and continues to rise at an unprecedented rate. What about the pressing and increasing needs for industry's water?

Sedimentation. Your students might collect in quart jars water that runs off from various sloping areas after a heavy rainfall. They might select cultivated fields, plowed both on the contour and up-and-down slopes, school grounds, park, or wood lot. After the jars have stood overnight students may compare both the amounts of material settled out and the sizes of the soil particles. Is the bulk of the material made up of fine or coarse particles? From what area did the largest amount of soil come? Why did that area lose more soil than the others?

This experiment can be used to start a discussion on sedimentation, the troublesome result of runoff. Soil is washed from where it is needed to where it clogs river channels, fills reservoirs, and harms aquatic life.

Along with municipal and industrial pollution, siltation is a costly and difficult problem. Some runoff is unavoidable, but man can do much to minimize it by proper watershed management.

6-4. Purification of Water

City Water Supplies. *Sedimentation.* Allow a tall jar of muddy water to remain standing for a time and ask students to note what happens. How do large cities use this principle in their water systems?

Use of Chemicals. To 1 cubic centimeter of an alum (aluminum sulfate) solution, add drop by drop a solution of a base, such as sodium hydroxide. Students may note the white precipitate, aluminum hydroxide.

Now take two tall jars, add some particles of fine clay to both, and stir. To one of the jars add some powdered alum and slaked lime (calcium hydroxide). A precipitate of aluminum hydroxide forms at once. Allow the two jars to remain undisturbed for 24 hours. The water to which the chemicals have been added should be very much clearer than the other, for the sticky precipitate of aluminum hydroxide and the heavy calcium sulfate drag the fine particles of clay with them as they settle to the bottom. Fortunately, the sticky precipitate can drag down with it entangled bacteria as well as tiny particles of suspended matter.

Your students might be interested in finding out where and how chemicals are added to their water supply.

Filtration. Students may make up a sample of impure water (Sec. 11-5). After washing a heaping tablespoon of clean sea sand in an evaporating dish with 50 cubic centimeters of distilled water, pour the wet sand upon a filter paper in a funnel, allow it to drain, and discard the filtrate. Then filter half the impure water through this sand. Students may compare the clearness and color of the filtrate with that of the impure water. Separate small portions of the filtrate may be tested for sulfate, representing dissolved solids, and for dissolved ammonia, representing dissolved gas. (They will be found present.) The sand has simply removed the suspended solids.

Ask a student to report on municipal filtration beds.

Aeration. Ask students to taste some freshly distilled water. Now they may aerate it by pouring it back and forth from one beaker to another. Does it have a different taste? Why and how do cities aerate their water?

Chlorination. As a teacher demonstration take a crystal of potassium chlorate and add 1 cubic centimeter of concentrated hydrochloric acid to it in a test tube. Cover the tube, not too tightly. Immediately you will have a sample of the greenish-yellow, highly poisonous gas, chlorine. (To stop the reaction, add water; this will give a sample of chlorine water.)

Students might examine pond water under a microscope, then add a drop of chlorine water and examine again.

Why is drinking water chlorinated? Does your community chlorinate its water? Students should now be ready to investigate the kind of water treatment plant set up in their community. One such municipal system is pictured in Fig. 6-6.

Coppering. If possible, students might collect some green algae from a neighboring pond in two jars. Samples may be examined under a microscope. To one add a few crystals of copper sulfate and leave overnight. Samples from both jars should be re-examined under a microscope.

Why is copper sulfate added to lakes and reservoirs?

Removing the Hardness from Water. Can one of your students get a sample of boiler scale or find a picture of it? What about the efficiency and safety of a boiler lined with such a coating? What would be the effect of boiler scale on the amount of fuel needed?

Students may have observed that softening water with soap is a wasteful and expensive method. They might also have observed that it is a messy, sticky method, injuring fabrics and depositing scum on bath tubs. Students might try washing fabrics with soap in softened and unsoftened water, comparing the results on the fabric over a period of time.

Temporary hard water can, as the student now knows (Sec. 6-1), be removed by boiling. (This is actually done in many factories by using the waste steam from boilers to heat large tanks of temporary hard water prior to use in the factory. Such a method is not practical, however, for home use.)

Students might add some limewater to a solution of a carbonate, boil, and note the precipitate. (This is a cheap method of softening large quantities of hard water, either temporary or permanent. Many industrial plants use this method.)

Any kind of hard water may be softened by means of suitable chemicals that will precipitate troublesome metallic ions. Here is a demonstra-

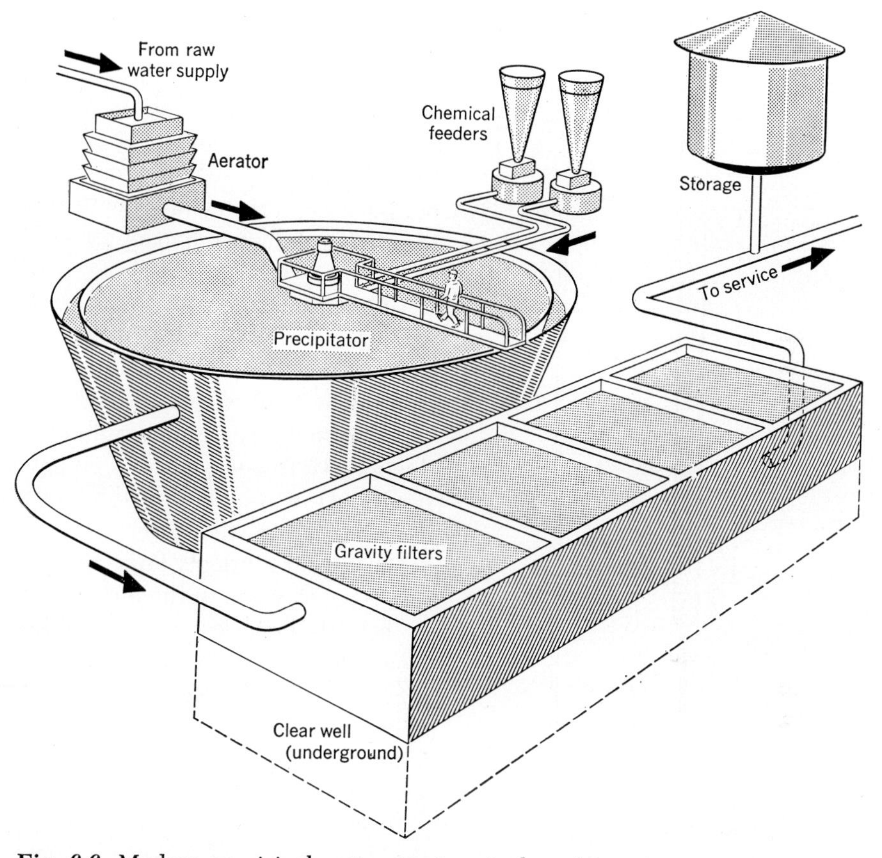

Fig. 6-6. Modern municipal water treatment plant (capacity to meet over-all needs of a community of 20,000). *Aerator* removes taste and odor, oxidizes iron and manganese; *precipitator*, a giant mixer and "strainer," uses coagulation, precipitation, and a filtering action to remove hardness, iron and manganese oxide, dirt, and silt; *filters* of graded sand and gravel remove remaining turbidity, provide clear, "polished" water. (This clarified water is generally chlorinated to kill bacteria.) (*Courtesy of Permutit Company.*)

tion you might try: Obtain some hard water or make it artificially with a little magnesium or calcium sulfate. Using four test tubes with equal amounts of hard water in each, add to one of them ¼ gram of sodium carbonate (washing soda), to another the same amount of sodium tetraborate (borax), and to a third, trisodium phosphate. Shake well. Add soap solution by means of a medicine dropper or burette, drop by drop, and compare the lathers formed in the softened waters with that of the unsoftened. Students might report on how water is softened in their homes.

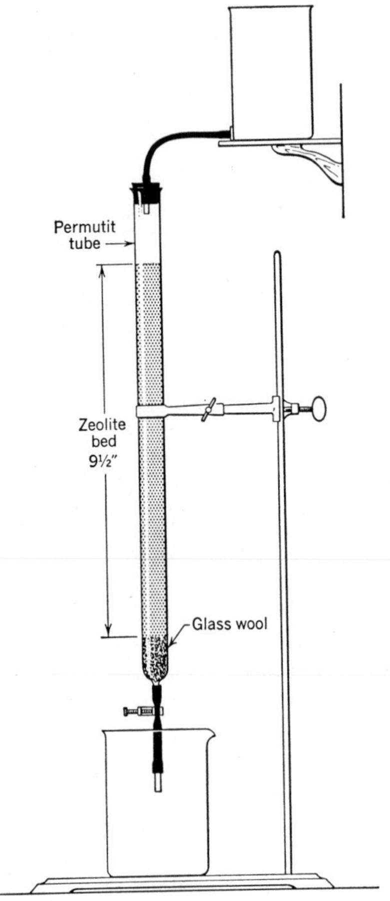

Fig. 6-7. Apparatus for softening water with Permutit.

You might write to the Permutit Company, 50 West 44th St., New York, for a complete lecture table water-softening demonstration (Fig. 6-7). Or you might use an iron pipe or glass cylinder about 12 inches long. Tie fine cheesecloth around the bottom and fill the cylinder with zeolite clay or permutit, a manufactured clay.

Test hard water with liquid soap, adding it drop by drop until you have a successful permanent lather. Run some hard water through the water-softening apparatus, and make the soap test once more. Compare results. How many drops of soap were needed in each case?

Have your students find out how this type of water softening is used in homes, factories, and hospitals. How is the zeolite regenerated?

Someone might report on the demineralizing of water by the two-step ion-exchange method, and the role of synthetic resins in this process.

Although water treatment is still the largest use of ion exchangers, there are now many other applications as a result of the more recent introduction of synthetic ion-exchange resins. Students might be interested in finding out what these new uses are.

Sewage Disposal Plants. Would it be possible to arrange a field trip to a sewage disposal plant and have students see for themselves how the sewage is treated (Fig. 6-8)? How is the effectiveness of the treatment measured? What is primary treatment? Secondary treatment? Why is complete treatment rarely used?

A number of steps are involved in the treatment of municipal sewage before it can be discharged downstream with safety. Here is a quick summary:

1. The polluted water must be collected and delivered to the point of treatment.

2. Inorganic solids (sand, gravel, glass) are quickly removed by screening and settling.

3. Organic matter, whether floating or settled, is removed by skimming

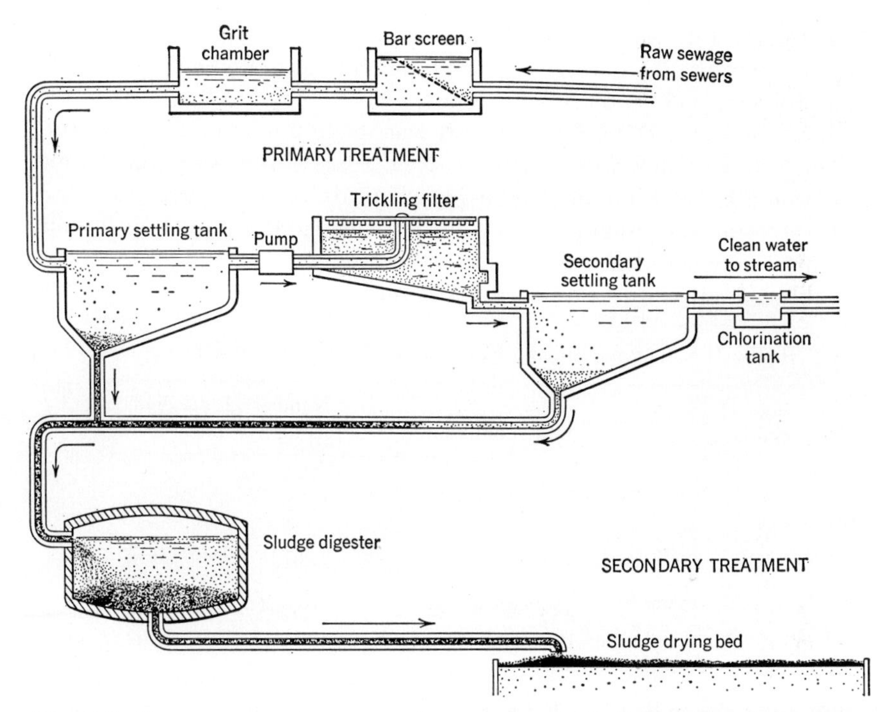

Fig. 6-8. How a sewage treatment plant works. (*U.S. Public Health Service.*)

and settling. Anaerobic bacteria (able to live without air) go to work on this organic material and decompose it. This solid forms a sludge which has value as a fertilizer.

The effectiveness of treatment is measured by the biochemical-oxygen-demand (BOD) and the suspended-solids removal (SS). Primary treatment takes out about 35 per cent of the pollution, which in many cases is enough, as the river itself can usually help in accomplishing the purifying process.

4. Secondary treatment follows if the remaining liquid is still too high in "organic loading." Usually the water is sprayed into the air, or in some cases air is pumped through the liquid and the aerobic bacteria begin to

attack it. If the effluent discharged to the receiving waters is still too high in bacteria, it must be chlorinated.

Intermediate treatment is 65 per cent removal, and complete may be as high as 90 per cent. The cost of the complete treatment would be beyond the finances of most communities and would actually be unnecessary unless the water had to be reused for drinking.

6-5. Fluorine in Drinking Water

A Study in Interpretation of Data. One technique found useful in teaching interpretation of data is to permit students to examine data relating to a problem, such as the following:

In December, 1955, a final analysis was made public on a 10-year experiment in Kingston and Newburgh, New York. This was the concluding report on 2,139 children in Newburgh, where the water supply has 1 part of fluorine in every million parts of water, compared with 2,255 children of Kingston, where there is no fluorine in the water.

Table 6-1 gives a record of decayed, missing, and filled teeth among

Table 6-1. Comparison of Findings in Newburgh and Kingston

Age of children	Number of children		Number of decayed, missing, or filled teeth	
	Newburgh (fluorine)	Kingston	Newburgh (fluorine)	Kingston
6–9	708	913	672	2,134
10–12	521	640	1,711	4,471
13–14	263	441	1,579	5,161
15–16	109	119	1,063	1,962

children of the two cities at the end of the 10-year controlled experiment. Do the figures bear out the following conclusions?

1. The younger a child is when he starts drinking fluoridated water, the more effectively is tooth decay reduced.

2. Among the children who drink fluoridated water, the number of missing, decayed, or repaired teeth will be between 40 and 58 per cent lower, depending on age, than among the children who do not drink the water.

While this dental study was going on, the Department of Health studied the health of all the children over the 10-year period and found no significant differences between the two groups of children.

Dr. Harold C. Hodge, professor of pharmacology at the University of Rochester School of Medicine and Dentistry, gave fluoridation a clean bill of health, as far as safety is concerned. He said that the key to the whole safety question is that the kidneys eject fluorine into the urine almost as fast as the human being drinks it. Apparently only a minute fraction is retained to strengthen teeth. He sees no danger of fluorine poisoning. Opponents of the program have argued that the method may yet prove dangerous, that there have been cases of "fluorine illness," and that the chemical could be applied to teeth in other ways.

At least two other studies have been carefully recorded. The first is the health study of a group of people who have been drinking fluoridated water all their lives in Bartlett, Texas, compared to a group in nearby Cameron, who drink unfluoridated water. Second, a statistical observation has been made of the matched populations of sixteen fluoride-drinking and sixteen non-fluoride-drinking cities to check long-term effects.

In examining the results of studies like these, one needs to be convinced of the reliability of the data. Are there, for instance, any "hidden factors" which may have affected the end result but which do not appear in the evidence adduced?

Various municipalities in our country will need to examine these and newer findings, listen to pros and cons critically, weigh the evidence, and decide whether or not to fluoridate their water supplies. Mayor Wagner of New York asked the city's Board of Health to answer these four questions when making a final recommendation:

1. Is tooth decay so serious a health problem in the city that fluoride should be put in city water?

2. What will be the effect on tooth decay if the water is treated?

3. If fluoridation is adopted, what is the best and most economical way to make the fluoride available?

4. What guarantees are there that, if put in city water, the fluoride will be harmless to individuals and beneficial to public health?

There is excellent material here for class discussion: the role of research, the weighing of evidence, the reaching of conclusions on the basis of the available evidence, and the role of the citizen in the final outcome. Could your class perhaps "play" a Board of Health and work through this problem?

To learn the collective views of an international group of experts, your students might study the first report of the World Health Organization, *Expert Committee on Water Fluoridation* (Columbia University Press, New York, 1958).

6-6. Increasing Our Water Supply: Planning

Preventing Water Waste at Home. Ask your students to examine the faucets in their homes. Do any of them leak? Students might measure the waste caused by a faucet drip for 10 minutes. They might then calculate waste (in gallons) for 1 hour; 1 day; 1 month; 3 months (the usual period of a water bill). What does the waste cost their families?

Here is a statistic: New York City wastes some 200 million gallons of water per day because of leaks and careless use. "How much water does our community waste?" might be a question to consider.

Show the class one or more types of water faucets used in homes (Fig. 6-9). Take each apart and show how to replace the washer. Have stu-

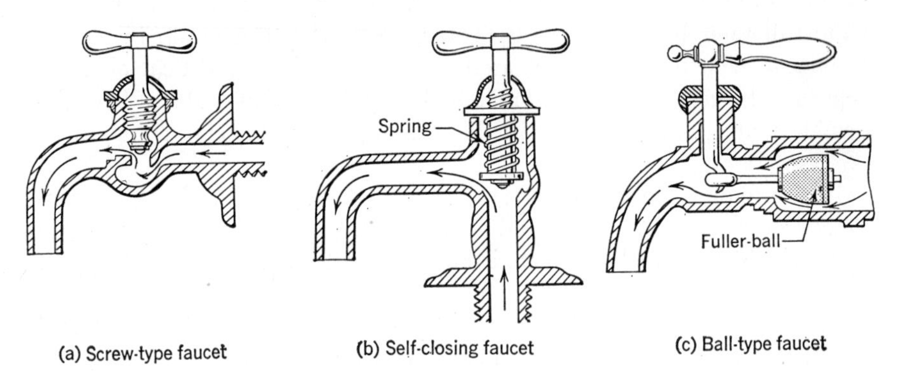

Fig. 6-9. Three common kinds of faucets. Repairing faucets saves water.

dents note the difference between hot water and cold water washers. Demonstrate the repairing of a faucet if more than the washer needs replacement. Instructions for faucet repair may be found in *Handbook for Teaching of Conservation and Resource Use,* page 191 (Sec. 19-3*h*). Your students can now take on the job of repairing the leaky faucets in their own homes.

Show the class how a leaky toilet flush tank can be repaired by adjustment of the float or by replacement of the plunger ball. Deteriorated examples of these items can be compared to new parts and hints given as to how to make proper adjustments of each.

Discuss emergency measures that can conserve water during dishwashing, laundering, and bathing. Your class might compile a list of "do's" and "don'ts" for emergencies.

Things That Industry Can Do. Can water be recycled or reused by industry? Have a student report on the successful reuse of water at the Kaiser Steel Company in Fontana, California (Fig. 6-10). Another student might find out about the use of treated sewage effluent by the Bethlehem Steel plant near Baltimore, Maryland.

Things That Communities, States, and Regions Can Do. You might show the movies from the Living Water Series: *Nature's Plan* and *Man's Problem* (Encyclopaedia Britannica Films). The emphasis is on the vital importance of proper care of our watersheds. There might follow a class

Fig. 6-10. The water system of this steel mill includes the recovery and reuse of water, even that from the plant sewage. (*Kaiser Steel Corporation.*)

discussion on important water conservation measures such as reducing runoff, increasing infiltration, and impounding water for surface storage.

Ideas That Are Being Tried or Suggested. Can students suggest changes in vegetative cover that might reduce evaporation and transpiration losses in certain areas (Sec. 3-14)?

Examine the suggestions of replenishing ground water by artificial recharge with flood waters, treated sewage effluents, or ordinary surface water. Write for a *Survey of the Direct Utilization of Waste Waters* (State Water Pollution Control Board, Sacramento, Calif.).

What about desalting sea water by distillation (Sec. 11-5)? Discussion might emphasize that it is still a slow and costly process.

Do we have enough evidence on the efficacy of cloud seeding as a rain maker (Sec. 11-10)?

Perhaps your students might try to reproduce an experiment carried on by the Bureau of Reclamation. It has been found that a thin coating of hexadecanol (cityl alcohol) spread on the surface of water in a laboratory setting cuts evaporation losses by almost two-thirds. The Department of the Interior is experimenting to see whether this method will work on large water areas.

Students might be referred to a good summary of various ways of conserving water in the August 31, 1957, issue of *Science News Letter*. The article, Making Water Plentiful, was written by Edward Hedrick.

Is more education needed in your community on water supply problems? What would pollution abatement laws, rigidly enforced, do for your water supply?

More Basic Research Needed. It may be that as research scientists learn more about certain natural phenomena, new and important clues to our water supply problem will be forthcoming.

Do we know all there is to know about how lakes and streams remain in ecological balance? The routes followed by water-laden clouds? The manner in which moisture condenses and falls as rain? The intimate linkage of soil erosion and sedimentation with an efficient water supply?

The other side of the problem of too little water is the problem of too much water where it isn't wanted (Fig. 6-11). We are still far from knowing all the answers to the question of controlling floods, although we do know how intimately the solution to the problem is linked to proper watershed management.

Fig. 6-11. The problem of "too much water." The entire village of Oslo, Minnesota, was flooded by the waters of the Red River in 1950. (*U.S. Soil Conservation Service.*)

Much research is now going forward on all these problems, some of it private, some of it government-sponsored. The Coweeta Hydrologic Laboratory in North Carolina, run by the U.S. Forestry Service, and the Water Research and Information Center at Texas A. & M. College are two important projects. Your class might write for literature.

Some of today's students will tomorrow be in the forefront of research. All of our students will be citizens and with them will rest the decision, directly or indirectly, as to whether basic research will be adequately encouraged and financed.

A National Water Plan. Here is something your class might want to know about:

In January, 1956, President Eisenhower sent Congress a long-range program for development of the nation's water resources. The program, representing the joint thinking of all the Federal agencies dealing with water resources, was prepared by a special Cabinet committee.

In submitting the report to Congress, Mr. Eisenhower said that the water resource policies the United States adopts "will have a profound effect in the years to come upon our domestic, agricultural and industrial economy."

The recommendations of this committee, and what Congress has done and will do with these and future findings, make up-to-the-minute material for class discussion, particularly after students have become familiar with the water resource problems of our country. Students may follow closely, once their interest is aroused, the steps taken in a democracy as it tries to meet a national need.

7
A Study of the Soil

In this chapter you will find a selective study of the soil: how it is formed and what are its biological, physical, and chemical characteristics. This leads to techniques of soil testing and soil improvement. Aspects of erosion and erosion control are included in a section on keeping the soil where it belongs.

HOW SOIL IS MADE

Perhaps you would like to start a study of the soil with a film from the Living Earth Series called *Birth of the Soil* (Encyclopaedia Britannica Films).

7-1. Profile of the Soil

When it is possible, have students examine an exposed, vertical section through soil, such as an area where excavation for a building is under way. Other times it may be possible to dig down several feet along a slope. At times you may find a washout of soil along a slope, so that a vertical cross section is already present.

What sorts of layers are found? Do the layers differ in color, texture, or composition? Why? Where are nearly all the plant roots found? Try the road builders' soil test (Sec. 7-7) on soil from the different layers. What can be learned by this means about the composition of the layers? From these layers, take samples of soil and find their differences in the amount and kind of animal and plant life (Sec. 7-6).

Students might examine soil samples from various localities by means of a soil auger (Fig. 7-1). Students may enumerate several factors that have changed bedrock to subsoil. How has topsoil been formed? Later you may want to indicate the role of topsoil in holding water.

Fig. 7-1. Examining soil brought up by a soil auger. (*New Hampshire Fish and Game Service photo, from Learning to Use New Hampshire Resources.*)

7-2. How Rocks Become Part of Soil

To lead into a discussion of the part played by rocks in soil formation, students will need to learn something about the weathering of rocks. Perhaps they can find a sample of granite that is beginning to crumble. They might take two pieces of limestone or fine sandstone and rub them together. After quite some rubbing, they should succeed in obtaining a very small amount of fine material. How, in nature, is this "rubbing" accomplished?

Weathering by Frost. On a field trip ask students to look for samples of soft rocks with cracks in them. Fill the cracks with water and allow the water to freeze (out of doors, if weather permits, or in the freezing unit of a refrigerator, if it doesn't). As the water expands in freezing, it may widen the crack. Your students might also try the Barrd test (Sec. 13-18). Under what climatic conditions and at what season would frost be the main weathering force?

Weathering by Expansion and Contraction. Students may already know something about the effect of temperature changes on rocks. Some will recall experiences at campfires. A piece of sandstone thrown into such a fire will perhaps "explode."

In the laboratory you might heat very thoroughly a piece of rock composed of layers (shale or slate) on a hot plate for several minutes. Quickly drop the rock into a pan of ice water. The rock may crack.

Students might examine at close range rocks that reveal exfoliation or peeling away of layers. When rocks are heated during the day there is expansion of the materials in the rock. At night sudden fluctuations may bring the temperature below freezing. The alternate expansions and contractions in rock cause exfoliation. This mechanical weathering due to fluctuations in temperature is prevalent in arid regions as well as in moist, cold ones.

Weathering by Chemical Action. Pour dilute hydrochloric acid on limestone. Note the action. Chemical decomposition and solution may be the main weathering forces in seasons other than winter. Your students will recall that roots of plants give off carbon dioxide (Sec. 3-13), which becomes carbonic acid (Sec. 7-10) in the soil. Students should be able to explain how mosses, lichens, and seedlings aid in chemical weathering.

Chemical weathering has great effect on breaking down rock in equatorial regions where there is heavy rainfall and soluble materials are carried away by the percolating action of water.

Perhaps this is the time, too, when students may want to compare this wearing down of rock with the formation of sedimentary rock from soil as shown in a sedimentation jar (Fig. 7-2). What effect has the enormous pressure of water on this rock formation?

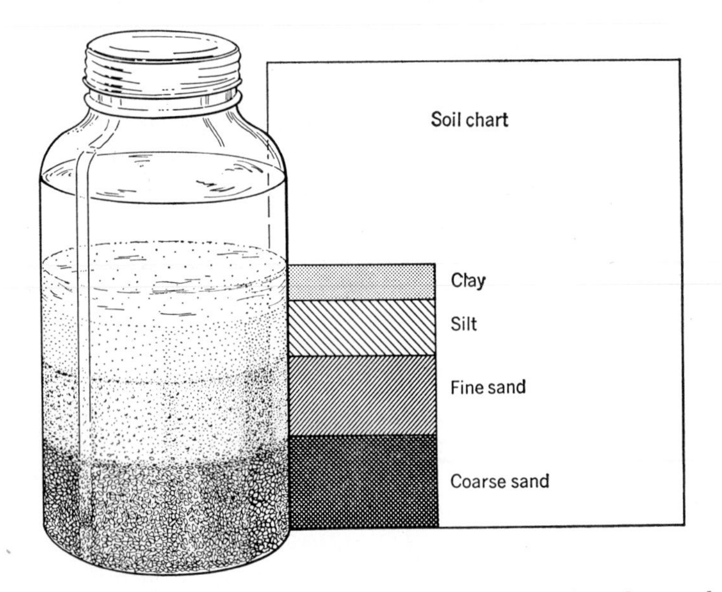

Fig. 7-2. A soil sample is shaken up with water and allowed to settle.

Is the pulverizing of rock all there is to the making of soil? To answer this question students might plant seeds in two flower pots, one of which contains soil and the other of which contains rock that has been crushed. Water both equally. Note results over a period of time, after the seeds have germinated.

7-3. Plants Are Soil Makers

Plants That Start with Bare Rock. Students might, on a field trip, examine bare rocks and make note of the lichens (Sec. 3-18) that cling to their surface. Lichens are able to dissolve a small part of the rock surface as they grow, thus forming minute amounts of soil. Students may notice that mosses and ferns are able to gain foothold on sections of rocks upon which there is a vestige of soil.

Pioneer Plants. If you can find exposed sand and gravel from a river bed that has changed its course, students might make note of the first plant invaders. These are usually annual weeds that hold the raw mineral stuff in place. The new vegetation encourages the invasion of animals; their droppings add organic matter, thus starting a soil-building process.

Leaves Add to Soil. Students may study at firsthand the continuous progression of dead leaves into soil. On a field trip plan to include a visit to a place where you will find the cut grass and leaves from a garden kept in a compost barrel or the layers of leaves on the floor of a wooded area. Have students examine the uppermost layers of leaves. Can they be identified? Can students also identify those leaves buried several inches? What has happened to the leaves still farther down? What organisms in the soil are responsible for these changes? What effect on the balance in nature would result if soil fungi and the bacteria of decay disappeared?

7-4. Rotting Wood Builds Humus

Students might bring back from a field trip some rotted wood from an old tree stump or log. They might note how easily it crumbles, adding organic matter to the soil and eventually forming part of soil humus. Suggest to your students this experiment: Dry the rotted wood, crumble it, and put it in a container. Weigh both. Pour water onto the wood and let the wood absorb it, adding more water if needed. Let it stand long enough for the wood to be completely saturated. Drain off any excess water, but do not squeeze the wood. Weigh the wet wood and container again. Usually the results show that the dry wood has absorbed four or more times its weight in water. Rotting wood, by soaking up and holding rain water or melting snow, helps make good humus in the forest soil.

BIOLOGICAL ASPECTS OF SOIL

7-5. What Makes Up a Unit of Soil?[1]

When on a field trip, blocks of soil about 6 inches square and 6 inches deep may be cut from different areas such as meadow and woods. When these are brought back to the classroom, the clods may be broken up on paper towels (Fig. 7-3). All plants should be removed and the roots shaken free of soil and small animals. The various kinds of plant roots and animals (snails, insects, worms, etc.) may be placed in separate piles or put into jars. After the soil has dried sufficiently it may be sifted through ½-, ¼-, and ¹⁄₁₆-inch mesh sieves and made into separate screened piles. The various plant and animal fragments may be separated out from each. Students might compare the materials found in the various blocks of soil. How do they differ in animal life and decayed plant matter?

Fig. 7-3. What do you find in a unit of soil?

7-6. What Living Things Are Found in Soil?

Your students may make a more careful study of the living organisms found in their unit of soil. They might look for earthworms, nematode worms, sowbugs, larvae and pupae of insects, eggs of small reptiles. What is the role played by these living things in making a healthy soil? Then students might examine bits of soil under the microscope. Samples of soil may also be incubated on petri dishes that contain nutrient agar (Sec. 18-1*a*). Many kinds of bacteria and especially fungi should become apparent as colonies. The USDA Yearbook *Soils and Men* (1938) describes a great variety of organisms, plants, and animals found in the soil.

[1] Many of the techniques described in Secs. 7-5 through 7-7 were adapted from *Conservation: A Handbook for Teachers* (Sec. 19-2*b*).

Students may also explore the living organisms in a decaying tree stump or log.

PHYSICAL ASPECTS OF SOIL

7-7. Some Simple Tests

Crumble Test. Students might bring to class samples of different kinds of soil (forest, open field, clay, loam, or sandy soils, or—if they live in the city—playground, park, or garden samples). Ask students to rub pinches of the soil in the palms of their hands. Which kind of soil crumbles most easily?

The "Feel" of Soil. Students may also begin to recognize soils by their feel. Thus, sandy soil is gritty; silt feels floury or like talcum when dry, and moderately plastic when wet; clay is harsh when dry, plastic and sticky when wet.

Particle Size Test (Road Builders' Soil Test). Using sedimentation jars, students may perform the following test on various soil samples: If a quart glass bottle or jar is filled about two-thirds full of water, enough of the soil sample should be poured in so that the water just overflows. With a hand or a cover over the jar, it should be well shaken and then allowed to stand until the soil settles.

Students will notice the layers of soil in the bottle (Fig. 7-2). Where are the biggest particles? For each sample tested students may make a record, by holding a card against the bottle and marking the location of the various layers. Each layer may then be labeled (sand, gravel, humus, clay). As students compare the cards they will note significant differences, depending upon the kind of soil they started with. Why would a test like this be useful to road builders?

Percentage of Sand, Silt, and Clay in Soil. A group of students might find this an interesting experiment: Shake up 2 tablespoons of fine soil in a pint jar about three-quarters full of water. After allowing it to stand for a minute, pour the muddy water into a second jar. What remains in the first jar is mainly *sand.*

After the second jar has been standing 5 minutes, pour the muddy water into a third jar. The sediment remaining in the second jar is largely *silt.* Now add more water to the third jar, shake it vigorously, and allow it to stand for a few hours or perhaps till the next day. When the water is poured off the residue is almost altogether *clay.*

Students may then dry the residues and weigh them or measure their volumes in a graduated cylinder. The percentage of sand, silt, and clay in the soil, by weight or by volume, may then be calculated. Students might note the fineness of the particles of each sample and examine them under a magnifying glass.

Compactness Test. A pencil or sharpened dowel rod may be pushed into the soil with the palm of the hand until it just begins to hurt. Try this technique on various areas and soils (lawn, woods, playground, paths). Measuring the distance the pencil goes into the ground will give a rough comparison of the compactness of the soil in the different areas.

Which are the most compact soils? The least? Which soils contain most grass roots? Most earthworms? What effect would there be on compactness after a rainstorm? (Equal amounts of water could be poured on the various spots and new tests made.) Does compactness of the soil have anything to do with the absence of grass from a path? How can soil be made less compact?

Percolation and Capillarity. *Which Kind of Soil Holds Most Rain Water?* Bring the demonstration in Fig. 7-4 to class. In preparing the

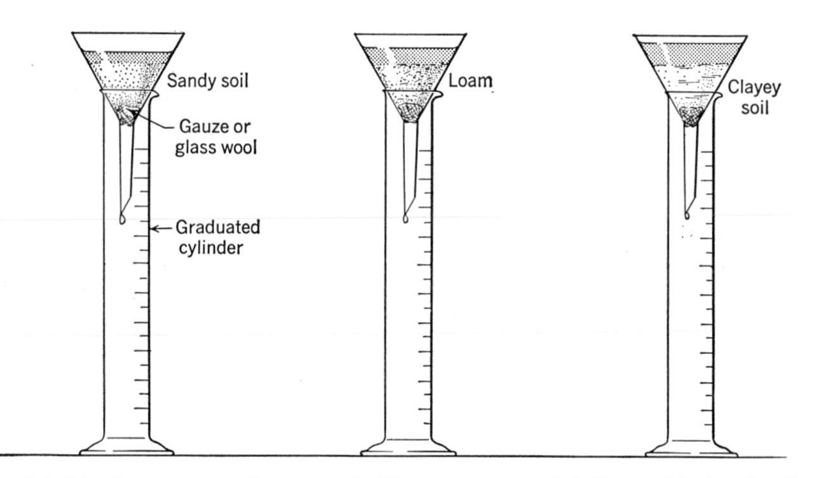

Fig. 7-4. To demonstrate the water-holding capacity of different kinds of soil.

funnels, first insert a bit of gauze or glass wool into the stem of each. Then fill one funnel with sandy soil, another with loam, and a third with soil rich in clay. Have a student pour equal amounts of water into each funnel. If you use graduated cylinders to catch the runoff of water, students may be able to describe their results with more accuracy. Which kind of soil permits water to pass through most quickly? How can the difference in rate be explained? What is meant by "percolation"? Compare both the amount of water and the amount of sediment from each soil sample. Which kind of soil retains the most water? Is water left standing on the surface of any of the soils? Would this kind of soil be good for gardening? Pour more water on each soil sample. Which soil allows water to pass through it readily, yet does not lose much soil? Which soil acts most like a sponge? Does the crumble structure (friability) of the soil have anything to do with the ease with which water enters and is absorbed by the soil? What ingredients might be used in preparing a good soil for crops?

Which Kind of Soil Absorbs Most Water? At another time, you may use the same demonstration as in Fig. 7-4 for another purpose. Instead of pouring water into the funnels of the different soils, fill the graduated cylinders with water and watch the rate of absorption of the water from the cylinders by the soil types. What kind of soil seems best for absorbing water? In which kind of soil materials would plant roots receive available water? What is meant by vadose water?

One student might reproduce the demonstration using cheesecloth as a wick, as shown on page 144 of the USDA Yearbook *Water* (1955). Here you will find described capillarity and the hydrostatic principles involved

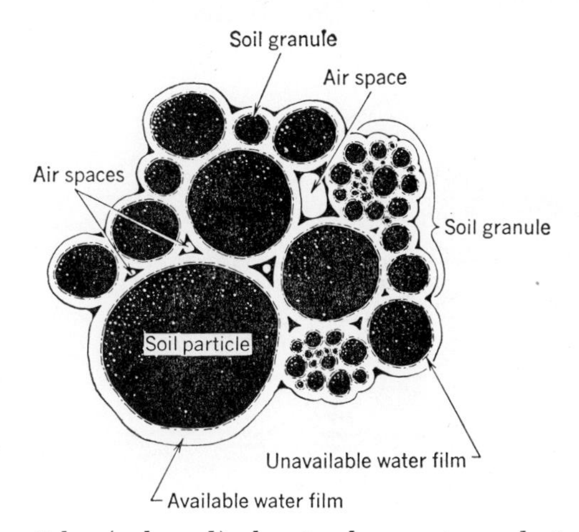

Fig. 7-5. Soil particles (enlarged) showing how water and air are held in the soil. (*Cornell Rural Leaflet, vol. 49, no. 4.*)

in the transmission of water in soil, regardless of the soil texture or structure.

In performing and discussing these experiments students will come to realize that the amount of open space in soil has a lot to do with the ease of water's flowing through and being retained (Fig. 7-5). In sandy or gravelly soil, with its large spaces, water will go through readily but will not be held. Loam, on the other hand, with its smaller spaces between smaller particles, will take up water more slowly and retain it for a longer time. Particle size, however, is only one of several soil requirements to be considered in studying soils. Some others are acidity (Sec. 7-9), amount of organic matter (Sec. 7-6), amount of minerals available to plants (Sec. 7-11), and internal or subsurface drainage.

CHEMICAL ASPECTS OF SOIL

7-8. Sweet, Sour, Neutral

In order to grow well, plants require certain conditions of the soil. Most plants need a soil that is almost neutral, although there are some that thrive best in an acid or "sour" soil while others require an alkaline or "sweet" soil.

In order for your students to understand the meaning of these terms, they will need a working knowledge of acids, bases, and neutralization. Or, vice versa, when your students are studying acids, bases, and salts, direct application of this knowledge may be made by soil testing. This will lead to learning ways in which improper acidity or alkalinity of the soil may be remedied.

What Is an Acid and How Does It Act? Prepare dilute solutions of

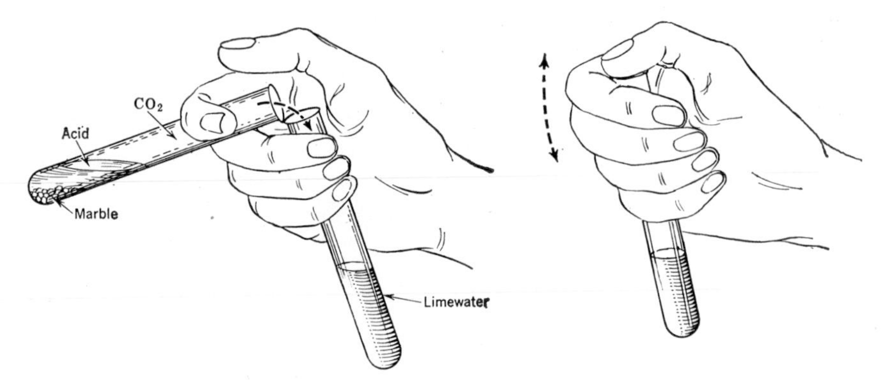

Fig. 7-6. To show the action of an acid on a carbonate. (Be sure to tilt the mouths of the tubes shown at the left close to each other—at right angles, if possible.)

four common acids, hydrochloric, sulfuric, nitric, and perhaps tartaric or acetic. (Always pour the concentrated acid, especially in the case of sulfuric acid, *carefully* into the water.) Students may test each of these solutions in turn with any of the following which are available: red and blue litmus paper, hydrion paper, bromthymol blue solution, phenolphthalein solution, methyl orange solution.

Ask students to try the action of each acid on granulated zinc (using powdered zinc with tartaric acid). In every case except nitric acid, a test for hydrogen may be obtained by applying a lighted splint. (Nitric acid, being an oxidizing agent, releases various other gases, depending on the metal used and the concentration of the acid.)

They might try the action of each acid on marble and test the evolved odorless gas with limewater (Fig. 7-6). In the case of tartaric acid, precipitated chalk (finely powdered calcium carbonate) should be used. Why?

In each case, the product is carbon dioxide. Elicit from students that this test may be used to identify a carbonate. Later they may use this test in soil analysis (Sec. 7-11).

Have students compare the formulas of the acids they have used. When dissolved in water, any acid supplies hydrogen ions. As your students advance they will want to learn that the hydrogen ion (proton) is a very additive particle, forming hydronium ion $(H_3O)^+$ with water.

What Is a Base and How Does It Act? Prepare dilute solutions of four common bases: sodium, potassium, calcium (limewater), and ammonium hydroxides. Students may make the same indicator tests for bases as for acids and compare results.

They may rub each solution in turn between their fingers, washing their fingers well between each test. Sodium and potassium hydroxide will have a particularly slippery, soapy feeling.

Carbon dioxide may be bubbled through the solution of a base (Fig. 6-2) for about 5 minutes. The treated solution should then be removed and tested for a carbonate by adding dilute hydrochloric acid (Fig. 7-6). There should be effervescence, which will turn the limewater milky when the test tube is shaken. What substance has been formed? This reaction has application in soil treatment, when lime (which, when moist, forms the base, calcium hydroxide) is added to acid soil to neutralize it.

Examining the formulas of several bases, your students will see that bases all have OH radicals in common. When dissolved in water these become hydroxyl ions, which are responsible for the similar characteristics of bases.

What Happens When Acids and Bases Get Together? Laundry soap may be used for a base. Students might add to a half test tube of water a piece of soap the size of a pea. This may then be dissolved by heating. Half the solution should be poured in a tumbler of water and tested with litmus. Another test tube should be half filled with vinegar (tested with litmus to reveal its acidity). The vinegar may then be added slowly to the soap solution, which is tested frequently with litmus of both colors. If this experiment is performed carefully, one can stop at the neutral point, when the blue litmus stays blue and the red remains red.

Another way to perform this experiment is to dissolve a pellet of sodium hydroxide (not to be handled with the fingers) in 20 cubic centimeters of water in a test tube. About 15 cubic centimeters of the solution may then be poured into an evaporating dish and dilute hydrochloric acid added, a little at a time. The solution should be stirred constantly and tested by applying the wet glass stirring rod to litmus until there is no basic reaction.

Next, the 5 cubic centimeters of sodium hydroxide left in the test tube and the acid should be diluted to one-fifth their strength. These much-diluted solutions of acid and base may be added drop by drop to the solution in the evaporating dish, to bring the liquid to the neutral or end point where it affects neither red nor blue litmus paper.

Students may evaporate the neutral solution slowly to dryness, avoiding spattering. The residue may be examined and tasted. What is it? Help your students to become aware that the OH^- of the base unites with the H^+ of the acid to form the almost un-ionized water, HOH, leaving the salt, Na^+Cl^-, in solution.

For more advanced students neutralization may be performed as a quantitative experiment with some additional knowledge. Required to prepare 10 grams of sodium chloride by neutralization:

Calculate the weight of chemically pure sodium hydroxide required and the weight of concentrated hydrochloric acid needed. (This should be thought through by the students with some aid, if necessary.)

$$\begin{array}{ccccc} x \text{ grams} & & y \text{ grams} & & 10 \text{ grams} \\ NaOH & + & HCl & & NaCl + H_2O \\ 40 & & 36.5 & & 58.5 \end{array}$$

Weight of pure 100% NaOH $\quad x = \frac{10 \times 40}{58.5} = 6.8$ grams

Weight 100% HCl $\quad y = \frac{10 \times 36.5}{58.5} = 6.2$ grams

Weight of conc. HCl (usually 38%) $\quad \frac{100}{38} \times 6.2 = 16.3$ grams

Volume of conc. HCl $\quad \frac{\text{Weight}}{\text{Density}} = \frac{16.3}{1.2} = 13.6$ cc

Weigh the sodium hydroxide in a weighed evaporating dish and dissolve in 25 cubic centimeters of water. Allow the solution to cool. Measure out 14 cubic centimeters (a slight excess) of concentrated hydrochloric acid and dilute it with water to 25 cubic centimeters. Run it into a burette. Allow 20 cubic centimeters of the hydrochloric acid to flow into the evaporating dish. Add a few drops of phenolphthalein solution. Then pour the 25 cubic centimeters of sodium hydroxide into the dish. Stir well. The solution should turn pink. From the burette add the hydrochloric acid, a few drops at a time, stirring well after each addition. The color may deepen as the neutral point is approached. The acid should then be added drop by drop. Consider the neutral point reached when a single drop of acid changes the pink color to colorless.

Evaporate at once on a water bath. Why? (Since the experiment is quantitative, spattering is avoided.) When the water has all evaporated, heat cautiously and then intensely with a bunsen flame directly under the dish to remove any traces of acid or mechanically enclosed water. Continue heating until all snapping and crackling (decrepitation) ceases. Weigh. Taste.

If desired, students can purify the crystals by dissolving them in water, filtering and recrystallizing, removing each crop of crystals as soon as an appreciable quantity has formed and long before the filtrate has evaporated to dryness. These crystals may then be examined under a microscope and preserved. Students can make microphotographs of these crystal structures by means of camera and microscope or enlarger.

pH: The Acid-base Measuring Stick. Test a sample of distilled water with litmus paper of both kinds. Students will find that there is no reaction.

The position of water between acids and bases has given chemists the idea that a scale of acid and base strength can be devised with water at the mid-point (7). Your students are now ready for a discussion of the pH scale (below 7 increasingly acidic; above 7 increasingly basic) and how it can be used. Control of pH is important in soil testing, but it has many other applications as well. It is needed in sugar manufacturing, water purification, paper making, baking, canning, jelly making, and other food industries, as well as in bacteriology and medicine.

7-9. Soil and Its pH

The pH value of most soils falls in the range between 4 and 8 (Fig. 7-7). A pH value of 6.5 (just a bit on the acid side) is desirable for most crops. In humid regions, soils are usually acid as a result of losses by leaching and crop removal of such basic elements as calcium, magnesium, and potassium (Sec. 7-10). In arid or semiarid regions one is apt to find alkaline soil.

Testing Soil for pH. Students may collect samples of soil from different regions, such as rich garden soil, soil from a wooded area, from a beach, from a desert area if possible, along a whitewashed wall, or from a swamp. They may take samples of soil from the surface as well as samples about 5 inches deep. The samples should be packed individually in newspaper and transported in a bucket.

In class, students may test soil in this simple way. Moisten strips of blue and red litmus paper and lay one of each color on individual glass slides. Place a pinch of one soil sample on the top of the strips of litmus on one slide. Then do the same with other slides and other samples of soil. Perhaps the soil needs to be moistened a bit. When students turn over each slide they should be able to see whether the soil is acidic or alkaline.

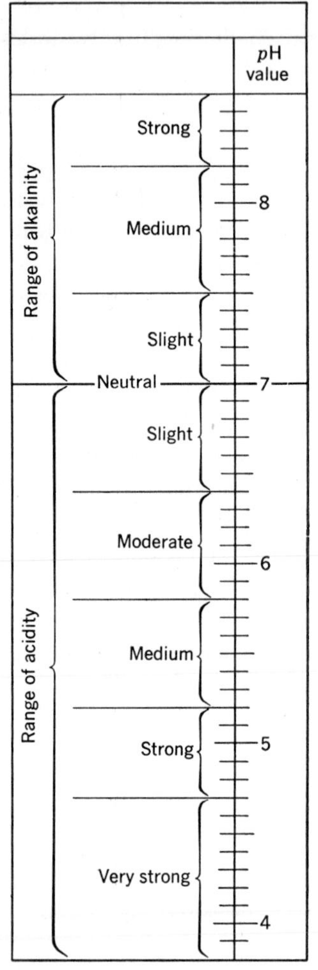

Fig. 7-7. The pH measuring stick for soils.

Have groups of students check each other, each group using different indicators (Sec. 7-8). When a liquid indicator is used, have students place a pinch of the soil sample in a small watch glass or white dish. Then add a bit of the liquid indicator such as bromthymol blue or others you may select. Tilt the dish so that the color of the liquid may be examined.

Press a strip of hydrion paper into a moist sample of various kinds of soil. Using the color guide on the roll of paper, decide which soil is most acid. Are any neutral?

Procure a pH test kit from your county agricultural agent or from the department of agronomy at your nearest land grant college. Follow the simple instructions accompanying the kit.

Simple inexpensive outfits for soil acidity tests (pH) may be ordered from Soil-Tex, Edwards Chemical Company, East Lansing, Mich., or from La Motte Chemical Products Company, Baltimore, Md.

What Causes Soils to Be Acidic or Basic? Test with hydrion or litmus paper decaying organic matter and limestone (parent material). These are two factors which affect the pH of soil. Another might be leaching. The pH of the soil, however, is only one factor among many that affect the kind of plant communities existing in a particular soil.

Is the pH Correct? Test the pH values of gardens, vegetable patches, and lawns in your vicinity. Is the pH correct for the use to which the soil is put (Table 7-1)?

At times, a very acid soil is desirable, for certain kinds of plants grow best in soil somewhere between pH 5 and 4, for example, azaleas, certain ferns, hydrangeas, ladyslipper, sheep laurel, sweet pepperbush, stagger bush, trillium, maple-leaved viburnum, mountain ash, pitch pine,

Table 7-1. pH Values Suitable for Some Common Crops

pH 6.5 to pH 7.5	alfalfa, sweet clover
pH 6.0 to pH 7.0	red and white clover, sugar beets, cabbage, beans, peas, carrots, cucumbers
pH 5.5 to pH 6.5	wheat, oats, barley, rye, most grasses, onions, tomatoes, most fruits
pH 5.0 to pH 5.5	potatoes, tobacco, watermelons, blueberries, certain flowers
pH less than 5.0	soil usually too acid; should be limed

scrub oak, among many. Here are just a few plants that thrive in slightly acid soil of a pH between 5 and 7: privet, mountain laurel, juniper, apple, hemlock, linden, most oaks, bittersweet, goldenrod, wintergreen, Virginia creeper, coleus, begonia, bayberry, chokeberry, candytuft, chrysanthemum. Almost neutral soil, with a pH of 6 to 8.0, supports such plants as barberry, honeysuckle, hawthorn, lilac, crocus, grape hyacinth, alyssum, crab apple, locust, sugar maple, pear, cherry, elm, ash, ailanthus. When these plant-soil relationships are well known, a student may be able to judge the pH of the soil as he recognizes a few of the kinds of plants growing in a given area. What happens when soil gradually changes its pH, as minerals are leached and possibly make the soil more alkaline? What kinds of plants will succeed each other in this area?

Incidentally, if you have the opportunity to develop a nature trail (Sec. 9-5) or outdoor garden (Sec. 8-3), you may need to remedy the pH of the soil for some reason. Might your class set up a soil-testing service for neighboring lawns and gardens?

7-10. Chemistry of Soil Conditions

Students can understand the chemistry of these pH soil conditions quite easily if they consider them step by step. First, they will need to become acquainted with basic and acidic oxides (anhydrides).

Basic and Acidic Oxides. Place a *very small* piece of potassium (or sodium) in a clean dry iron pan resting on a tripod. Directing a sharply focused nonluminous bunsen flame downward on the metal, cautiously burn it. What is the result? Add a few drops of water and test with litmus.

Burn a small piece of calcium as in the potassium test above. Burn a 2-inch strip of magnesium ribbon over a clean mortar, allowing the product to drop into the mortar. Moisten with a few drops of water and grind to a thin paste. Test with litmus. (This will be a slow change.)

In all three of the above tests the student will discover that bases are formed. Going back to the problem of soil, he will now see that potassium, calcium, or magnesium are base-forming (metallic) elements, and their removal from the soil will produce a sour or acid condition.

Line a deflagrating spoon with asbestos paper and fill with flowers of sulfur. Ignite the sulfur in a flame and lower the spoon into a clean bottle of air. Remove it when the sulfur has burned for about a minute and add a few cubic centimeters of water to the bottle. Shake. Test with litmus.

Repeat the sulfur test using red phosphorus instead of sulfur.

Burn a piece of charcoal (carbon) in a bottle of air. Heat the charcoal until it glows and then hold it by means of a forceps in the bottle. Add a few drops of water, shake, and test with litmus.

In cases of the sulfur, the red phosphorus, and the carbon, the student has been dealing with acid-forming (nonmetallic) elements. This knowledge, too, has application in soil chemistry as, for example, when sulfur is used to overcome alkaline soil conditions.

What Can Be Done to Correct Acid Soil? Students may test some weak acid, like vinegar, with litmus. Then, ask them to add to 2 drops of the acid some powdered limestone or precipitated chalk (both calcium carbonate). Effervescence will be noted. Water may be added to the residue, which is then tested with litmus. The acid reaction should be gone.

Liming is the process used to correct soil acidity. This consists in adding to the soil ground limestone (or sometimes hydrated and burnt lime, marble dust, mash, chalk, or oyster shells). The limestone will act on the acid in the soil and in addition will restore to it calcium. In the case of dolomitic limestone, magnesium as well as calcium is added to the soil. In practice, one neutralizes an acid soil by adding powdered limestone, about 80 pounds to every 1,000 square feet of soil.

What Can Be Done to Correct Alkaline Soil? Sulfur, as the student has discovered, is an acid-forming element. Powdered sulfur spread on the soil slowly oxidizes, eventually forming an acid that is able to neutralize the alkalinity in the soil. A student might like to try this out. In practice, when acidifying soil, about 25 pounds of flowers of sulfur are added to 1,000 square feet of soil.

A fertilizer can be added to increase acidity of the soil if it is selected so that it will hydrolize to produce an acid reaction. Thus ammonium sulfate is added to increase both the acidity and the nitrogen content of the soil. If the nitrogen content is already high enough, aluminum sulfate may be added.

Hydrolysis. Your students will need to understand hydrolysis in order to comprehend the chemistry involved above. Conversely, if you happen to be studying hydrolysis, the above may be used in a practical application.

To learn what is meant by hydrolysis, solutions may be made of the following salts: sodium chloride, sodium carbonate, ammonium sulfate, and aluminum sulfate. Test each with pink and blue litmus. Your students may be surprised to find that only the first is neutral, the second being basic while the other two are decidedly acidic. They will want to know why. Refer them to a chemistry textbook for explanation.

7-11. Identifying Dissolved Minerals in the Soil

Soil and Its Minerals. Students might add equal volumes of distilled water to weighed samples of good soil and of poor soil. The mixtures

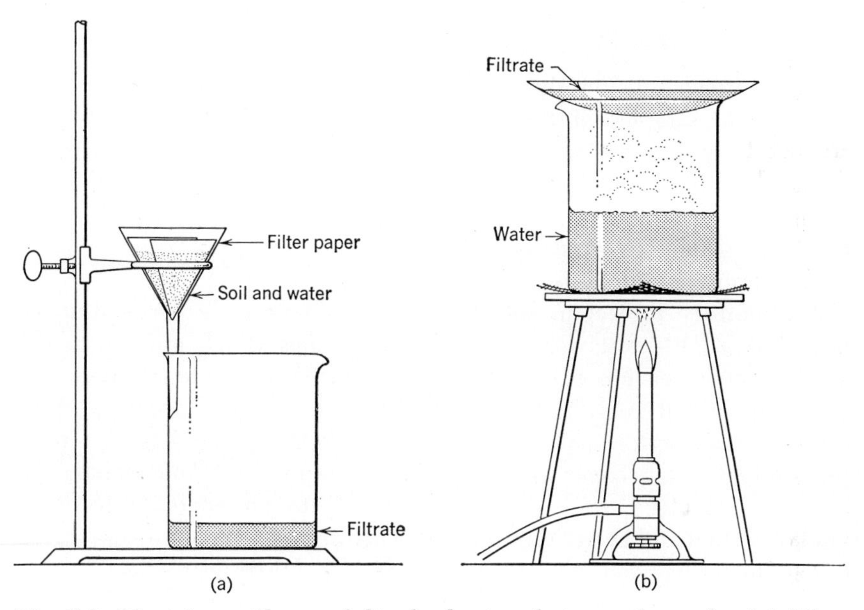

Fig. 7-8. Obtaining evidence of dissolved minerals in a soil sample. (*a*) Filter a well-stirred mixture of soil and water; (*b*) evaporate the filtrate on a water bath to avoid spattering.

should each be stirred and filtered (Fig. 7-8*a*). When the filtrates are evaporated (Fig. 7-8*b*), the residues of dissolved minerals may be noted and weighed. How do they compare?

Students might collect some dead leaves and dry them out so that they will burn readily. The leaves may be burned in a can or on a metal sheet and the color of the ashes noted. After pouring water over the ashes and stirring well, the nonsoluble material should be filtered out. The filtrate is then evaporated and the residue noted. What is it? Tie this in with the need for fertilizers in order to supply minerals for good plant growth. Students will become aware that the soil itself would be of little value to plants were it not for dissolved minerals.

These supply the nourishment needed for growth and development of plant life. Further connections might be made with problems of human nutrition.

Soil Testing with Commercial Kits. There are a number of kits, varying in price range, on the market. Here are a few companies selling portable rapid-soil-test kits:

La Motte Chemical Products Company, Baltimore, Md.
Sudbury Soil Testing Laboratory, South Sudbury, Mass.
Urbana Laboratories, Urbana, Ill.
Edwards Chemical Company, East Lansing, Mich.

Using quick, commercial tests, your students may make a soil analysis of the various soils in their community.[2] Students may compare the nutrients in samples of topsoil, subsoil, virgin soil, and field soil by testing. They may test samples of commercial fertilizer and of barnyard manure for plant nutrients. Or they might submit samples of the soil around the school to a state laboratory for analysis of available plant nutrient content. At this time you might want to plan a field trip to see soil-improving practices.

A Chemistry Project in Soil Analysis. When your chemistry students have learned the tests for common anions (ions which migrate to the anode and hence are negative) and cations (positive ions), they can do a simple soil analysis by applying their knowledge. Some of these are not the tests ordinarily used in commercial testing kits, but once the student has become interested in soil testing and understands the chemistry involved, he may want to go on to the more professional kind of testing and even delve into the chemistry of the more complicated tests, which involve a good deal of organic chemistry.

Here, then, are some of the tests interested students can quite easily perform:

Making a Soil Extract. Put ½ teaspoon of soil in 10 milliliters of distilled water. Shake for about a minute, and filter. (The filtrate contains the dissolved substances in the soil.)

Testing for Nitrogen. The nitrogen in the soil will be found as nitrate or nitrite anions, or ammonium cations.

NITRATE. Using a little of the soil extract, add a cold, concentrated, freshly prepared solution of ferrous sulfate (made by grinding a few crystals with a few cubic centimeters of water). Then pour 5 cubic centimeters of concentrated sulfuric acid through a thistle tube to the bottom of the test tube (or carefully down the side of the slightly inclined test tube). If a brown ring forms at the boundary between

[2] Careful directions for a complete soil analysis, along with reagents to prepare and color charts to procure, are given in *Test It Yourself!* (Sec. 19-2*w*).

the acid below and the solution above, the original solid contains a nitrate.

NITRITE. Repeat the test for a nitrate, substituting acetic acid for sulfuric. A brown coloration throughout indicates the presence of a nitrite.

AMMONIUM. To a sample of the soil add a solution of a nonvolatile base (e.g., sodium hydroxide). Heat gently, if necessary. If a gas comes off which has the odor of ammonia (and which produces a white smoke of dispersed ammonium chloride when brought near a filter paper wet with concentrated hydrochloric acid), ammonium ion is present.

Testing for Phosphorus. The phosphorus in the soil is in the form of phosphate and can be tested in this manner:

PHOSPHATE. To the soil extract add a few cubic centimeters of ammonium molybdate solution made slightly acid with nitric acid. Heat gently and watch for the formation of a yellow precipitate of ammonium phosphomolybdate, which shows that a phosphate is present.

Testing for Potassium. The simplest test for potassium, which exists in the soil as potassium salts, is the flame test with cobalt glass. Dip a platinum wire into soil moistened with dilute hydrochloric acid and hold in the outer edge of a nonluminous flame. A lavender or orchid flame coloration is characteristic. This may not always be visible, particularly when other metallic ions are present. Look at the flame through two layers of cobalt glass, and the lavender glow of the flame will reveal the potassium. The characteristic faint red potassium line, when viewed through a spectroscope,[3] will also identify the potassium. (The blue line is hard to find with a small, inexpensive spectroscope.)

Testing for Calcium. Calcium, too, exists in the soil in the form of salts of varying degrees of solubility.

To the soil extract add ammonium oxalate solution. If a white precipitate forms that proves soluble in hydrochloric acid but insoluble in acetic acid, a calcium compound is present.

A calcium compound confers an orange coloration to a nonluminous bunsen flame. This coloration reveals its characteristic green and orangish-yellow lines when viewed through a spectroscope.

Testing for Common Anions. CARBONATE. Add to a sample of the soil some dilute hydrochloric acid. If there is an effervescence and the gas that escapes is odorless and turns limewater milky, a carbonate is present.

SULFATE. To the soil extract add barium chloride solution. If a white precipitate insoluble in hydrochloric acid forms, a sulfate is present.

[3] A small direct-vision spectroscope such as that manufactured by Bausch and Lomb, 730 Fifth Ave., New York, is a fine addition to a high school chemistry laboratory.

An inexpensive color and spectroscope kit put out by Science Materials Center may be obtained from the Library of Science, 59 Fourth Ave., New York.

CHLORIDE. To the soil extract add a few cubic centimeters of silver nitrate solution. If a white precipitate forms, add to one portion of it ammonium hydroxide and to the other nitric acid. If the precipitate is soluble in ammonium hydroxide and insoluble in nitric acid, a chloride is present.

KEEPING SOIL IN PLACE

7-12. Importance of Vegetative Cover

To realize the importance of vegetative cover, grow different kinds of plants in class. Secure three nursery flats and fill them with garden soil. In the first, plant grass seeds; in the second, peas; and in the third, clover. After the plants have started to grow, test water runoff and absorption from time to time by sprinkling each flat with the same amount of water. Which plants seem to supply the best ground cover? Why?

Binding Power of Roots. Bring to class paper cups containing moist sand in which some twenty-five oat or mustard or radish seeds have been growing for about 10 days. With a firm tug, lift out the plants and show students how the entire mass of sand is bound by the plant roots. If the seedlings have been watered sparingly the root system will be more extensive than if they have been watered excessively.

Have students figure out the advantages of this binding action of the roots of plants. Why is a grass cover often planted along a hillside?

Here is an experiment that a group of students might like to demonstrate: Into two large wide-mouthed jars or fish bowls may be fitted U-shaped cups built of ¼-inch mesh wire screening. The bottom of the screen should extend more than halfway down the jar. After finding an area where good grass is growing and where there are trampled bad spots, students may cut small samples from each and put them into the wire baskets and then place them in the water-filled jars (Fig. 7-9).

Why does the water in the jar with the root-filled soil stay almost clear?

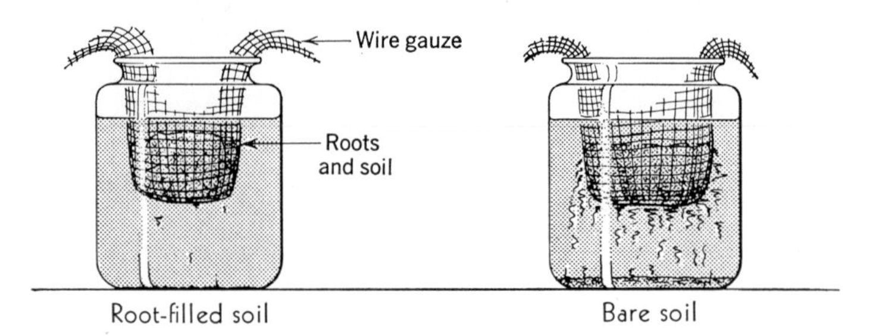

Fig. 7-9. Experiment to show the binding power of roots.

7-17. Soil-saving Project

A committee of students might make a survey of the community to learn which kinds of soil-saving practices are used. In a farming area students might get explanations directly from experts; in city schools the school lawn or roadsides might be areas for observation. Then students may use reference texts such as the USDA Yearbooks *Science in Farming* (1943–1947); *Crops in Peace and War* (1950–1951); *Farmers in a Changing World* (1940); *Water* (1955); *Land* (1958).

Students may report to the class on the value of crop rotation, strip farming, contour plowing, irrigation, letting land lie fallow, green manure, terracing, replenishing ground water, and the kinds of minerals that should be in fertilizer (Secs. 8-8 to 8-12). They may want to report on the role of radioactive tracers (Sec. 16-13) in fertilizers to discover the rate at which different minerals are absorbed by the soil, and also the amount of leaching of these valuable minerals from the soil. What kinds of plant cover might be used on a hillside? How might trees serve as windbreaks?

Is there something your students can actually do to save soil on the school grounds, around their own homes, or in the community?

They may want to check erosion in many regions around the school grounds. Students working as a club or on a group project might engage in planting young saplings as one way to reduce soil erosion by water or wind, or to cover a burned-over area. They should be able to receive help in this project from a county agent or forester.

Other activities along this line giving practical experiences in working with soil are suggested in a nature trail (Sec. 9-5), a school garden (Sec. 8-3), and a tree census (Sec. 9-2). You and your students will doubtless think of other ways of translating learning into useful action.

8

Growing Living Things in Farm and Garden

This chapter deals selectively with techniques for getting acquainted with a farm (or a garden), its purposes, problems, and conservation practices. The mineral needs of plants for healthy growth, the value of fertilizers, the possibilities of soilless culture are explored by experiment. Food, the major product of the farm, as well as fibers and other produce are included with many identifying tests. There is emphasis on the close interrelationship between the modern farm and science.

GETTING ACQUAINTED WITH A FARM

8-1. Field Trip to a Farm

To young people who do not know firsthand the life of a farm, a carefully planned field trip will open vistas and increase understanding. Proper use of the farm terrain, kinds of crops and their healthy growth, kinds of livestock, their care and usefulness, methods of improving livestock, machinery and its uses, water supply, problems of marketing, these are some of the possible areas of learning.

If your students have a chance to chat with the farmer, to ask him questions when he acts as guide, if they can watch, or better, if they can share in the work of field, garden, or barn, and if they can visit informally with the family and have a dip in the swimming hole with the children, they may begin to get the flavor of a way of life different from their own. If the field trip can be an extended one so that regular participation in the various phases of farm life can be included, the experience may be a memorable one indeed.

8-2. "Farming" at School

A Farm Model. The construction of a farm model can be an absorbing project, requiring study, group planning, and manipulative work. These are some of the practices that can be shown: reforestation of a steep, rocky area; strip cropping; fencing of a wood lot; gully control; wildlife protection runways; rotated pasture; a farm pond; and grassed waterways.

This project[1] could be made even more meaningful if it were coordinated with actual farm mapping under the direction of an expert from the Soil Conservation Service.

An ingenious teacher[2] has added a variation to a farm model project by presenting to his class a model of what might be a farm with its hills and valleys. Their problem is to assume that they own this land and must reclaim and improve it so that it could be a successful farm business.

This might be the time for students to learn about the services rendered to farmers by the Soil Conservation Service through soil surveys. A farm is usually made up of several different kinds of land, each being suited to specific uses. There are eight different land-capacity classes (Fig. 8-1). To make the best use of his land the farmer should know its classification.

When students have "classified" the land on their model, they should lay out the farm into sections and plan the crop rotation of each. They might plan methods of handling the woodland and reclaiming eroded gullies. The location of the house and barns with necessary roads presents problems in water supply, sanitation, and engineering that will require the students to make a thorough study of a practical situation.

A Miniature "Farm" with Drainage Tiles. Fields that are swampy in spring may dry out in summer, and thus produce a negligible corn crop. In Iowa a Dutch boy[3] had seen his family solve this problem by laying a series of sloped drainage tiles, constructed of short lengths of baked clay pipe fitted together with gaps wide enough to collect water but not wide enough to become clogged with dirt. The boy made a miniature "farm" to demonstrate to his class. Perhaps this may suggest a similar experiment to one of your students.

[1] For details as to the way one teacher guided such a project, you may refer to the article by John F. Adams, Whitingham High School, Jacksonville, Vt., A Model Farm, on p. 160 of *Conservation Handbook* (Sec. 19-3*h*).

[2] Malcolm Campbell, Dorchester High School, Dorchester, Mass., A Farm Study, *ibid.*, p. 161.

[3] Al Vorwald, student at Xavier High School, Dyersville, Iowa. His story was told by John Woodburn in *Six Ears of Corn Where One Grew Before* (copyright 1957 by Street & Smith Publications, Inc.), reprinted from *Science World*.

Fig. 8-1. A small watershed illustrating different land-capability classes. (*U.S. Soil Conservation Service photo.*)

Fill a glass tank without any drainage outlet with loam. Fill a second tank containing miniature tiles draining into an overflow (Fig. 8-2) with the same kind of soil. Plant both tanks with corn and treat them to the same conditions of sunlight, temperature, and watering. The corn in the tank without drainage should turn out to be sickly and yellow, with dwarfed root systems. Tall, vigorous corn with well-developed root systems should result in the drained tank.

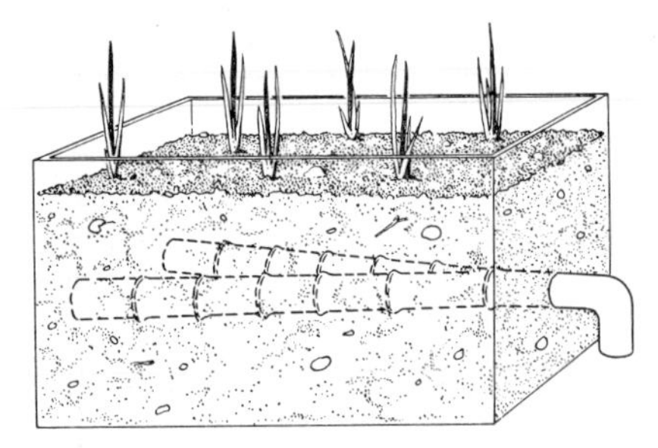

Fig. 8-2. Miniature "farm" with drainage tiles.

Why do plants fail to do well in undrained soil? Elicit from students that the high water level restricts root growth to a layer of shallow soil. When the summer sun bakes this layer, the plants wither. Another reason is that wet soils are cold and seeds are slower to germinate.

(Water with its high specific heat (Sec. 11-13) warms much more slowly than the same weight of soil.)

Why will soil above drainage tiles stay moist and not wet? Excess water is drained off and capillary action (Sec. 3-10) will draw moisture upward and keep it available for crops when summer's sun begins to dry the soil.

A School Farm. Fortunate the school that can work out some arrangement to have its own farm, to which students may come for work and study. Here experiences might be shared by the rotating of groups throughout the school year, while some students might work on the farm during the summer months in a work-camp situation.

School camps and school forests are already valued additions to the programs of a number of schools. School farms, though presenting more difficult problems, offer still another challenge and opportunity for the most vital of all learning experiences—a living one.

If a school farm seems too ambitious an undertaking, a school garden might be possible.

8-3. A School Garden

A school garden has multiple uses, many of which students can contrive and carry through to completion.

In this area of ground you may want to teach many farming methods by example. Arrange an area illustrating terracing, especially where ravages of soil erosion by water are indicated. Try planting a cover of vegetation and observe the binding effect of roots (Sec. 7-12). There may be a way to measure the amount of runoff of water in an exposed region and this covered region. There are other uses, for example, studies in mineral deficiency of plants or grass, an examination of the ingredients and proportions of minerals in fertilizers (Sec. 8-11). Why are nitrates, phosphates, and potassium compounds used in specific proportions for certain kinds of crops?

You may want to teach the entire reproductive cycle of seed plants as they grow in the school garden or as they are started in a school greenhouse. The means used to improve the quality of seeds introduce work in heredity (Sec. 4-10). After a breeder has obtained a desirable plant, how does he propagate this type? Here students may try out some methods of vegetative propagation (Sec. 4-4) to show how this method perpetuates a constant type since there has been no fertilization or union of genetic material from two strains. Students may plant bulbs from the middle of October to the middle of November. In this way they may watch the growth of a plant, using the bulbs to illustrate an asexual method. What color flowers develop? Why can the color be printed on the container with certainty? A few precautions in planting bulbs may be in order: Plant daffodil, tulip, and hyacinth bulbs about 5 to 6 inches deep; crocus bulbs may be planted only 3 inches down in a good loam soil. When the flowers have bloomed, pinch off the pistils so that vigorous bulb formation takes place.

There are other projects. Some students might make a study of a few square feet of soil to learn the kinds of organisms found in soil (Sec. 7-6), and others might take a census of the number and kinds of insect pests (Sec. 8-7). In class, some students may suggest an experiment using weed killers, or insecticides (Sec. 8-7), or even a project using

Table 8-1. When to Plant in Every Section

Name of plant	North	Central	South	Gulf and Southern California
Bachelor's button	Apr.–June	Mar.–June	Feb.–May	Oct.–May
Carnation	May–Sept.	Apr.–June	Mar.–May	Sept.–May
Daisy, painted	Apr.–Sept.	Mar.–June	Feb.–May	Aug.–May
Four o'clock	May–June	Apr.–June	Jan.–May	Sept.–May
Gourd	May–June	Apr.–June	Mar.–May	Feb.–May
Marigold	Apr.–June	Mar.–June	Feb.–May	Jan.–May
Morning glory	Apr.–May	Mar.–June	Feb.–June	Jan.–June
Nasturtium	May–June	Apr.–June	Mar.–June	Any time
Petunia	Apr.–June	Mar.–June	Feb.–May	Sept.–May
Scabiosa	May–June	Apr.–June	Mar.–May	Feb.–May
Scarlet runner	May–June	Apr.–June	Mar.–May	Feb.–June
Stock	May–June	Apr.–June	Feb.–June	Any time
Sweet alyssum	Apr.–June	Mar.–June	Feb.–May	Any time
Sweet peas	Mar.–May	Mar.–Apr.	Dec.–Mar.	Aug.–Mar.
Zinnia	May–June	Apr.–June	Mar.–June	Feb.–July
Beans	May–July	Apr.–Aug.	Mar.–Sept.	Feb.–Oct.
Beets	Apr.–July	Mar.–July	Feb.–Oct.	Any time
Carrots	Apr.–June	Mar.–July	Feb.–Aug.	Any time
Corn	May–June	Apr.–July	Mar.–Aug.	Feb.–Sept.
Cucumbers	May–June	Apr.–July	Mar.–Aug.	Mar.–Sept.
Lettuce	Apr.–Aug.	Mar.–Sept.	Feb.–Oct.	Feb.–Nov.
Onions	May–June	Apr.–June	Mar.–Oct.	Sept.–May
Peas	Mar.–May	Mar.–Apr.	Feb.–Mar.	Jan.–Mar.
Radishes	Apr.–Aug.	Mar.–Sept.	Feb.–Oct.	Jan.–Nov.
Rutabaga	Apr.–July	Mar.–July	Feb.–Oct.	Any time
Squash	May–June	Apr.–July	Mar.–Aug.	Mar.–Sept.
Swiss chard	Apr.–Aug.	Mar.–Sept.	Feb.–Sept.	Jan.–Oct.
Tomatoes	May–June	Apr.–June	Mar.–June	Mar.–July

plant growth hormones to encourage rapid rooting of cuttings (Sec. 4-6).

Perhaps one of the simplest yet most important objectives of a school garden might be to create out of ugliness a spot of loveliness and beauty. Your students might like to contact the National Garden Institute, a division of Friends of the Land, 1368 North High St., Columbus, Ohio, to learn of their School Garden Service Bureau.

You might find the following paper-backed books of help in a gardening project: *The Handy Book of Gardening,* by Albert E. Wilkinson and Victor A. Tiedjens (Signet Key Book, New American Library, 1955), or *The Garden Gate,* by Samuel Caldwell (Greenberg: Publisher, Inc., New York, 1954).

Planting Schedule. Table 8-1 gives a planting schedule for some of the common varieties of flowers and vegetables. What are the climatic factors that cause this variation in planting time from section to section?

An Indoor Garden. At the time of year when students can no longer work in an outdoor garden, there are many interesting and valuable experiences with plant life that they may have indoors.

A large shallow packing box or an unused sandbox makes a good receptacle in which to plant an indoor garden. Put pieces of broken crock or stones in the bottom of the box before filling in with earth. Bore a few small holes in the bottom of the box. Why?

If you have several such boxes, control experiments may be set up with different kinds of soil, soil enriched or unenriched with fertilizer, different amounts of water or of light.

Window boxes, too, may be used for experiments with all kinds of plants—squash or pumpkins, morning glories or nasturtiums, bulbs, etc.

IMPROVING WILDLIFE HABITATS

8-4. On a Farm

Cover for Wildlife. "Clean farming," the elimination of hedgerows and edges, is not good for wildlife, which must have suitable cover to survive.

When visiting a farm, notice what the farmer has done to protect wildlife (Fig. 8-3). Perhaps he has taken steps toward increasing the "edge" of his fields so that there will be places where rabbits, quail, and songbirds can live and raise their young.

Should there be opportunity for a school farm, your students will find valuable information from these USDA pamphlets: *Shrub Plantings for Soil Conservation and Wildlife Cover* (Circular no. 887) and *Multiflora Rose for Living Fences and Wildlife Cover* (Leaflet no. 256).

Your students may be summer campers. By proper cutting operations, camp areas may be kept in many stages of vegetative growth and have maximum numbers and kinds of wildlife. "Interspersion," or mixing of

Fig. 8-3. Notice the "edge" of the field. This farmer supplies cover for wildlife. (*U.S. Soil Conservation Service photo.*)

cover types, is the important thing to remember in making an area more favorable to wildlife.

Excellent information for improvement of a farm for wildlife may be found in the booklet *The Farmer and Wildlife* (Wildlife Management Institute, Washington, D.C.) or in *Making Land Produce Useful Wildlife* (USDA Farmers' Bulletin no. 2035).

A Farm Pond. Farm ponds sometimes fit well in a farmer's crop-raising plans. Technicians of the Soil Conservation Service frequently include ponds in plans they make for a farm, and advise the landowner how to manage them for high yields of fish.

An understanding of food chains, of the role of predator and prey, is needed to determine the management of such a pond.

Is there a place for a pond on your school property or in your students' summer camp area? Perhaps students could have one built and manage it for fish. The State Game and Fish Department or local office of the Soil Conservation Service can advise how to go about it. You will find that many valuable conservation practices are associated with a farm pond. These bulletins should prove helpful: *Farm Fishponds for*

Food and Good Land Use (USDA Farmers' Bulletin no. 1983) and *List of Publications on Farm Fish Ponds* (Wildlife Service, Fishery Leaflet no. 24).

8-5. At School

A School Sanctuary. Here is another idea you might find stimulating. A project of unusual interest has been going forward at a school in New England under the guidance of the biology teacher.[4] Approximately a dozen students, working three afternoons weekly, are well started on the development of nearly 50 acres of abandoned farm and forest land into a nature study area, a sanctuary for wild flowers and wildlife. Cleaning old access roads and cutting new trails, controlling the silting of the streams and pond, thinning the forest, improving the field borders, rebuilding a dam—these are some of the measures already under way.

A photographic project has been initiated to record change of habitat and inhabitants at permanently marked sites throughout the area. "It is expected," writes the teacher, "that biological and ecological studies, identification and marking of local species or points of interest, and publishing of descriptive literature will be undertaken eventually by the students to record changes over the years."

If Yours Is a City School. Though students who live in the city need to understand their relationship to and dependence on the land, they will also need a fuller understanding of their own brick-canyoned "habitat." Wildlife, to city folk, means squirrels, pigeons, sparrows, starlings. Observation of these small creatures, their nests, their eating and mating habits, their chances for survival, brings vivid learning.

Window boxes, indoor gardens, or Japanese gardens are possible when outdoor experiences are difficult and rare.

If you teach in a city school your students would find much helpful material in the leaflet *City Nature* (National Audubon Society, New York).

Planning a city or town community for healthy, productive, and happy living is conservation in a true sense. Too often, rapid urban development fails to include enough schools, enough parks, enough play space, and adequate transportation.

Might your students build a model of a good community—*their* future community? They would need to study the many requirements of such a community. What would be the best use of the available space? How many of the needs of the population would it be possible to meet? How could provision be made for expected growth?

[4] Herbert R. Drury, Putney School, Putney, Vt.

Your students have learned that in planning a farm, experts from the Soil Conservation Service may be consulted. In planning a town or city, who are the possible consultants? Does your city have a planning commission? If so, might one of its members be of help by discussing the commission's work with your students?

FRIENDS AND FOES OF THE FARM

The farmer has allies and competitors in his struggle to produce food, fiber, and chemicals. Perhaps you might begin this unit by having students list in separate columns, as they come to mind, all the farmers' friends and all his foes. Have any been forgotten? What makes a living organism a friend of man? A foe?

8-6. The Farmers' Friends

The Earthworm. How many earthworms are there in an acre of well-drained fertile soil? Students might mark out foot-square areas and go down to the depth of a foot. How many earthworms do they encounter? Have them estimate how many there might be to the acre. According to USDA figures, there should be millions.

Students may become aware of the countless holes earthworms dig (Fig. 8-4) as they transport earth from one level to another, mixing organic material near the surface with underlying soil particles. Earthworms help make good soil structure, so essential to proper aeration, drainage, and root growth.

How do the numbers of earthworms in poor, neglected soil compare with those in fertile soil? Students might investigate and draw conclusions.

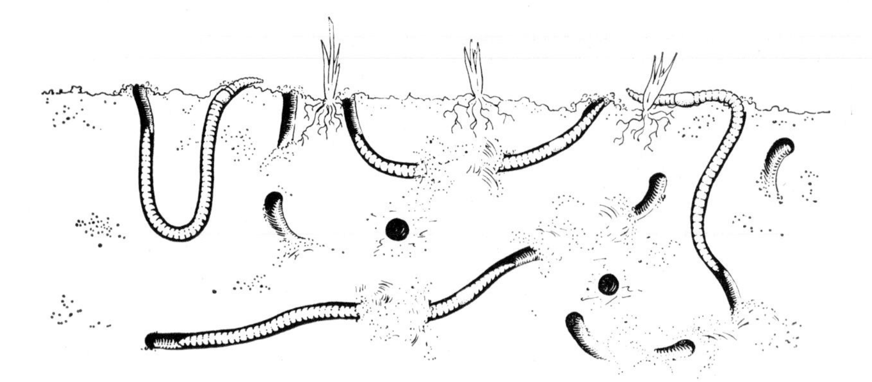

Fig. 8-4. Earthworms dig holes in the soil and help to make good soil structure.

The Farmers' Winged Allies. Your students may have the opportunity to observe the eating habits of birds in their natural outdoor habitats. Analysis of the contents of birds' stomachs by scientists has shown amazing collections of worms, grasshoppers, beetles, bugs, weed seeds, mice, rats, and moles, depending on the bird and his particular diet.

Here is a situation your students might ponder. Suppose a farmer decides to cut down the thicket around his cornfield. By so doing, he forces the nesting quail to go off to another thicket, perhaps his neighbor's. The next year, the chinch bugs invade the first farmer's cornfield and his crop is ruined. Why might the neighbor's corn flourish? Why is it essential for a farmer to know something about "upsetting the balance"? Can your students find other examples of what happens when the balance is not maintained?

This might be the time to discuss the offering of "bounties" for birds such as the hawk. Is the hawk an enemy or a friend? Do bounties help in the long run?

Insects. In gaining understanding of insects, both those which are friends and those which are foes of man, your students should, if possible, have opportunity for observation in the field. Insects can be brought into the laboratory. A study of their life cycles will provide clues on methods of insect pest control. It may be that your students would be interested in making an insect collection. Many suggestions about insect study may be found in *A Sourcebook for the Biological Sciences* (Sec. 19-3*e*).

8-7. Pests and Their Control

Your students might review the parade of pests with which the farmer has to cope. First come the bacteria and fungi, tiny disease organisms that are carried by the soil and the seeds and then infect the growing plants; then come the insects, harmful to crops and annoying to livestock. Weeds are there, too, crowding out profitable plants and using their food. Then, there are the internal parasites that infest farm animals. How science has met and is meeting all these challenges makes a fascinating story and study.

One group of your students might learn how seeds are disinfected before they are put into the ground (Sec. 4-2). They might devise experiments to try out the efficacy of the treatment. Another group might report on the ways growing plants are protected and saved. This would include a study of insects and their life cycles followed by an investigation of insecticides and fungicides, old and new, as well as methods of application. Included, also, should be reports on the rotation of crops as a method of combating pests; development of disease-resistant strains; the practice of burning diseased plants rather than plowing them under.

Still another committee might experiment with weed killers, sharing its findings with the class. How animal parasites may be destroyed makes yet another topic, while the protection of plants during storage and their packaging for sale add a final chapter to the story. A helpful pamphlet called *Chemistry and the Farmer* may be obtained from E. I. du Pont de Nemours & Co., Wilmington, Del.

The Fungus Pests. Ask students to find examples of fungus pests, the smuts and rusts and mildews that plague the farmer. They may be able to find blackberry rust or wheat rust. Perhaps they may collect samples of the powdery mildews on poplar leaves, lilac, Virginia creeper. Still other rusts are found on apple and cherry leaves.

If the infected leaves are wrapped up to keep them dry and then soaked in water for several hours, the scrapings may be mounted on clean slides in a drop of the liquid.

What part do the molds and mildews play in the wastage of food? How does a knowledge of the life cycles of fungi help in combating certain of them?

What are the requirements of fungi for growth? (Food, warmth, moisture, air.) Students might illustrate how canning, dehydrating, refrigerating, special treatment with ultraviolet light, antibiotics, or radioisotopes destroy fungi and not only "preserve" but also "conserve" food.

Perhaps your students would be interested in trying their own experiment with food preservatives (Sec. 8-14), or in setting up an exhibit to illustrate the various methods.

Insect Pests: Biological Control. Insects have natural enemies that can help man in his warfare with pests. Have a student report the story of how the fight against Japanese beetles was won by infecting them with bacterial disease.

A simple type of biological control is the putting of goldfish in a garden pond to eat mosquito larvae. A complicated type is the campaign which exterminated the screwworm fly (which is devastating to livestock) on one of the islands of the Caribbean.

Work of this sort is being carried on by entomologists, and students might write to the Department of Agriculture for information.

Insecticides. If there are insect pests on the school grounds, students might try the use of specific insecticides, following directions carefully and making note of the effects (Fig. 8-5). A student might report on the immunity certain insect pests build up against insecticides. Why is the United Nations concerning itself with this problem?

The Pros and Cons of Pest-control Measures. You might pose this question to your class: What are the dangers involved when man attempts to control the spread of pests?

You might suggest that your students look up the history of the gypsy moth, the insect that was deliberately brought to the United States from France for the purpose of cross-breeding with silkworms. After the gypsy moth had defoliated millions of trees in the northeast, the Department of Agriculture instituted a 5 million dollar aerial DDT-spraying cam-

Fig. 8-5. In a controlled test, Mexican bean beetles have destroyed untreated plant on left, while plant on right has been supplied with proper insecticides and is not affected. The attacking beetles are killed. (*E. I. du Pont de Nemours & Company, research laboratory.*)

paign in the spring of 1957 and sprayed 3 million acres of New York, New Jersey, and Pennsylvania.

Your students might discuss the pros and cons of such wholesale spraying. Was it effective in wiping out the gypsy moth? Was the DDT harmful to other species? Was there danger to fish? Does a more careful study of the effect of pesticides on fish and wildlife resources seem indicated?

Do we know enough about the long-range effects of chemical poisons like DDT on humans?

A letter like the following, appearing in a daily newspaper, may serve as the basis for a thoughtful class discussion:

> TO THE N.Y. HERALD TRIBUNE:
>
> We own a week-end home in a large wooded area on Long Island, adjoining one of its largest state parks. We were especially proud to call this land our bird sanctuary, since we were able to observe and list over sixty different varieties of birds, including a long list of the small members of the vireos and parulidae families. After DDT spraying twice had gone over the area a few weeks ago, I found four of these lively little callers dead on the ground, and the woods themselves entirely deserted by them. Larger birds than these, the thrushes and the grain eaters, seemed to be unaffected. Whether these small birds died from the spraying itself or from eating poisoned insects, I would not dare to decide.
>
> I would like to add still another observation: Along the sandy cliffs of Long Island's north shore, especially in our parts, scores of cliff swallows had their domicile, and waves of them could always be watched, especially in the later part of the afternoon. Since the spraying, the cliffs seem deserted. I was in the vicinity for several days and did not see even one bird. However, since I did not find any dead birds on the ground, I conclude that the birds withdrew instead of being killed.
>
> I wish to offer these observations to those who are speculating about the question whether nature's biological control or that of man's chemical control by spraying has actually a greater value. Or whether at least we ought to consider limiting such sprayings to amounts which will not have such a detrimental effect upon our bird population, or be more careful and selective in regard to the areas treated.
>
> DR. E. HARMS
> *New York, August 1, 1957*

Study of a Weed Killer. That 2,4-D destroys broad-leaved plants may be shown in a part of the lawn or in a flower pot. Sow grass in several flower pots full of a light loam soil. Then plant some sample broad-leaved plant, such as a mustard or a plantain, among the growing grass plants. Leave some of the flower pots untreated, and spray the other flower pots of grasses and broad-leaved plants with 2,4-D. Keep the untreated plants in another room while this spraying is under way. Have students watch the changes in the treated flower pots. In a few days, they should observe the broad-leaved plants begin to wilt, and probably in two to three weeks the broad-leaved plants will have shriveled and disappeared. Does the weed killer affect the grasses?

Elicit from students an explanation of why weeds take over a cultivated area so rapidly. What traits that have survival value do they possess? Uproot weeds from the lawn or garden and compare their roots and rate of growth with other cultivated plants. How do you explain their high immunity to plant diseases?

Weed Control by Insects. There might be a student report on the story of Klamoth weed and its control by introducing its European insect enemies, an account of which may be found in the July, 1957, issue of *Scientific American.*

WHAT PLANTS NEED TO GROW

Having studied with your students the need of plants for sunlight (Sec. 3-6), water (Sec. 3-9), and carbon dioxide (Sec. 3-7), you may want to go on with a study of the other essentials (Fig. 8-6). You might begin with the three primary plant nutrients, or chemical "trio."

8-8. Nitrogen

Nitrogen is essential to all life, animal as well as vegetable. The proteins of our flesh are nitrogen compounds. The interchange of this element between the earth's air, minerals, plants, and animals we call the nitrogen cycle (Sec. 12-3).

Modern farming has upset this cycle of nature for it removes nitrogen compounds from the soil faster than the cycle replaces them. The chemist has had to step in and make up this shortage by adding nitrogen in a form easily available to plants.

Although the air is a vast storehouse of nitrogen, this element is unavailable to plants unless it is "fixed" or in combined form. The legumes house nature's factory for fixing atmospheric nitrogen. Small amounts of nitrogen are fixed, too, in thunderstorms and washed into the ground by rain. Man has learned to imitate this method (the Arc process), as well as to devise others, such as the Cyanamide or Haber processes, of greater commercial importance. (Students may be referred to chemistry textbooks for details of these processes.)

Nitrogen-fixing Bacteria and the Soil. You may want to use this experiment in a study of plant nutrients as part of a broad study of the means of saving soils, or as an example of symbiosis in leguminous plants and the nitrogen-fixing bacteria in the nodules of their roots.

Students may bring to class some specimens of freshly gathered leguminous plants: clover, alfalfa, peanut plants, a bean or pea plant—all of these uprooted from the soil so the specimens have roots. In fact, students may gather these as part of a group field trip. An examination of the roots should reveal nodules, many of them (Fig. 8-7).

The nitrogen-fixing bacteria found in these swellings or nodules may be studied under the microscope. After washing off the soil, have students crush a nodule in a drop of water on a slide. With a dissecting needle have them spread this smear along the slide and set aside to dry. Should you want to stain these bacteria, use methylene blue (Sec. 18-1*p*). Place a drop of the stain on a slide in advance and let it dry.

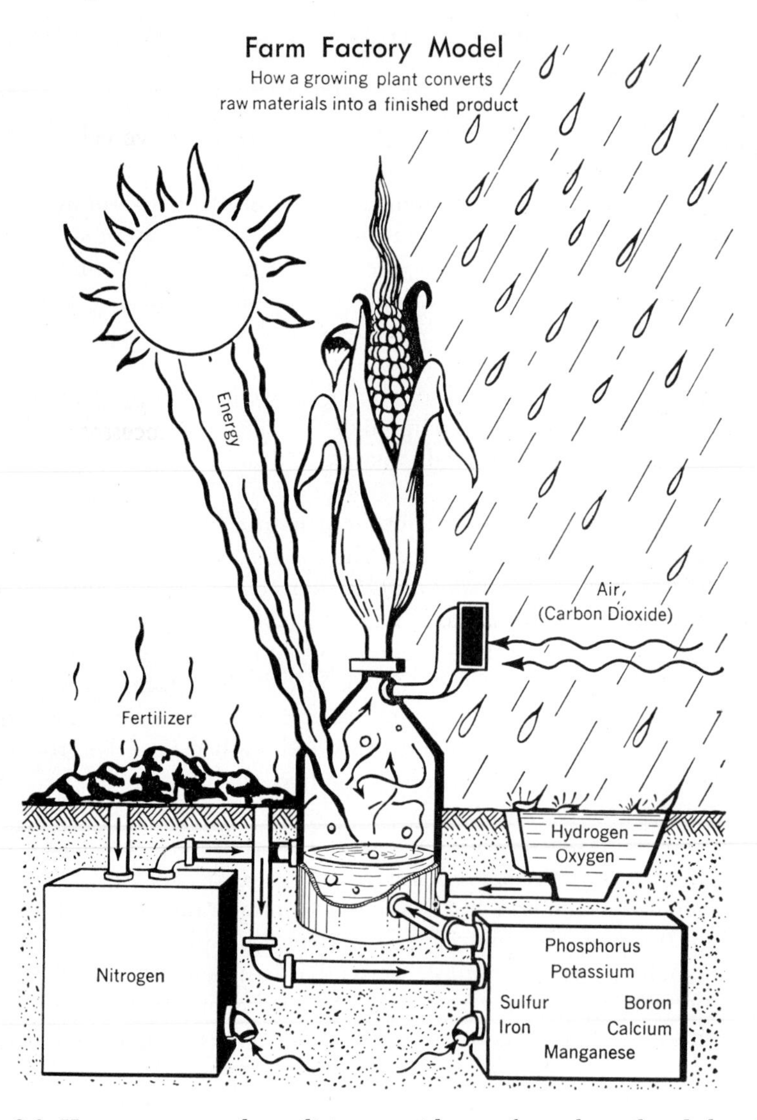

Fig. 8-6. How crops grow by utilizing nourishment from the soil and the air is shown in this simplified drawing. The role of fertilizer in supplying nutrients is also represented. (*From The Story of Farm Chemicals, E. I. du Pont de Nemours & Company.*)

Of what help are nitrogen-fixing bacteria to the soil? Why are leguminous plants used by farmers when rotating their crops?

Plant Growth Affected by Nitrogen-fixing Bacteria. This demonstration should be prepared weeks in advance of the lesson. Perhaps some students may get this material ready at home.

Sterilize several small pots of soil in an autoclave or oven. Nitrogen-fixing bacteria may be purchased from seed companies; these should be added to the soil of some of the flower pots. Then introduce an equal quantity of soaked clover seeds into all the flower pots. Students may examine the plants after some weeks of growth. Which pots have the more luxuriant growth?

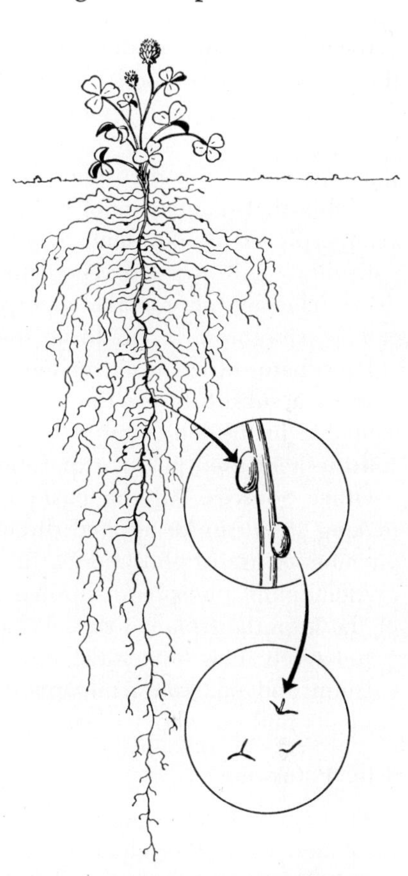

Fig. 8-7. Root system of the legume, red clover. Nodules are enlarged in upper circle. Lower circle shows the nitrogen-fixing bacteria in the nodules. (*From Cornell Rural Leaflet, Holes in the Ground.*)

Nitrates and Their Effect on Plants. On a field trip students may come upon a sandy patch of soil where the grass is pale in color. This may possibly be due to a lack of nitrates in the soil. Mark off an area 5 square feet or more. Would there be a change in the color of the grass if nitrates were added to the soil?

Have students scatter about 15 grams of sodium nitrate evenly over this area when the soil is dry. Then let them water the area so that the nitrate is absorbed. The remainder of the area should serve as a control. Watch the patch of soil over some weeks. Can students see a difference? Are the plants in the experimental area more green, more vigorous?

8-9. Phosphorus

Phosphorus, one of the three prime essentials for plant growth, is bound or fixed in very insoluble forms so that only a small part of the total supply becomes available in any one cropping season. Unsatisfactory plant growth is more often due to a shortage of this element than of any other plant food. Phosphorus is intimately associated with all life processes and is a vital constituent of every living cell. Without phosphorus there could be no life.

Rock Phosphate. Students may take a sample of rock phosphate (tricalcium phosphate) and try dissolving it in water. When it is filtered, the filtrate should be evaporated to see if any of the rock phosphate went into solution.

The trouble with rock phosphate for a quick fertilizer is that it is so insoluble that plants cannot utilize it for quite a long time.

Superphosphate. Students may then treat a little of the rock phosphate with dilute sulfuric acid. The acid should be rinsed out and the product dried. The solubility of the superphosphate may be tested as in the preceding paragraph. It should be somewhat soluble.

Phosphate rock is used for long-time soil-improvement progress rather than as a substitute for the more soluble forms. How would it become available in the long run? What in the soil might take the place of the sulfuric acid used in this experiment?

Other Sources. All the basic slag from the open-hearth process for making steel can be applied directly to the soil. It contains appreciable amounts of useful phosphorus. In what form would it be?

Ammonium phosphate supplies not only phosphorus but also another of the important plant foods. What is it?

Relatively new materials, now reaching commercial production, are calcium and potassium metaphosphate and alpha phosphate. Can your students find out about them and their advantages?

8-10. Potassium

Potassium, far too active to be used in the free state, is chemically combined with other elements in fertilizers. (To demonstrate the violent activity of the uncombined element, drop a piece of potassium, the size of a small pea, into a large battery jar of water and watch the action. Careful!) Potash (potassium compound, usually the carbonate), aside from helping plant growth in general, is said to "stiffen the straw" of grain crops. Although our soils are rather rich in potash, it is locked up in such a way that it is not readily utilized by plants and must, therefore, be supplied in the form of fertilizer.

Sources. Prior to World War I we were entirely dependent on foreign sources, notably the Stassfurt mines in Germany. When the war cut off these supplies, an intensive search was made to locate sources in our own country. Your students might find out where we now get our supplies. Any up-to-date chemistry textbook will be helpful.

Potassium Compounds in Plants. To identify potassium compounds in plants, students might burn some wood, moisten the ashes with water, and then apply the flame test for potassium compounds (Sec. 7-11).

8-11. Effects of Fertilizer on Plant Growth[5]

Experiment with the Chemical "Trio." This experiment may be done in a variety of ways. One could plant seeds like beans or barley, or set out plants like tomato. Use ten earthen pots (10-inch size) and fill them with clean sand. Plant seeds or set out plants in the pots. They should be stationed in a bright sunny place and should be allowed to grow without adding anything but water every morning and evening for 3 to 5 days after they are set out or have germinated.

After this interval, experimentation with fertilizers can be started. The pots should be numbered in pairs.

Pots no. 1 are the controls (nothing added except water); pots no. 2 are nitrogen pots; pots no. 3 are phosphorus pots; pots no. 4 are potassium pots; pots no. 5 have all the "trio."

Adding fertilizers:

Pots no. 2 (nitrogen): Sprinkle 1 level tablespoon of ammonium nitrate evenly on the surface of the sand. Add water to dissolve the salt and carry it to the roots. Repeat every four days.

Pots no. 3 (phosphorus): Bone meal, which is only slightly soluble, should be inserted in 2-inch holes made in the sand. Make six of these holes and divide 1 level tablespoon of bone meal among them. Smooth the surface and add water. Repeat every four days.

Pots no. 4 (potassium): Proceed as with pots no. 2, but use 1 level tablespoon of potassium chloride. Repeat every four days.

Pots no. 5 ("trio"): Add 1 level tablespoon of bone meal as directed for pots no. 3 and ½ tablespoon of ammonium nitrate and ½ tablespoon of potassium chloride, as directed for pots no. 2. Repeat every four days.

Once each day for about four weeks record the size, color, general appearance, and other characteristics.

You might want to have a class discussion to bring out the differences produced by each treatment. Applications to crop production, effects of leaching of soils, etc., can be made. Several students might make time-lapse photographs of the plants. Others of your class might prepare a bulletin-board display of photographs and observations. The whole project might lead into further research on fertilizers.

"Complete" Fertilizers. This might be the time to discuss commercial fertilizers of the "6–10–4" variety, having students learn that it is customary to express the composition of mixed fertilizers in percentage fig-

[5] Allen Gruer, Albuquerque, N. Mex., Effects of Fertilizer on Plant Growth, *Conservation Handbook*, p. 155 (Sec. 19-3*h*).

ures, giving first, the percentage of nitrogen, second, the content of phosphorus expressed as percentage of phosphoric acid, and third, the content of potassium expressed as percentage of potash.

8-12. Secondary and Minor Plant Foods

In recent years increasing attention has been given to the importance of the secondary elements in fertilizers—calcium, magnesium, and sulfur. Considerable investigation has been made, too, of the minor or trace elements (also called "micronutrients")—manganese, copper, zinc, boron, and iron. It was formerly thought that our soils contained sufficient trace minerals and that commercial fertilizers had enough of these elements as impurities or they were carried by other plant foods. Now, however, it is being realized that poor yields are often due to deficiencies of one or more of the secondary or minor elements (Fig. 8-8).

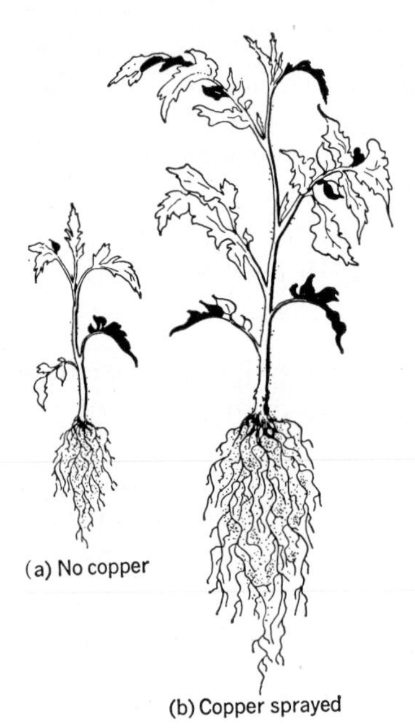

Fig. 8-8. Effect of a trace element on plant growth. (*a*) Tomato plant grown in the laboratory with all needed plant foods except copper; (*b*) this plant was grown under the same conditions except that a solution of a copper salt was sprayed on the leaves. (*California Agricultural Experiment Station, University of California, Berkeley.*)

Perhaps your young people can figure out why these deficiencies have become marked in recent years:

1. The development of more highly refined fertilizers carrying more nitrogen, phosphoric acid, and potash has reduced the valuable "impurities."

2. More intensive cropping, with emphasis on higher yields per acre, coupled with the fact that our soils are becoming older and more depleted are added reasons for the deficiency.

An excellent publication called *Our Land and Its Care,* describing good land management including the restoring of plant foods to the soil, may be obtained from the American Plant Food Council, Inc., Washington, D.C.

Still another pamphlet worth obtaining is *Make the Soil Productive,* International Harvester Company, Chicago.

Soil Improvement Preparations Containing "Trace" Elements.[6] Your students might be interested in testing out the value of secondary and

[6] West Coast Science Teachers' Summer Conference, 1954, reported in *The Science Teacher,* February, 1955.

minor plant foods. Some may want to devise experiments to show the importance of certain trace minerals. Here is one way of comparing soil improvement preparations containing trace elements:

In some areas the addition of trace elements makes noticeable differences in plant growth, and in others, very little. How does the soil in your area rate in this capacity? Two very useful materials containing trace minerals are pulp wastes from paper mills and commercial trace elements from a garden store. Which is superior in your area?

One way to find out is to take three shallow boxes and fill each with the same soil up to about 4 inches deep. If your students live in an area where things grow all winter they may mark off, with stakes and string, three plots each about a yard square.

Into one, students may sprinkle trace element minerals according to the directions given on the package. In the middle box or plot the soil should be left as it is. To the third, the same amount of pulp waste should be added as trace elements in the first box. All the plots should be raked uniformly.

Radish or other quick-growing seeds may be sown according to directions in each of these plots. They should be watered uniformly with a sprinkler. Students may keep a chart on each plot showing when the seeds sprout, how rapidly they grow, and how the produce, when mature, compares in size, taste, quality, and uniformity. What conclusions can your students draw? (NOTE: This type of experiment requires adequate replication.)

8-13. Soilless Growth of Plants

Hydroponics. Soilless growth of plants is a fine hobby for school or home. Any student interested in producing and experimenting with plants and in studying mineral deficiencies will find that this method makes possible year-round activity. The equipment is easy to make and the chemicals required are not expensive.

A very simple method is to prepare pint- or quart-sized, wide-mouthed bottles by fitting them with clean, one-holed cork stoppers. Nutrient solution (such as the one in Table 8-2) is then added. (Or nutrient solutions with one salt left out of each may be used when studying mineral deficiencies.)

Have students germinate seeds (Sec. 4-2) in sawdust, sand, or in a germination box. Students should then insert the root of a germinating seedling (or the stem of a cutting) into the stopper so that the cut end of the cutting or the root is submerged in the nutrient solution. As the plants grow, students may have to support the plants with dowel sticks which can be fitted into another hole made in the cork stopper if the cork is wide enough, or the shoots may be supported by an iron ring stand. Or students may want to grow seedlings in a container such as that in Fig. 8-9, which has a zinc mesh trough suspended in a container of nutrient solution. However, this mesh must first be coated with paraffin since the zinc is toxic. Bed the seedlings in excelsior or glass wool.

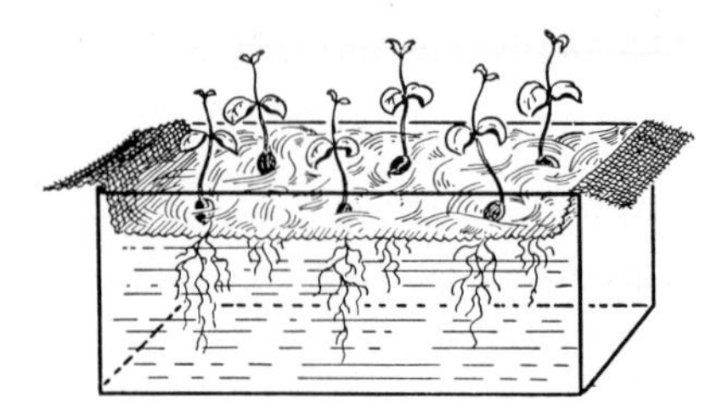

Fig. 8-9. Soilless growth of plants in nutrient solution. Seedlings are bedded in excelsior or glass wool in paraffined zinc mesh trough.

If the experiment is being performed to study mineral deficiencies, then compare the growth and appearance of the plants in each solution, using the complete nutrient solution as a control. Variations of this experiment might include trying different concentrations of solution as well as different degrees of acidity and alkalinity. The effect of aeration of the solution (using an aerator pump) could also be studied. Our experience has shown that aeration of the roots is an important factor for healthy growth of the plants.

Once your students have become interested in the soilless growth of plants they may want to learn about the various methods that have been successfully used by the amateur. A number of common house plants, wandering Jew, English ivy, rubber plants, *philodendron,* and many others may be successfully grown by means of hydroponics.

Many detailed methods for raising plants in soilless cultures (sand, water, or gravel) may be found in such textbooks as Carleton Ellis and M. W. Swaney's *Soilless Growth of Plants* (Reinhold Publishing Corporation, New York, 1947), or you might want to write for *Nutriculture* (Technical Manual no. 20–500, Adjutant General's Office, Publications Branch, The Pentagon, Washington).

For the beginner, there are simple directions for a project in hydroponics in *Living Chemistry,* by M. R. Ahrens, N. F. Bush, and R. K. Easley (Ginn & Company, Boston, 1957).

A Nutrient Solution for Hydroponics. You probably would want to prepare 5 gallons of nutrient solution, Table 8-2 (or modify in proportion the quantities given there). Weigh out each salt, and dissolve each separately in a pint of water. Then mix the four solutions, and add enough

Table 8-2. A Nutrient Solution

Monopotassium phosphate	KH_2PO_4	5.9 grams
Magnesium sulfate	$MgSo_4 \cdot 7H_2O$	10.7 grams
Calcium nitrate	$Ca(NO_3)_2 \cdot 4H_2O$	20.1 grams
Ammonium sulfate	$(NH_4)_2SO_4$	1.8 grams

water to make up 5 gallons. Students may notice that this nutrient solution contains the six main elements essential for the growth of plants: nitrogen, phosphorus, potassium, sulfur, calcium, and magnesium. These are combined in the first three salts in the formula for the solution. The ammonium salt is added to offset the rapid change in pH that results when plants absorb nitrogen faster than calcium (when the salt is in the form of calcium nitrate in the solution).

When a scale is not available, these approximate measures may be used: 1¼ teaspoons of monopotassium phosphate, 2½ teaspoons of magnesium sulfate, 4 teaspoons of calcium nitrate, ½ teaspoon of ammonium sulfate.

There are, in addition, trace elements which stimulate growth of plants (Sec. 8-12), which should be added to the nutrient solution students have made. Add 0.8 gram of each of these three salts: boric acid crystals, manganese sulfate, and zinc sulfate separately to pint containers of water. Then add 10 cubic centimeters of each of these three solutions to the nutrient solution.

Now you have 5 gallons of nutrient solution composed of three major salts, three secondary salts, and trace amounts of three trace element salts. Remember to check the pH of the culture solution, for it should be between 4.5 and 6.5 (Sec. 7-8); increased alkalinity seems to stop good growth of roots.

A Practical Substitute for Soil? In working with hydroponics, the soilless culture of plants, the question will naturally arise: Since this seems such an "easy" method as compared with growing crops in soil, why can't we substitute nutriculture for soil in the growing of food crops?

There is an excellent article in UNESCO's publication *Impact of Science on Society* (vol. VI, no. 1, March, 1955) entitled The Possibilities of Soilless Cultivation by JWEH Shotto Douglas. This describes successful hydroponic techniques, gives figures on yields, points out advantages and disadvantages, and attempts an answer to the question, "Should hydroponics replace agriculture?"

PRODUCTS OF THE FARM

8-14. The Farm and Food

Elicit from your students that one of the prime purposes of most farms is to supply food in the form of crops, both animal and vegetable, and in the form of dairy products.

Farm Surpluses and Conservation. Your students will gradually become aware of the tremendous importance of healthy, efficiently producing farms to keep our expanding numbers alive and healthy.

They may be puzzled by the apparent paradox of farm surpluses and the need for conservation. Have them dig a bit deeper. Are all our own people adequately fed? Are farm surpluses a local and perhaps transient phenomenon? Are retail prices of such products as meat, butter, cotton too high to compete with cheaper products? What about the world situation? What are some of the possible solutions? These are hard questions for which there are no easy answers, but you can help your students to make a start.

This may be the time your class might be interested in discussing parity—what it is, what its relationship to price is, and what its direct effect on the consumer is. For a clear exposition of parity and its problems you might refer your students to the article, What to Do? One Man's View (*The Yearbook of Agriculture,* 1954, page 395).

Cheap Food for the Millions. Your students might plan to get in touch with a nonprofit organization known as Meals for Millions Foundation, Inc., 115 West Seventh St., Los Angeles, which promotes and distributes a preparation called Multiple Purpose Food (MPF). This high-protein food, a soybean by-product fortified with minerals and vitamins, is available in tremendous quantities and is produced, according to the Foundation slogan, for "three cents a meal."

Food Preservatives. Here is a simple experiment illustrating the use of preservatives in food. Beans or peas that have been soaked overnight may be macerated and put into seven test tubes of water. One of the test tubes should be left alone, and one of the following chemicals should be added to each of the others: 1 teaspoon of salt, 1 teaspoon of sugar, 1 teaspoon of vinegar, ¼ teaspoon of boric acid, ¼ teaspoon of alum, a pinch of benzoate of soda. Students may, over several days, keep records of the conditions of preservation in each test tube (color, odor, etc.).

What other methods are there of preserving food? How valuable is food preservation as a conservation measure?

Food Testing: A Summary of Common Tests. Table 8-3 gives a summary of simple tests to identify the important components of food. For more complete directions, consult a laboratory manual of chemistry or biology.

Samples to be tested might include grape and cane sugar, nuts, flour, potatoes, cereal, butter, eggs.

Test for Vitamin C. Add a fruit juice (like orange, lemon, or lime) containing ascorbic acid (vitamin C), drop by drop, to an indicator called indophenol.[7] A point is reached where the color of the indicator turns from blue to colorless. (Disregard the in-between pink stage.)

In a laboratory lesson, students may take comparative tests of the quantitative differences in the vitamin C content of several fruit juices.

[7] Indophenol, as sodium 2,6-dichlorobenzenone, may be purchased from the Chemical Division of Eastman Kodak Company, Rochester, N.Y.

Table 8-3. Some Food Tests

Nutrient	Test Procedure	Positive Result
Starch	Add Lugol's solution (Sec. 18-1*o*)	Bluish-black color
Simple sugars		
Glucose or grape	Add Fehling's (Sec. 18-1*k*) or Benedict's solution (Sec. 18-1*d*) and bring to a boil	Color change from blue to green to yellow or orange
Sucrose or cane	Add Fehling's solution and boil. Add several milliliters of hydrochloric acid and boil. Neutralize with sodium hydroxide. Now apply Fehling's test	No color change Color change from green to yellow or orange
Proteins	Add nitric acid and heat carefully	Yellow color
Fats	Rub food substance on unglazed paper	Translucent spot
Minerals	Burn food substance in an evaporating dish	Ash remains
Water	Heat food substance in dry test tube	Drops of water condense on walls of dry tube
Vitamins	*a.* Some chemical tests, for example, for vitamin C *b.* Animal experimentation (devise feeding experiments with pure nutrients) *c.* Bioassay with microorganisms	*a.* Reactions with specific indicators *b.* Symptoms of specific deficiency diseases result *c.* Failure to grow

Prepare a 0.1 per cent solution of indophenol (Sec. 18-1*m*) for this lesson in advance. You will have to dilute the fruit juices twenty times or more, but this you must test before the class begins. For instance, in a laboratory lesson there would be no point in adding one drop of the fruit juice to the indicator to find it bleached immediately. Therefore, dilute all the juices you use equally, but be certain that about 10 drops of juice decolorize 10 cubic centimeters of indophenol.

Then, in the laboratory when students begin with 10 cubic centimeters of a 0.1 per cent indophenol solution in a test tube, they may find it takes 20 drops of juice *A* to bleach the indophenol, or 12 drops of juice *B*. Of course, if the juices were diluted to the same degree, then juice *B* would contain more vitamin C, since less of the juice was needed to bleach the indicator.

You may also want to extend this work to show how we often destroy the vitamin content of our food supply. Heat the juices to boiling and test again to find how many drops of juice must be added to bleach 10 cubic centimeters of the indicator. You might also want to test and compare the ascorbic acid content of canned, frozen, and fresh juices, diluting them all equally.

The Acids in Orange Juice: Paper Chromatography.[8] The relatively new technique of paper chromatography, of increasing importance in chemical analysis, can be adapted to secondary school analysis of inorganic as well as organic compounds. The purpose of this experiment is to show a method of using this technique in the analysis of citric and malic acids in orange juice. It is felt that with this background, an industrious student could go ahead on more advanced research into other components contained in this and other materials.

A method suggested by Dr. C. H. Wang of Oregon State College is given as follows: An old-fashioned vacuum desiccator is obtained with the top of the lid removed. A petri or crystallizing dish is placed in the bottom to hold the saturating solvent. A separatory funnel containing the same solvent is connected by means of neoprene tubing to a piece of capillary tubing drawn at the free end. A screw-type pinch clamp is fastened on the neoprene tubing to regulate the flow of the solvent. Whatman no. 1 filter paper, larger in diameter than the outside flange diameter of the desiccator, is processed as described in the next paragraph and, with wick attached, is placed across the desiccator as is illustrated in Fig. 8-10*a*.

The large circular filter paper is divided into four or eight parts, as is shown in Fig. 8-10*b*. *Do not fold* and do not touch with the fingers any more than necessary. Why these precautions? Two circles are drawn about the absolute center of the paper and slits are cut, by the razor blades shown in Fig. 8-10*c* (two single-edged blades separated by an extra nut between the blades, fastened to a strip of metal), from *near the outside edge of the filter paper* to the inner circle. The unknown and control acids are applied to a marked spot on the second circle. These spots should be kept as small as possible by applying with a drawn capillary tube and allowing each spot to dry before the next one is applied in the same place. The number of times the spot is applied is called the *level* of the compound. The level will vary with the compound and will have to be determined by experimentation. After the "spots" have been applied, a wick consisting of a 3- by 5-centimeter piece of filter paper rolled tightly is inserted in a small hole at the absolute center of the circular filter paper. When this is done, the large filter is ready to be placed in the desiccator.

During the time the filter paper is being prepared, the desiccator should be closed so that the solvent in the crystallizing dish can saturate the atmosphere. After the filter paper is placed in the desiccator, allow the solvent from the separatory funnel to drop through the capillary tube onto the wick at a very slow rate. The solvent should drip very slowly from the bottom of the wick into the crystallizing dish. After 3 hours

[8] From the West Coast Science Teachers' Summer Conference, 1954, in *The Science Teacher,* February, 1955.

Table 8-5. A Summary of Tests

Textile	Burning	Sodium hydroxide	Hydrochloric acid	Microscope
Cotton	Burns readily; little odor, little ash	None	Only slightly affected	Flat, twisted
Wool	Burns fast; gummy residue; smells of burning hair	Dissolves	None	Rough, scaly
Silk	Burns slowly; flame extinguishes itself; leaves small black bead; smells of burning hair	Dissolves	Dissolves slowly	Smooth, cylindrical; width irregular
Rayon	Burns very quickly; odor varies with type of rayon; fine gray ash	Swells or gelatinizes	Dissolves slowly	Smooth, cylindrical, striated
Nylon	Difficult to ignite; shrinks from flame; celery odor; round hard bead	Insoluble	Dissolves slowly	Smooth, cylindrical
Orlon	Ignites readily; not self-extinguishing; black bead; acrid odor	Fairly resistant	Not attacked	Twisted, striated
Dacron	Hard to ignite; shrinks from flame; pungent odor; round hard bead	Dissolves in boiling NaOH	Not attacked	Round, smooth, kinky in places
Spun glass	Does not burn; softens, forming round bead	No effect	Attacked by concentrated acid	Round, transparent
Saran	Ignites with moderate difficulty; self-extinguishing; acrid odor; black bead	Insoluble	Not attacked	Round

animal fibers, will turn pink litmus to blue because of the formation of ammonia (ammonium hydroxide when moist).

To Tell the Difference between Animal and Vegetable Fibers. Place a drop of a 2 per cent solution of sulfuric acid on samples to be tested and allow it to penetrate through the goods. Then place the samples between two pieces of paper and press with a hot iron. The vegetable fibers will char, but the animal fibers will remain as they were.

To Analyze a Mixed Material. Obtain a sample of a mixed animal and vegetable material such as wool and cotton, or silk and rayon. Put 2 teaspoons of lye in a pint of water. Boil the sample 5 to 10 minutes. Any wool or silk will dissolve, while cotton, rayon, or linen will remain. This experiment may be done quantitatively, by weighing the sample "before"

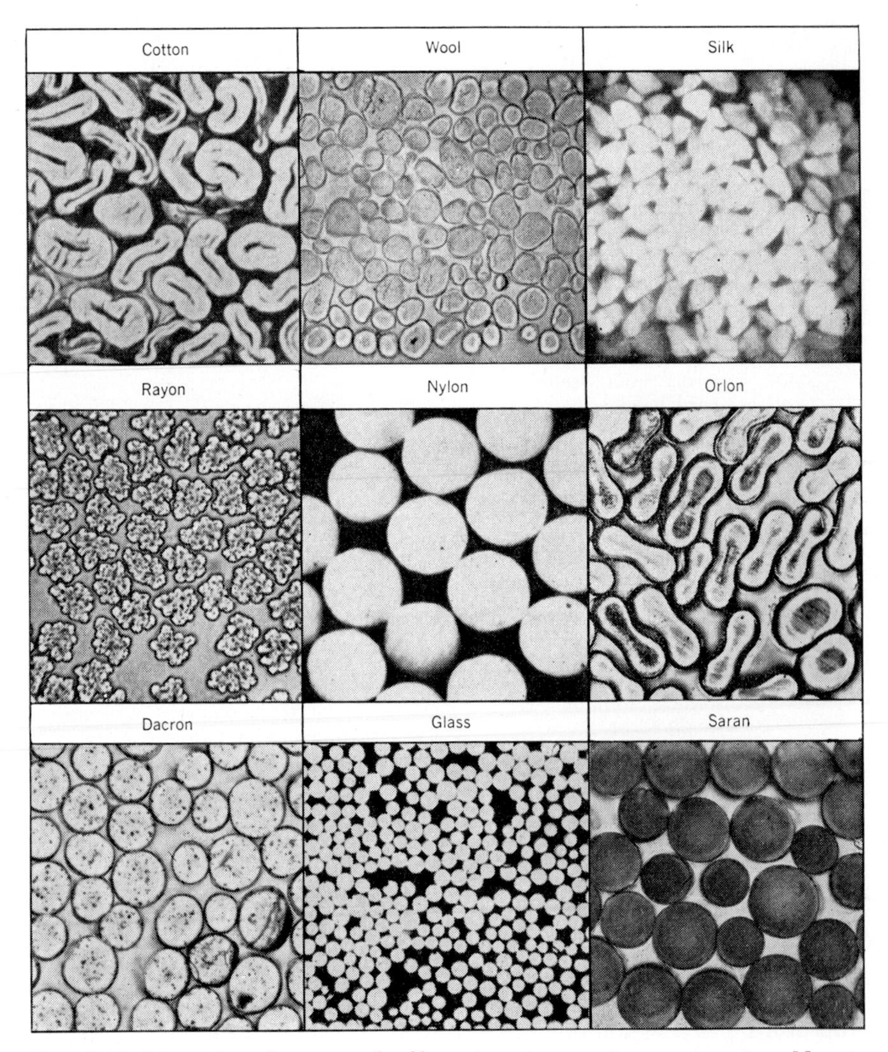

Fig. 8-12. Natural and man-made fibers in microscopic cross section. No attempt has been made to standardize magnifications. (*Modern Textiles.*)

and "after" and calculating the percentage of each fiber in the sample.

Other simple fiber tests may be found in *Test It Yourself* (Sec. 19-2*w*) and in *Living Chemistry.*[10] Students who are interested in man-made fibers may write to *Textile World,* 330 West 42d St., New York, for a complete chart called *Synthetic-fiber Table.*

"Technical and Production Data of Sixteen Principal Synthetic Fibers and Metallic Yarns" may be obtained from *America's Textile Reporter,* 286 Congress St., Boston, Mass.

8-16. Other Farm Products

Ethyl Alcohol from Sugar. This is an experiment students might do alone or in small groups: Dissolve 60 grams of grape sugar in about 600 milliliters of water in a liter flask *A*. Warm this solution to 40°C. Then add to it one-third of a yeast cake (powdered). Arrange apparatus as in Fig. 8-13*a* and set aside in a warm place for 48 hours. Then note the condition of the limewater in test tube *B*. Note the odor of the fermented mixture. Distill the solution in the liter flask, attaching the flask to a Liebig condenser as shown in Fig. 8-13*b*. When 150 cubic centimeters of distillate has collected in the receiving flask, stop the distillation, discard down the sink the residue in the distilling flask, and replace it with the distillate.

Redistill this and test the second distillate for proof spirits (at least 50 per cent alcohol) *at once,* when drops of it *first drip from the condenser.* This test is made by taking a small piece of asbestos paper in a forceps, wetting the paper with the distillate as it drips from the condenser, and then holding it for a moment in the bunsen flame. The liquid will then burn with a pale blue flame if it is of proof spirits quality. Continue making this test at brief intervals until the distillate no longer burns. Then stop the distillation and measure the volume of the distillate. What are the uses of ethyl alcohol?

Soap from Fats (by the Cold Process). Students may dissolve 10 grams of sodium hydroxide in 45 milliliters of water and allow it to cool. When cold, the lye should be poured slowly into 75 grams olive oil (or cottonseed or cocoanut oil, although they are not as satisfactory), stirring all the time with a stirring rod or egg beater. The mixture should be stirred until the lye and oil have reacted sufficiently to give the mixture the consistency of honey (15 to 30 minutes). Then it should be poured into a pasteboard box with wet sides, wrapped up in a wet towel, and put in a warm place for 2 weeks.

Your students might study the chemistry of saponification. What important by-product is formed? Why did we salvage fats during the last war? Why is homemade farm soap a "soft soap"? (When wood ashes are

[10] *Op. cit.*

leached for alkali, a potassium rather than a sodium compound is obtained; this makes the soap soft.)

What substitution products for soap are now widely used? From what raw materials are they made?

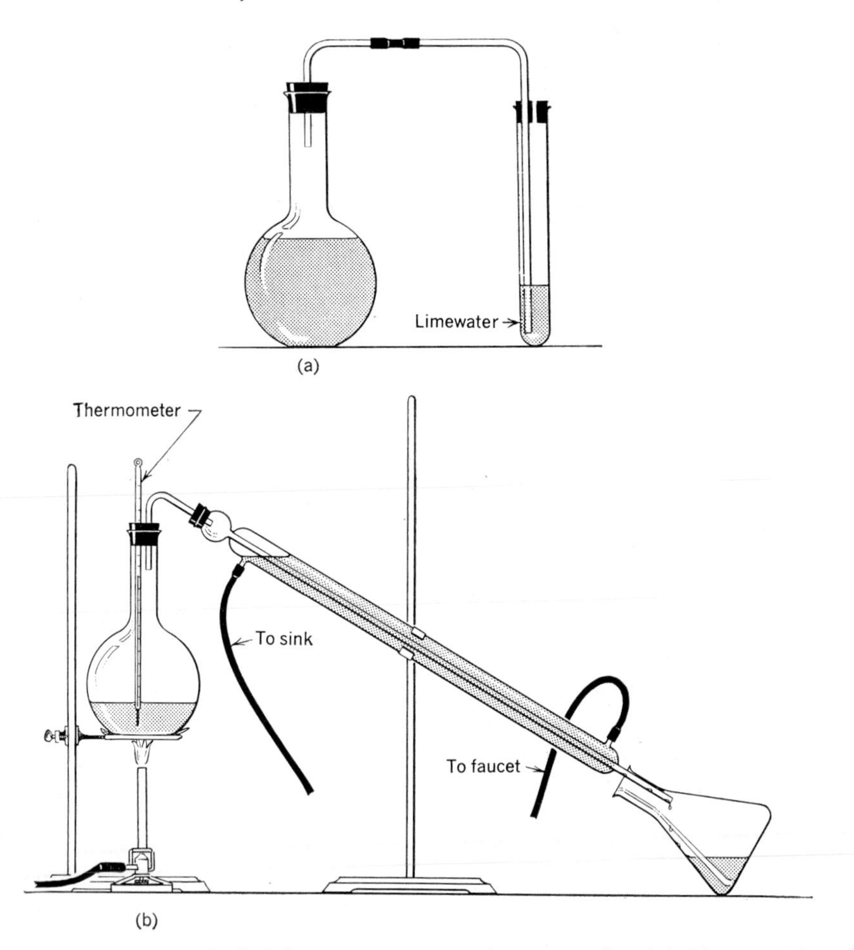

Fig. 8-13. Making alcohol from grape sugar. Apparatus for (*a*) Fermentation of grape sugar with the aid of yeast; (*b*) fractional distillation of the ethyl alcohol obtained in (*a*).

Starch from Potatoes. Here is a simple experiment for students to try: Reduce a clean new potato to a fine pulp by first peeling it and then grating it on the medium-rough surface of a regular kitchen grater. Soak this for 5 minutes in a small amount of cold water, pour it all into a stout linen or cheesecloth bag, and squeeze out all the liquid into a clean iron pan. Repeat this, wetting the pulp and squeezing three times. The starch is carried mechanically through the cloth and settles at the bottom of the pan. The clear water may be poured off and the starch dried.

Make starch paste of a portion of this starch and apply the iodine test to it (Sec. 8-14). From what other vegetables is starch prepared? How is starch prepared on a large scale?

Dextrin from Starch. Starch is converted into dextrin at 205°C. Students may heat 20 grams of finely powdered starch in a porcelain dish, stirring constantly with a teaspoon for 8 to 10 minutes, taking care not to burn the starch. After this time, the material should be cooled, 100 milliliters of water added, and the mixture stirred and filtered. The filtrate should then be evaporated down to 50 milliliters. The dextrin may be precipitated by adding denatured alcohol, until a light coffee-colored precipitate permanently appears. This should be filtered (or allowed to settle), dried, and a paste made of it. Students may test its sticking qualities. What happens molecularly when dextrin is made from starch? What are some of the uses of dextrin?

Solid Fats from Vegetable Oil. Vegetable oils have long been important foods for many peoples. In solidified form they can be used as a substitute for animal fat or lard. Ask your students what is the advantage of this. Elicit from them that when vegetable oils are used in this way one step in the "food chain" is saved; consequently this means a cheaper product than that obtained from animal sources.

For detailed directions on hydrogenation of oil see *Test It Yourself!* (Sec. 19-2*w*).

Other Farm Products of Importance. Committees of students could study, arrange exhibits and make reports on other industrial products of the farm. Here are some suggestions:

Rayon, cellophane, dynamite, plastics, lacquers, photographic films from wood or cotton; casein plastics from milk; nylon from corncobs and bulbs; glue, paint, varnish, lacquer, and products used for coating paper from soybean oil.

8-17. The Farm and Chemistry

A Cooperative Venture. There is an interesting interrelatedness between the farmer's and the chemist's work, which you as a science teacher may want to accent.

The farmer of today relies on the chemist for help in fighting insects, fungi, plant diseases, weeds. The farmer could hardly get along without the products of chemical research—improved fertilizer, plant hormones, poultry and livestock feeds. In addition, chemistry has had a hand in improving living conditions on the farm, providing healthier surroundings, and helping to eliminate many backbreaking tasks. Through the science of chemurgy, industry has now found increasing use for farm products or the residues of these products. Wood and cotton, grains and sugars, corncobs, soybean oil, and others are needed for these gigantic and expanding chemical industries.

Nevertheless, the farmer faces stiff competition. Soap substitutes, plastics in place of leather, synthetic textiles instead of cotton or wool, all have played a part in cutting down the use of farm products and increasing surpluses.

Students will be interested in following the reports of President Eisenhower's bipartisan committee called the Commission on Increased Industrial Use of Agricultural Products.

The Commission has already come up with some exciting suggestions for new uses and new crops. Cashmere from corn, fiber from poultry feathers, antibiotics from cereal grains, growth of a crop called "grear," with countless industrial applications, are only a few of the proposals.

What a fine exhibit your students might make to show the products of the chemist for the farm and the farm for chemistry. Some of the traditional experiments in a chemistry course, like the destructive distillation of wood (Sec. 10-12) or alcoholic fermentation (Sec. 8-16), will take on an added dimension as students begin to recognize these interrelationships. Here, too, may be found many examples of science used creatively in the service of man.

9

The Forest and Living Things

In this chapter you will find suggestions for giving your students a firsthand acquaintance with the forest and its living things—trees, cover, animal life—as well as its enemies—insects, disease, and fire. Man's continuing need of the forest and of forest products is explored and ways of giving students direct experience in forest management are indicated.

THE LIVING FOREST

9-1. Starting a Forestry Unit

If you live in a community where trees abound, or even if you live where they are scarce, there are many outdoor activities that may be used to lead into conservation education. These activities ought not to be treated as isolated exercises but as links in the growing chain of understanding of the wise use of our resources—in this case, our forests.

Many of the topics dealt with in this chapter are included in *Suggestions for Integrating Forestry in the Modern Curriculum,* by the U.S. Forest Service. You might find this an invaluable pamphlet for suggesting still other areas to be explored by your class. Many ideas, too, have been gleaned from *Conservation: A Handbook for Teachers* (Sec. 19-2*b*).

The Forest Community. Here is one way in which a unit on forestry might be started. Ask your students, "What besides trees do we find in a forest?" As they enter the woods, students will observe with varying degrees of perception.

At the end of the trip, they might compare notes and begin to sense how many and various are the living things that constitute a forest community. What is the relationship of these living things to each other and to their environment?

There might be some discussion of the differences in forest communities as one goes from north to south or east to west across the United States.

9-2. A Study of Trees

Tree Identification. Learning to identify trees is not in itself conservation, but it is a helpful step in learning to read the language of nature. The kinds of trees we find in a region tell us much about the fertility of the soil as well as its moisture. Foresters need to know which trees to cut and which to preserve in order to keep the forest productive. The kind of wildlife, too, is dependent to some extent on the kind of forest in an area.

You will find books like the following helpful: *Trees: A Guide to Familiar American Trees,* by H. S. Zim and A. C. Martin (Simon and Schuster, Inc., New York, 1952); and *Knowing Your Trees* (Sec. 19-5*w*).

Tree Census. As a pleasurable means for gaining skill in the identification of trees and shrubs, students might be assigned small areas around the school, along nearby streets, or in a wooded region. In these regions they might record the kinds of trees and their size. They may measure the trunk at a designated height, perhaps 4 feet up from the ground.

Which types of trees serve for shade, which might be used as wind breaks, and which would attract birds to nest? Thus, students learn that certain trees and shrubs are valued for individual uses.

Age of Trees: Cross Section of a Tree Trunk. Students may examine the layers and rings of a cut tree trunk, and count the rings to determine age. Next, they might find out the functions performed by the inner and outer layers of bark, the sapwood, and the heartwood in a living tree (Fig. 9-1*a*).

Determining a tree's age, noticing irregularities, may open up discussion of possible causes of injury—such as old fire scars (Fig. 9-1*b*), too little rainfall. The width of the ring indicates the wetness of the year. Many successive narrow rings may indicate droughts or a hard struggle for life in a forest which is too crowded (Fig. 9-1*c*) or too poor in its soil.

City teachers may contact the Park Department, which supervises city trees and discards infected ones. City park departments will no doubt cooperate in supplying a freshly cut log for studying cross sections.

Sample Core of a Tree Trunk. If you can arrange to have the help of a forester, he might show your students how the recent rate of growth of a tree may be determined by means of an increment borer.

Your students might obtain information through UNESCO about a new instrument which can automatically compute the age and annual growth of trees. A core of wood taken from the tree trunk is fed into a machine which then both counts the number of concentric rings and measures the width between them. What effect might such "automation" have in assessing the results of forestry programs or in more accurately forecasting forestry resources?

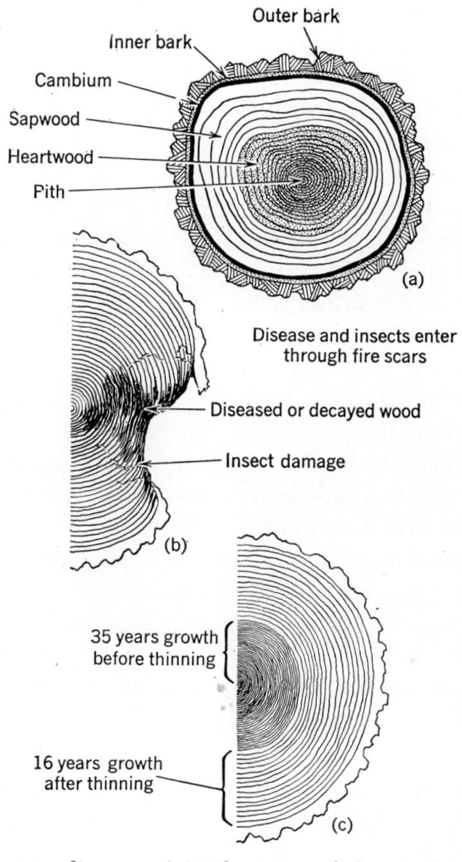

Fig. 9-1. Cross section of a tree. (*a*) The parts of the trunk; (*b*) effect of fire; (*c*) effect of crowding followed by thinning.

Counting Whorls. Students might examine pine trees of different sizes and observe how the branches grow in whorls around the trunk. Have them count the number of whorls of branches or branch scars along the trunk from the ground to the top of the tree. For some species of pine, such as white, red, Austrian, Scotch, the number of whorls gives the age of the tree. Many others grow irregularly, producing several whorls each year. To check this, the number of annual rings on a branch may be counted, or if there is good reason to do so, the tree may be cut down and the annual rings in the stump counted and compared to the number of whorls.

A Study of Leaves: Blueprints. There are times when a set of blueprint outlines of leaves may be an aid in identification of trees and shrubs. This technique may be useful for younger children, too. Perhaps these prints might be displayed on a bulletin board with the challenge that students should locate the trees and bring a leaf to school to see whether they can match the blueprints.

The technique is simple enough. Tape one end of a sheet of cardboard as backing to one side of a small pane of glass about 6 inches square. Cut the cardboard to fit the size of the glass. Insert a sheet of blueprint paper between the glass and the cardboard backing. Now lay a leaf on the surface of the blueprint paper and expose the print paper to sunlight for a few minutes or until a strong print is produced. Then remove the blueprint paper, rinse it in water and hang each of these up to dry as photographic prints are dried. Finally flatten them under some weight.

Similarly, students may want to make outlines of leaves on photographic paper. They may use the same kind of frame suggested for blueprint paper. Caution students to handle the photographic print paper in darkness. An electric light bulb may be substituted for the sunlight. The paper will then need to be developed, fixed, and rinsed. In this kind of activity, students learn a skill as well as subject matter.

Leaf Skeletons. You may want to develop a library of lantern slides of different leaves; this may help students in keying out plants and in learning to identify weeds and cultivated plants.

One suggested method is this: Prepare a solution by dissolving 4 ounces of sodium carbonate in 16 ounces of boiling water. Then add 2 ounces of calcium hydroxide and boil for 15 minutes. Filter the solution after it has cooled. When leaves are to be prepared they should be boiled in this solution for about an hour. Then the soft parts of the leaves may be rubbed away so the tougher web of veins remains. These skeletons may be mounted with library paste on cards or inserted between two lantern slides and then taped.

Changes with the Seasons. Note and discuss the effects of seasonal changes upon trees. Your students might keep a written diary of changes observed in one tree throughout the school year.

If, for instance, a study of why leaves fall is linked with results of their falling, the protection of soil, the checking of runoff through water storage, the aid to wildlife, or, on the negative side, the increase of fire hazard, then the study becomes a way of pointing up conservation concepts.

Autumn Coloring. As the fall season approaches, we anticipate the beauty of a countryside aglow with color. Many of us start wondering what makes the leaves turn from green to brilliant yellow, orange, or red.

Early in autumn your students might make observations of the color changes, noting also the daily weather, temperature, humidity, length of daylight, and occurrence of frost. Clear, bright days and cool, crisp nights seem to be the most favorable conditions. Though lack of moisture, fungus attacks, and frosts play a part, scientists now believe that length of day is an important factor.

The shortening of daylight seems to cause a decrease in production of the plant hormone, auxin. This, in turn, results in the formation of a layer of cells (absciss layer) at the base of each leaf. These cells act to separate the leaves from the branches so that little food and water can circulate. Each leaf, therefore, becomes isolated. No new chlorophyll is formed and as the old gradually disintegrates the dyes and pigments in the leaf, which had been masked by the green, are revealed in their vividness.

The reds and purples are a function of the sugar content of the leaves. With sudden frost, the sugar is trapped in the leaves and cannot move down the stems. The leaves finally turn brown as a result of the action of tannins on the protein matter.

9-3. Some Field Trip Techniques

To begin to explore the out of doors—a wood lot, a forest, a glen—you might want to consider these suggestions:

Trip 1: What Did You See? This might be a pure and simple walking trip with no comment or explanation by the teacher until the end. Then only would he ask, "What did you see?" The extent and acuity of the students' observations often reveal, to an unsurpassed degree, the truly gifted youngster.

Trip 2: What Is a Plant? On a second trip the teacher may ask students to bring him a plant (Fig. 9-2). Students will at first bring leaves, blossoms, or a stem with leaves and flowers. Only a "whole" plant, uprooted with the dirt still clinging to it, will bring home to the students that the plant is an organism, rooted in the soil and dependent on it.

Trip 3: What Makes the Difference? On this trip the teacher would lead the group to a small clearing or opening where sun-loving plants could flourish. "Why," he might ask, after students had had a chance for observation, "don't the plants in the clearing look the same as those on the wooded side of the trail?"

Trip 4: On Which Side Does the Moss Grow? The purpose of the next trip might be to examine a large mossy inclined tree. The teacher would ask, "On which side is the moss?" The youngsters might decide it was the east side. "Why not the north?" would be the next query. The students would have to figure out that the moss grew on the surface down which the rain ran. Would this be on the same side for all the trees? This would be the side not only that got the wettest, but also the one that was least exposed to evaporation. If someone happened to identify the tree as a sycamore, well and good; but identification at this point might not be as important as the understandings gained through attempting to resolve questions.

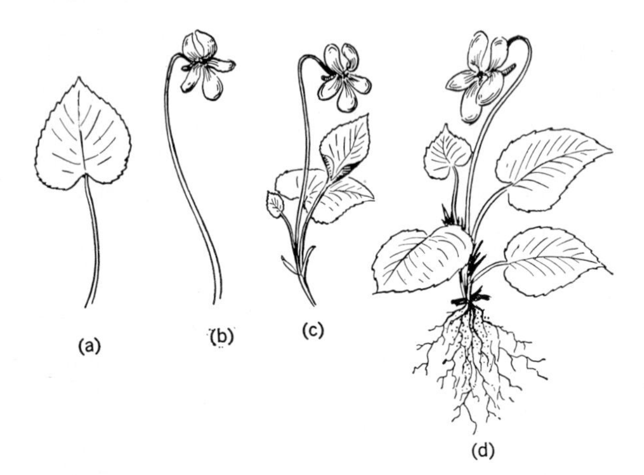

Fig. 9-2. What is a plant? Is it (*a*) leaf? (*b*) flower? (*c*) stem-leaf-flower? (*d*) root-stem-leaf-flower?

With paper or plastic bags brought for the purpose, the youngsters might collect samples of wood from a decaying log, some perhaps showing mycelia of fungi at different stages of decay. These could then be examined and classified on return to class, with the aid of a magnifying glass or microscope.

Trip 5: A Time for Listening. This trip could be for picnic lunch beside a stream. The lunch time, quietest time in the day, would provide opportunity for the youngsters to become aware of woodland noises: bird song, frog voices, trees swaying, water music. If the teacher were asked to identify by their calls the names of birds, he would do so (if he could) and afterwards arrange in class for a playback of recordings[1] of bird songs and amphibian sounds.

Trip 6: When Is a Leaf Not a Leaf? The teacher would hold up a simple and then a compound leaf (Fig. 9-3) and ask, "Which is a leaf?" The objective, of course, would be for students to see that both are, and perhaps to note, in addition, variations in shape, color, margins, etc., again without the necessity of naming unless the question arose. Perhaps this trip would afford a place to see poison ivy growing beside woodbine, to note the long bare central petiole of the "untouchable" one and the five-fingered design of woodbine.

[1] Volumes 1 and 2 of *American Bird Songs,* and *Voices of the Night,* Cornell University Records, Ithaca, N.Y.

Trip 7: "The Old Order Changeth." Discover examples of trees which are disappearing from a certain woodland because they are being shaded out by larger, more vigorous trees—an analogy, perhaps, to examples of social evolution and change within the human species if we could but read it.

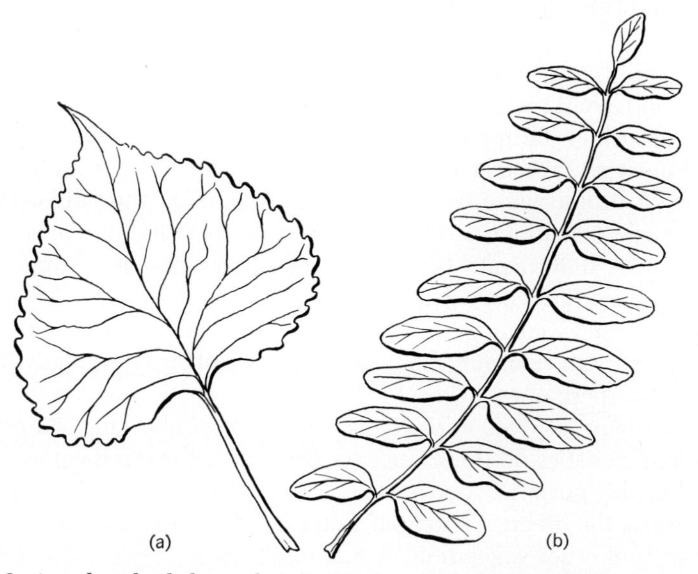

Fig. 9-3. Are they both leaves? (*a*) Simple poplar leaf; (*b*) compound locust leaf.

Trip 8: Plants, Too, Live in Communities. As the teacher and his class explore the glen they may find a number of examples of plant communities. A flourishing bed of ginger, for instance, illustrates how some kinds of plants do well together.

Trip 9: How Plants Get Their Names. A teacher might uproot a plant whose stem exudes a bloody juice when crushed. Even those youngsters who might not know it will come close to its common name, bloodroot. The teacher might try to illustrate other homely means by which many species have been commonly named.

Trip 10: A Lesson in Adaptation. Early in spring, a trip to the woods will be rewarded with the finding of many varieties of wild flowers. Students will notice that these small plants bloom and seed before the leaves of trees appear. Why?

Trip 11: Beware of Experts! A teacher, stopping by a small plant, shrub, or tree might ask students to identify it. If the identification is correct, the teacher might declare the answer false and find none to challenge him. If teachers, instead of *telling*, truly teach, students will learn, among other things, that experts can be wrong.

9-4. Other Observations in the Forest

The Forest Floor. When students are in the woods they may note the "spring" in their steps as they walk on the forest floor. What is the reason for this? Suggest that they squeeze a handful of the upper material and then let go. Does it come back to its original shape? Can students explain?

If the soil is moist, water may actually be squeezed out. Does this help students understand why it is recommended that trees be planted around reservoirs, on high farm land, and on the headwaters of streams?

The Forest as Protector of Soil. Do forests help prevent erosion? Students begin to find an answer to this question when they discover how the forest keeps soil moist. What evidences do they find of water held or checked in its movement? In a deforested area, what has happened to the soil? What differences in temperature and humidity do they find in a forested area as compared to a nearby open area? Can they explain the difference? On returning from this trip students may be ready to deal with some of these questions:

What varieties of trees in particular are used for checking soil erosion? What characteristics do these varieties possess that make them especially adapted to this purpose?

Which has the greatest potential water-holding capacity, the soil aided by forests and other vegetation, or man-built dams?

How do forests affect the quality as well as the quantity of water supply for human consumption?

Draw to scale a 5 per cent slope (Sec. 7-13), a 50 per cent slope, and a 65 per cent slope. On which would you expect to be able to check erosion with grass? With forest?

How a Forest Spreads. If your school is near the woods, then a field trip to the surrounding meadows might be planned to study how a forest spreads. Can students discover pioneer trees? Are they the light-seeded ones (ash, aspen, hemlock, maple, pine, and others) or the heavy-seeded ones (beech, hickory, or other nut-bearing trees)? Are the pioneer trees larger in the middle of the field or close to the woods? Why? Which side of the forest seems to be seeded most easily? Might the direction of the prevailing wind have anything to do with this? How important is natural reseeding to good forestry practice?

What kinds of trees are not able to germinate in their own shade? Students might investigate the shade-tolerance scale of tree seedlings. This might be a time to engage in a study of the succession of trees and the final emergence of the climax forest.

Do Trees and Cows Belong Together? Select two wood lots, a hardwood stand where cows graze, and another that is not grazed. In the two wood lots compare the following things: abundance of young tree and shrub growth, amount of leaves and duff on the forest floor, compactness of soil (Sec. 7-7), height from the ground of leaf-bearing branches, approximate age of the majority of the trees, and extent to which tree roots are exposed.

On the basis of your students' observations, do they think that healthy cows and a good crop of trees can be nurtured on the same land?

While you and your students are studying these two wood lots, you might compare their relative values as habitats for wildlife. Which wood lot has the most animal signs? What can you conclude about the relationship of cattle and wildlife in wood lots?

Flora and Fauna of the Forest. The delicate plants of the forest are often small and hidden. They can easily be passed over unless you can help your students to develop the seeing eye.

Students looking for early spring wild flowers will find them in deciduous forests where the sunlight can reach the soil. There are very few wild flowers in an evergreen forest. Why is this?

If you like to roam the woods in early spring to catch a glimpse of the first hepatica; if each year you visit the slope where the bloodroot blossom; if you know the haunts of the dogtooth violet and the rare and lovely lady's-slipper, then you may be able to transfer your enthusiasm to a few of your students. A lifelong interest cannot be taught, but it is, in some instances, quite readily "caught."

Indian Pipe: A Saprophytic Plant. Should you walk in the woods in late spring or early fall you may show students clusters of white Indian pipe. They grow in shaded spots under fallen leaves, so you may have to move aside these decaying leaves. Have students examine the plant relationship here. Since the plants are not green, they cannot make food; neither are they parasitic (Sec. 3-19). Have students explain what processes must go on in the soil; how materials of humus might be made soluble so they can enter the Indian pipe plants.

Students may want to compare these seed plants with mushrooms, which should be found in the same region. Perhaps it might be possible to transport some of these plants, in cushions of the soil they are in, to a terrarium in the classroom. A terrarium seems almost a requirement of a classroom interested in interrelationships among plants and animals. Students can make several, following the directions in Sec. 9-5.

Mushrooms as Saprophytic Plants. Students may bring in samples of mushrooms and of their relatives, the bracket fungi that grow on the sides of stumps of trees. In fact, they may want to learn to distinguish the poisonous varieties from common forms of mushrooms. Some students may learn to dry out the mushrooms and key out the forms so that they can be mounted in an exhibit case in school.

What materials do these plants remove from the soil or dead trees? What materials do they return to the soil? What do students observe to be the characteristics of the soil in which these saprophytes are found?

Perhaps some students may want to try to keep these mushrooms growing in a terrarium.

9-5. Creating Natural Habitats, Indoors and Outdoors

A Terrarium. Terrariums offer scope for the creativity and imagination of the designer. They may range from small fishbowl gardens to woodlands or deserts in large aquarium tanks (Sec. 5-9).

A terrarium may be prepared in this way: At the bottom of a tank add a 1-inch layer of coarse gravel or pebbles along with a few bits of charcoal. Over this spread a half-inch layer of sand. Over these layers add an inch layer of a light loam soil and plant the vegetation in this layer. Watch the amount of moisture needed and keep the terrarium covered (Fig. 9-4). Should mold occur in the tank, remove the cover

Fig. 9-4. A woodland terrarium.

so that its moisture content is reduced. An electric light bulb might be used to supply light during the winter months.

Culturing Mosses and Ferns. Students may collect specimens along with small amounts of soil. These may be transported in moist paper in a vasculum or the mosses or ferns may be wrapped in waxed paper. In class transfer the plants to terrariums.

Students may cultivate many kinds of mosses, such as *Polytrichum* and *Mnium,* and such liverworts as *Pellia* and *Marchantia.* Small specimens of many ferns can be maintained in a drier terrarium, along with club mosses and horsetails.

Nature Trails on the School Grounds. Students in one class in general science or in biology might take responsibility for this long-range project: a nature trail around school. Some students may make decorative wood markers in the shop, and others may paint these markers. Then the trees and shrubs need to be identified. Students may plant trees to attract birds; for example, there might be flowering crab apple, white oak, black cherry, box elder, elderberry, blackberry, Japanese barberry.

Birdhouses (Sec. 9-6) might attract permanent residents, too. Models of farming methods such as terracing or strip cropping might be included somewhere along the trail. Fallen tree logs might be towed to a spot convenient for study by a group of students. Spring flowers and ferns and mosses might be transplanted, in some of their soil, to a shady, moist area of the same soil acidity. In fact, a small artificial lake might even be constructed and stocked with plants and animals brought from another region some distance away.

Over several years, with planning and the imagination that students bring to such a project, a number of classes of young people might achieve such a goal through a pooling of their efforts. They may even plan a mimeographed guide sheet asking questions concerned with interrelationships between plants and animals. Lessons on soil pH (Sec. 7-9), identification of plants and animals (Sec. 4-9), tropisms (Sec. 3-15), reproduction and variations (Sec. 4-9), and anatomy of plants and animals might all be studied out of doors with living materials in their natural habitat. These are valuable, purposeful activities.

9-6. A Study of Wildlife

Signs of Wildlife. When your students are out in meadow or woods, they might see how many signs of wildlife they can find. There may be tracks, bedding spots, nests, signs of browsing and of leftovers such as chewed cones or nut husks. Feathers, bits of hair, droppings may also be discovered. Can your students piece together the stories that these signs tell? What needs and habits of a particular animal are reflected in these signs?

Making a Cast of Animal Tracks.[2] Students might find the tracks of some animal in snow, mud, or soft dirt. They might try a dog or rabbit track first, since there are plenty of these. Then perhaps they can find tracks of forest wildlife—raccoon, deer, or gray squirrel.

Here are directions for them to follow: Place a cardboard ring around the track and secure it with a paper clip. Push the ring gently into the ground or snow, so that plaster cannot run out under it. This wall holds in the plaster (Fig. 9-5).

For each cup of water poured into a tin can, sprinkle in about 1⅔ cups of plaster of paris. Allow this to stand for 2 or 3 minutes, then stir until smooth. The plaster should be about like pancake batter. It sets quickly, so do not dawdle. Slowly and gently pour the plaster into

[2] Cornell Conservation Corner Leaflet no. 3, Cornell University Press, Ithaca, N.Y.

the track, to a depth of about 1½ inches. The plaster should be liquid enough so that all air bubbles can float to the top.

Fig. 9-5. Materials needed for making a cast of animal tracks.

Let the plaster set. If it is fairly fresh, the cast should be ready to pick up in about ½ hour. When the plaster is hard, carefully pick up the cast, peel off the cardboard, and gently clean the surface with an old toothbrush.

The cast just made is called a *negative cast*. If you want a positive cast, one that looks just like the track on the ground, smear the negative with petroleum jelly, put a cardboard or clay wall around it extending about 2 inches above the negative, then pour in the plaster mixture. Let the plaster set, then remove the wall and separate the casts. This will not work on negative casts with undercuts, such as the cast of a deer track in mud.

Wildlife Needs Cover. Spend a little time with your class studying the requirements of animals (food, water, cover), then take your students out and examine the border of a woods, next to a field of grain or hay (Fig. 8-3). What animal signs do they find? Do they find more in the border areas than in the center of the wood lot? Can your students explain what they find? Do they think that wood borders would be improved for wildlife by the planting of food-bearing shrubs? Do hedgerows help?

Students may walk along any country road where the brush and shrubbery between the road and a field have not been cut down and burned. Can they discover whether the presence of hedgerows really makes any difference in the abundance of wildlife?

A Wildlife Census. Perhaps your students could help in taking a census of the wildlife in a given forest region. Such a project may be under way in your county or state, in which case you could very likely receive guidance from experts. The *Conservation Handbook* (Sec. 19-3*h*) on page 185 describes a census of small mammals, conducted by two biology classes at Smith Center, Kansas, in cooperation with a state census.

Whether or not your students have taken this or a similar census, they may want to find out whether the forest is under- or overpopulated with wildlife and just what the local wildlife problems are. This may lead to the making of shelters, feeding stations, or watering places for wildlife species in need of help.

Others of your group might be interested in cooperating with the

State Fish and Game Commission, or the Conservation Department, banding or marking some wild animals as a help in the study of wildlife.

All the work might be followed by a discussion of such questions as these: What are some practices in farming, forestry, industry, and commerce that are beneficial to wildlife? What practices are detrimental? Could any of these be economically changed to avoid such harm?

Ask your students to find out what are the benefits and the damages to forests caused by beaver, elk, deer, squirrels, woodpeckers, porcupines, or other animals found in your woods. Suggest that they find illustrations of what happens when a certain species of wildlife is overprotected by man. Where does wildlife fit into the balance of nature?

An excellent booklet on wildlife management in its many phases may be obtained from Boy Scouts of America, 2 Park Ave., New York.

Protection of Birds. The key to wildlife conservation is the improvement of the environment. In the case of birds this means providing plantings for food and cover. Look for an appropriate spot where your students can plant shrubs for shelter and nesting places, and other bushes to provide berries.

Encourage members of your class to join or help to organize a local group interested in the establishment of a bird sanctuary.

Certain of your students may be interested in building birdhouses for the school grounds or their own back yards. Specifications are available from the U.S. Fish and Wildlife Service, or perhaps from your State Department of Conservation or the National Audubon Society, 1130 Fifth Ave., New York.

Ask your students to suggest ways of preventing the wanton shooting not only of songbirds but also of crows, hawks, and owls.

Young people could turn over to the proper authorities in the community the stray cats, who, when they are abandoned, must kill to live.

A Tin Can Birdhouse.[3] Your students can build a tin can nest box, which attracts tree swallows as well as other birds.

Two-quart (No. 10) cans are best for these nests (Fig. 9-6*a*). These cans may be obtained from restaurants or other places that buy canned fruit and vegetables in quantity. An entry hole 1½ inches in diameter should be cut two-thirds of the way up the can. The edges of the hole should be bent over or filed smooth. The top cover of the can should be cut off completely. A wooden lid should then be cut so that it projects about 1 inch in front and ½ inch at the sides.

Two screw eyes, projecting downward from the bottom of the lid, one on each side of the can, make it possible to hold down the lid by passing a heavy wire through the eyes and through holes punched in

[3] *Science Newsletter,* Apr. 21, 1956.

the sides of the can. Using this method, the lid can be removed for cleaning the nest in the fall. Another wire, passed through holes punched about two-thirds of the way up the can in the back, will serve to hold the can firmly to its support. The can should then be painted green, after which it is ready for bird housekeeping.

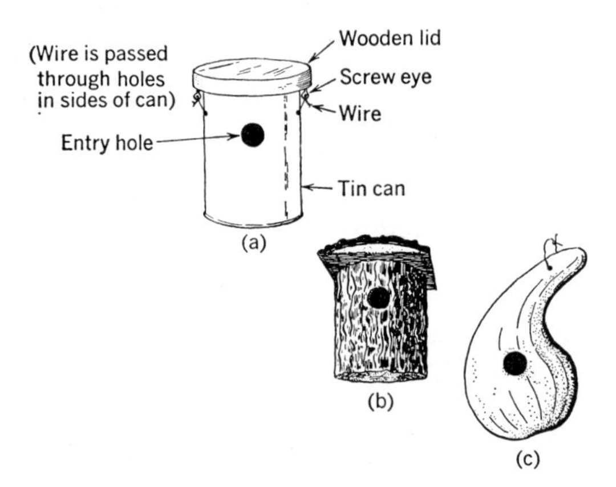

Fig. 9-6. Some homemade birdhouses. (*a*) A tin can; (*b*) a hollowed log; (*c*) a hollowed gourd.

If tree swallows are wanted as occupants, the can should be placed on a post in an open area, where there are few trees or shrubs; otherwise wrens are likely to use it. Of course, other birds will use the can nests too, if they happen to arrive first and are tough enough to defend their new home.

The nests should be placed as early as possible because tree swallows start looking for a home in early spring. If the birds find the nest and its surroundings to their liking, they are apt to return.

Wildlife in the Classroom. Many teachers have encouraged their students to bring all kinds of animals to the classroom for temporary observation, feeding, and first aid, if needed. Woodchucks, opossums, snakes, birds of various kinds can thus be studied at firsthand. Feeding habits can be noted and food chains traced, so that students become aware of each animal's place in the web of life.

Getting acquainted with animals in the classroom is a first step toward an understanding of the reasons for wildlife conservation. It also presents an opportunity to build up attitudes that will lessen the wanton and senseless killing of our wildlife, still so prevalent. A helpful pamphlet, *First Aid and Care of Small Animals,* can be obtained from the Animal Welfare Institute, 350 Fifth Ave., New York.

Museum of Living Things. Students may be trained to keep cultures of microscopic living materials (Sec. 5-11) as well as larger plants, invertebrates, and vertebrates, throughout the school year in the laboratory or class. In fact, a museum of living things may be maintained in a section of a laboratory or classroom. Student curators may work as a club with the responsibility for training freshman members each year. In this way a group of highly skilled students may continuously be available for service.

An Indoor Field Trip. Classes may come to the museum on indoor field trips. Your students may want to prepare a mimeographed "guide." Many ecological relationships among living things in different habitats may be maintained. For instance, in terrariums (Sec. 9-5), plants and animals may be placed in an arid environment. Cactus plants and horned toads might be a start; for a swampy terrain use amphibia, some mosses, willows, red maple seedlings, marsh marigolds, and other acid-loving plants. Prepare a terrarium so that it represents a wooded area with ferns, mosses, seedlings, Indian pipe, spring flowers, *Lycopodium,* amphibians such as newts, tiger salamanders, and different frogs. Also prepare a fresh-water aquarium and a marine aquarium (Sec. 5-9).

Students are cooperative about bringing in living materials when the teacher considers it important work. Many lessons in behavior, reproduction, classification, food chains, ecological successions, etc., may be taught in a museum of *living* things. Also, think of planning nature trails on the school grounds (Sec. 9-5).

Wildlife Regulation. At some point you will want your students to consider the laws regulating wildlife. Discussion of the necessity for a closed season will surely be in order. Federal laws dealing with migratory birds, and state laws, dealing also with hunting and fishing, should be familiar to your students.

It is most important for your students to understand the "why" of regulation. If you succeed, your students will know that wildlife resources have real and lasting value, that they will be important to many others in time to come, and that as individuals all of us have responsibility for their protection.

9-7. Enemies of the Forest

Insects and Disease. Your students might make a survey of the tree insects in the community. At the same time they could begin to find examples of the close relationship between insects and tree diseases. They will want to discover, too, what kinds of insects and fungi are beneficial to the forest. The question, "How are birds effective in forest insect control?" will lead to the study of a chain of ecological relationships. If there has been a forest fire your students may get direct evidence of the relation that exists between the fire and insects. Are fires apt to follow forest insect and disease epidemics? Are insects and diseases apt to follow fires?

Next, you may want to channel discussion to the important query, "What can we do about all this?" First, your students could find out the name, title, and address of the persons or officers in their city or state to whom tree insects and disease infestations should be reported and what service can be obtained. Specimens prepared for shipment should accompany letters.

Your students might welcome the challenge of conducting a campaign to destroy certain tree insects such as the tent caterpillar—planning carefully, securing the cooperation of appropriate organizations, arranging a program of publicity through papers and radio, with speakers throughout the school. Certain problems could finally be offered for consideration. Here are several:

1. Given an insect with the following characteristics, what would be some measures of control you could use?

a. The larvae have to crawl up the tree trunk.

b. The eggs have to be laid on seasoned logs.

c. The insect has to live on cambium of a weak tree or freshly cut logs for only a few weeks before it bores in to live in the sapwood or heartwood.

2. What instances can you cite in which insects, birds, or animals were introduced to control some other insect or animal and the introduced species became as much of a menace as the one to be controlled?

3. Why may great harm result from using a poison spray or dust (Fig. 9-7) in a forest (Sec. 8-7)?

Fig. 9-7. Spraying insect poison by airplane. Can such spraying of forests be harmful as well as helpful? (*U.S. Forest Service.*)

4. Why does the continuous harvesting of timber as it matures reduce insect and disease attack?

Termites: Wood Destroyers. Old tree stumps, wet logs, and sometimes, alack, old beams in a home provide shelter and food for colonies of termites.

Students should try to find a decaying tree stump that contains such a colony. This might be a time for study of symbiosis. Students may report to the class on the role of the flagellated protozoa that live in the intestine of termites and digest the wood that the termites ingest. Since the termites have no means of digesting the wood they consume, they are dependent upon the activities of the flagellates that abide within. Since both organisms help each other, this is not a case of parasite and host.

You may want students to examine these flagellates as a microscope lesson. Collect termites in the field and transport them to the laboratory where they may be kept in closed jars. Add a bit of sugar and some water from time to time to the wood particles in which the termites live.

On a clean slide add a drop of physiological salt solution (Sec. 18-1*t*). Place one termite on the slide. With one forceps hold the termite's body to the slide as you pull off the head with another forceps. Watch how the intestine and other organs of the viscera are removed with the head. Discard the other parts of the body; tease apart the intestine in the water and mount this material on a clean slide. Examine under low and high power of the microscope for the graceful flagellates.

Students may want to find out how the termites become infected with the flagellates, or what would happen if the flagellates were removed from the termites. As a matter of fact, termite eggs may be hatched under sterile conditions. Without flagellates the termites will starve to death in sawdust!

Students might also use a termite colony to study the social structure within this group.

To the homeowner, an invasion of termites may become a major calamity. How may wood used for construction purposes be protected from termites (Sec. 9-11)?

Forest Fires: How Do They Start? Have one of your experienced Scouts build a fire with a single match. Can forest fires start in as simple a manner? Students will think of burning cigarettes, smoldering trash, the friction of a steel cable drawn over a punky log, a stroke of lightning—any of these can provide the spark that ignites disaster.

Disaster: A Typical Year. Ask your students to do a bit of research. Can they find out the number of millions of acres burned by wood fires in our country in a typical year? Have them calculate what percentage of our annual timber crop this represents. Perhaps they might estimate how many new homes this yearly sacrifice to Baal might have built.

The Trees Left Standing. Students might examine the damage to trees scarred by fire. What evidences do they find of injured bark? Of insect infestation? What has happened to the ground cover and duff (Fig. 9-8)?

Fig. 9-8. A forest fire not only ruins timber but also destroys ground cover and duff. The resulting erosion washes away the topsoil and exposes parent rock material. (*U.S. Soil Conservation Service.*)

Other Results of Forest Fires. Make some wood ashes. Dampen them and test with litmus paper. The test should prove alkaline.

After a forest fire, not only is there possible damage to the soil, but rain washes lye from wood ashes into the streams, thus annihilating fish and fish foods. Fire destroys the natural leafy shade and permits the sun's rays to raise the temperature of streams and ponds. This kills off many kinds of fish that cannot live in warm water.

A forest fire, the destruction of fish—the interrelations are there, even if they are not always obvious.

Here Is How You Can Help. Evolve with your students common-sense procedures for behavior when in the woods. Topics they will want to consider are matches, smoking, making and breaking camp, how to put out a campfire, brush burning, etc. You might have them discuss, too, what procedures to use should a fire get out of control.

This might be the time to study the nature of burning (Sec. 10-4), and the principles and practices to apply in putting out fires (Sec. 10-9).

THE FOREST AND MAN

9-8. Forest Management

Begin Right in Your Own Yard. Students might survey the trees in their school yard, around their homes, on their street, or in the nearest park to see what needs to be done to save them. There may be broken branches or openings in the bark that should be painted with creosote to keep out wood-boring insects and fungi of disease.

A Field Trip. Visit an industrial forest or a farm wood lot with your students. If possible secure the services of a forester as guide. Make careful preparation for the trip. Here are some of the opportunities for observation and learning: finding trees of different ages from seedlings to mature saw timber; noting how forests reseed themselves naturally; watching demonstrations of proper cutting methods, of log transportation; observing evidences of forest fire protection and protection from destructive grazing.

Follow-Up: Some Classroom Activities.[4] Find pictures of good and bad forest cutting and list the differences shown. Find out how the slash (branches and tree tops left in lumbering) may be disposed of so as to reduce dangers of forest fire after logging operations. Give several reasons why old trees, not young ones, should be cut.

Report on ways in which waste in lumbering has been decreased. How does the use of what might otherwise be waste enable the operators to reforest, protect from fire, and use other conservation measures?

Find out the differences in logging for timber and for pulpwood. What is there about each process that makes conservation difficult?

Other classroom activities and many thought-provoking questions may be found in the U.S. Forest Service booklet, *Forest Conservation in the Social Studies and Sciences.*

A School Forestry Project. When you are ready to begin plans for your own forestry work, you might want to write to your State Con-

[4] From Ward P. Beard, *Teaching Conservation,* The American Forestry Association, Washington, D.C., 1948.

servation Commission to find out if there are any school forests in your state. Your school might like to take part in one that has started, or start one itself (Fig. 9-9). If you are hemmed in by the canyons of the city you might still want to share in a forestry project (Sec. 9-9).

Students might write to the State Forestry Department to learn how forests are handled as crops. They should be able to describe how forests aid in watershed maintenance, in flood control, in checking soil

Fig. 9-9. Students of Norman, Arkansas, High School have a laboratory session in forest management on their "school forty." (*U.S. Forest Service.*)

erosion. They should learn, too, of the value of thinning out forests, as well as the uses of lumber in our economy. Much valuable information is available in the USDA Yearbook *Trees* (1949). The USDA film, *The River,* which can be rented from state film libraries, gives a picture of economic factors associated with forests and flood controls.

A School Wood Lot. Is there a wood lot on your school property? Or one nearby? Management of a small wood lot is an excellent school-forest project. You will probably need the help and guidance of a trained forester, who will explain to your students the fundamentals of forest management, resulting in the production of a continuous crop. Following his instructions, the ripe trees may be marked with chalk. The poorly formed or damaged trees, and those species that are worthless as timber trees, may also be marked for cutting. The trees that should be encouraged to grow may be banded or tagged.

You may want to establish a tree nursery. This will involve the gathering of cones to obtain seed, the planting and care of the seedlings, and their final transplanting in the school forest or other areas in the community where they are needed.

Eventually this wood lot project might result in a demonstration stand to show "before and after" conditions. The students will have a living laboratory in which to observe what happens to wildlife food and cover in the woods; what are the results of thinning as far as low ground cover is concerned; and what part, in general, a forest plays in nature's intricate web of life.

Saving Trees in a City. Cities need trees not only for beauty and shade, but also to relieve the vast and oppressive dazzle of concrete and asphalt during the summer.

Plane trees, with remarkable ability to survive urban dirt and gasoline fumes, were planted along New York's Third Avenue when the "El" was torn down. Two years later, many of them were either dead or dying. The Boy Scouts got busy, applying emergency care to several hundred trees, loosening the soil around them, and packing in vermiculite to retain rain water. The Park Department recommended that cultivating the soil around the trunks of the trees and pouring on three pails of water twice a week would do much to keep the trees alive.

Who says there isn't "forestry" conservation work to be done on city streets?

9-9. Forests in the Larger Community

National Forests. We are all of us, no matter where we live in America, part owners of our public forest lands, about 161 million acres worth, scattered from Puerto Rico to Alaska. Students may find out that these forests were established mainly for the production of timber and protection of our watersheds and streams. Discuss with your class that wood and water are only two of the important resources of our national forests, for they provide forage for livestock, homes and food for wildlife, and recreation for all.

Your students may find out more about this heritage of ours and the work of the forest rangers in the U.S. Forest Service booklet, *In Your Service* (A1B136).

National Parks. Perhaps a student has had the opportunity to visit one of the National Parks and will recount his science experiences and explorations. Perhaps he has slides or pictures to show.

Another student might report on the history of our park system, extending from the West Indies to Alaska, from Maine to Hawaii. What about the thousands of new visitors who flock to the parks each year? Are we, as a people, supplying sufficient staff and funds to meet the new situation?

Do your students know about "Mission 66," whose objective is an adequately developed and staffed National Park system by 1966, golden anniversary year of the founding of the Park Service? How important do your students believe this "mission" to be?

Wilderness. Should our wilderness areas be left undisturbed? What value have they to wild creatures? To adventurous men for exploration, for refreshment, or for scientific study? Has the wilderness greater value for other purposes?

As "space" becomes an increasingly rare commodity, there is growing pressure to cut down on the wild places of the earth and to develop them for purposes of civilization, making commercial use of their valuable natural resources. Is this wise? Is it necessary? These are questions to which there are no easy answers. Yet teachers as citizens and students as future ones will need to weigh in the balance values both tangible and intangible and to make their voices heard.

Forests: World Education. "Arbor Day" or "Arbor Week" is celebrated in many lands under many different names. It is called "Greening Week" in Japan, "The New Year's Day of Trees" in Israel, "The Tree-loving Week" in Korea, "The National Festival of Tree Planting" in India.

In all these countries and many others, people are beginning to gain an understanding of the importance of forests to their welfare and prosperity. Civilizations have, indeed, disappeared through lack of this understanding. The threat of such disaster is by no means a thing of the past; it may be seen in the spread of dust bowls and "deserts on the march."

The Food and Agricultural Organization (FAO) of the United Nations has held world forestry congresses to focus attention on this problem and to help with its solution. They believe that starting in the schools (Fig. 9-10) is the most effective way of "inculcating an awareness of the values of trees and woodlands, and for keeping these values present even in the adult mind."

Continuity of purpose and effort is vital to the success of this plan, involving as it does school forests. It is not enough to put trees into the ground. Unless the trees are cared for by providing light, water, space, and fertile soil and by guarding against damage, the fruits of the planting are thrown away. Schools are well suited to care continuously for the young trees planted in the neighborhood, especially when forestry and maintenance of woodland become a regular feature of their activities.

Students might set out miniature posts and use "controls" at the same time. Examine after some weeks and later after some months.

Discuss with your students the protection of wood as a conservation measure (Fig. 9-12).

Treating Wood with a Pesticide. Protecting wood used in construction from termites is an excellent conservation measure. A student might report on the new pesticides dieldrin and chlordane which, it is claimed, can free the homeowner of termite problems for more than 10 years if applied once to the soil around the house under construction. These pesticides are supposedly not harmful to plant life. Why is this consideration important?

Using Wood Substitutes. Have students collect and arrange displays of the new plastic materials which are being used in place of lumber. Of what are these plastics made? What is the "raw material" situation in regard to the making of these plastics? Do plastics made from wood save lumber? You might want to write for the free pamphlet, *The ABC's of Modern Plastics* (Baklite Company, 30 East 42d St., New York).

Can paper be made of substances other than wood? Your students might bring in a report on *bagasse,* the fibers left over from sugar cane after the sugar has been extracted, which are now being used for certain kinds of paper. Encourage your students to bring in news clippings with up-to-the-minute information on products developed as substitutes.

9-12. Our Future Supply of Wood

A Danger Signal [7]

WARNING: U.S. NEWSPRINT LOW:
SUPPLIES CALLED AT DANGER POINT.

> Newsprint supplies have reached a "dangerously low point" and experts don't see "how the anticipated deficit after 1958 will be overcome," the government reported today.
>
> Despite the newsprint shortage, the report by the Commerce Department predicted United States newspapers will increase in circulation and size over the next decade.
>
> The report predicted that smaller daily and weekly newspapers particularly "will be penalized by inadequate supply" of newsprint for at least the next few years.

A news clipping like the above can initiate a discussion of our forest resources—the tragic story of what we have done, the hopeful story of what we are doing in some places, and the story of what we must still do. How "dated" is the report? What is the present situation? What about the future?

[7] From a UP report from Washington, Jan. 10, 1956.

If your students become truly absorbed in forests, the science aspect will be only one of the many facets of their interest. They may, for instance, be stimulated to find out how the U.S. Forest Service guards and manages our forests; how national, state, and municipal forests function; what they offer and where they are; what industry is doing to meet the challenge of shrinking timber; what the role of the man-in-the-street is when it comes to our forests.

Students might write for the U.S. Forest Service pamphlet, *People and Timber: A Review of America's Timber Resources.* Two statements from that publication are particularly significant. "About 50 million acres, an area equivalent to 10 per cent of all our Nation's timberlands, need planting to become productive in a reasonable time," and "The real key to our future timber supply lies in the hands of the '1 out of every 10 American families' who own our small forests—these lands can be made more productive." These "1 out of 10 families" send their children to our schools.

Tree Farming: Industry's Answer. Ask your students to find out what the large paper and pulp industries are doing to ensure a continuing crop of trees. They might write for *Tree Farming in the Pacific Northwest* (Weyerhaeuser Timber Co., Tacoma, Wash.) or *Growing Paper on Tree Farms* (Crown Zellerbach Corp., San Francisco, Seattle, Portland, Los Angeles, or New York).

Notice that companies are beginning to realize that tree farming is not only "enlightened self-interest" but good "public relations" as well.

Your students might write to the American Forest Products Industries, 1816 N St., N.W., Washington, D.C., for these booklets: *Forest Facts* (for various states) and *Our Growing Wood Supply* (containing a summary of all the information in the Forest Facts series; revised annually).

Understanding and Action: A Student's Answer. Understanding the forests and our dependence on them, not only for products, but, more importantly, for healthy soil and healthy life on earth, is an educational "must."

Respect and love of the woods, coupled with the knowledge that a stand of trees, whether forest or wood lot, is not a mine to be exploited and stripped but rather a crop to be nurtured and wisely managed, is a second important lesson. If our students have truly made these learnings their own, then responsible action should be the outcome.

PART 3

Conservation as a Study of Interrelationships between Matter and Energy

10
A Study of Matter

This chapter is concerned with matter and some of the fundamental principles governing its behavior. One important chemical change, the nature of burning, has been selected because of its relationship to the securing of energy from fuels and also because burning, as fire, can destroy material resources—forests, fossil fuels, buildings. Activities in fire prevention and fire fighting are therefore included.

A study in wood chemistry has been chosen to illustrate a way of dealing with *one* (only one) fundamental resource in a chemistry class.

CHEMISTRY AND CONSERVATION

10-1. A Point of View

Chemistry, the study of matter, its properties and behavior, is basic to the study of conservation. After all, our material resources are "matter." We have only to touch on matter to find that we are immediately encountering problems of resources—resources which are not laboratory curiosities but the very stuff upon which man's existence depends.

It is tempting to present this study of matter by emphasizing the magic tricks the chemist can play upon it. How much more vital, how much closer to reality does chemistry become when it is firmly linked to our students' lives and the problems they face as individuals and as members of the human family.

If we teachers hold this point of view it may be that we can bring to our chemistry classes an added dimension of interest and meaning. All of us are already teaching conservation without perhaps being conscious of it. We have only to go a step or two further—make the connections, bridge the gaps—and we will be doing an even better job.

10-2. Principles That Govern Changes in Matter

Law of Conservation of Matter. You might bring to class a freshly scoured iron nail and a very rusty one. The first is ready for use, the second for the junk pile.

You might emphasize that we have not changed the amount of iron by allowing the nail to rust, but we have definitely changed its usefulness. There is only a certain amount of iron available to man on earth. One of his present problems is to make and keep this iron useful.

Law of Definite Proportions. Chemistry teachers usually employ a metal (iron, copper, or zinc) along with powdered sulfur to show the difference between a mixture and a compound. It is possible to perform this experiment in a quantitative way and thus bring home to the student the meaning of the law of definite proportions.

Using a balance that is accurate to the nearest decigram, weigh out, or ask a student to weight out, 5.6 grams of powdered iron ("iron by hydrogen" or electrolytic iron). Now add 3.3 grams (an excess) of flowers of sulfur to the iron and mix well. Place the mixture in a weighed hard-glass test tube, and clamp to a ring stand. Heat until a glow passes up the tube, and continue heating until all the excess sulfur has burned off. Cool the tube and weigh. You now have the weight of the tube plus the compound, ferrous sulfide. By subtracting from this weight the weight of the tube and the original iron, you have obtained the weight of the sulfur with which the iron combined.

Repeat the experiment, using the same amount of iron but substituting 3.4 or 3.5 grams of sulfur. (You might suggest that different students try out varying weights of sulfur with a fixed weight of iron and then pool results.) The students learn that a given amount of iron will take on only a definite amount of sulfur no matter how much may be available. This reaction is simple enough so that students can appreciate and understand it both qualitatively and quantitatively.

Law of Conservation of Energy. The chemist is particularly interested in the conversion of internal chemical energy (potential) into other forms of energy.

Burn a wooden splint. Draw attention to the heat produced, and also to the visible products, ash and smoky gas.

When we burn a fuel, are we interested in the visible products or in the invisible energy liberated? (Ash and smoke are usually necessary nuisances, and the less the better.)

When a fuel is burned to produce heat it is serving a useful purpose for man. When, however, a forest or an oil well goes up in flames, we are wasting energy in addition to destroying a valuable resource.

10-3. Atoms and Molecules

Matter Is Discontinuous. Take a familiar substance like water, and ask your students to think about it in terms of its stuff. Is it, for instance, continuous or is it made up of discrete particles with spaces between? Dissolve some salt in it. If it were continuous, where did the salt go?

Or you might try this: Take exactly 1 quart of water and pour it into a 2-quart container. Now pour an exact quart of alcohol into the same container. The mixture will be somewhat less than 2 quarts because some of the particles of alcohol slipped into the spaces between the particles of water.

This will lead to a discussion of the various theories about the nature of matter, beginning with the ancient Greeks.

Dalton's Atomic Theory. Atoms are indivisible particles. Atoms of one kind are alike in size and weight but differ in these respects from other kinds of atoms. Compounds are formed by the linking of atoms with one another. These are the familiar postulates of Dalton's atomic theory.

Have your class look into a kaleidoscope. The design changes; the number of particles remains constant. We may rearrange atoms into new patterns by forming various compounds but we are not changing the sum total of elementary particles at our command. This is, in essence, Dalton's picture of atoms.

"What about atom smashing?" a student may well ask at this point. Discuss with your students the attack on the atom (the "indivisible") and elicit from them that this work did not take place until long after Dalton's time. Neptunium, plutonium, and the rest of the man-made elements were unknown resources just a few decades ago. Isotopes (atoms of the same element differing in atomic weight), were also undiscovered in Dalton's day and so we must now modify his statement that all atoms of the same kind have the same weight.

You may want to emphasize Dalton's enormous contribution to science even though his theory has needed modification. You can help your students realize that the fundamental laws governing the behavior of matter are not changing; it is rather man's knowledge of these principles that keeps growing and deepening.

Showing the Motion of Molecules. If you have a sealed tube containing mercury and some small blue glass beads,[1] heat the mercury gently. The molecules of mercury are set in such rapid and violent motion that the beads (gigantic in comparison to the mercury atoms) hop about at a great rate.

[1] This molecular motion demonstrator can be obtained from a supply house (Sec. 18-3).

Or you might examine grains of pollen suspended in water under a microscope to see that all the particles are moving about rapidly and irregularly.

If you have a Brownian movement apparatus,[2] you may show the motion of cigarette smoke molecules as they are bombarded by molecules of air.

Elements: Their Abundance. Almost every chemistry text has some-

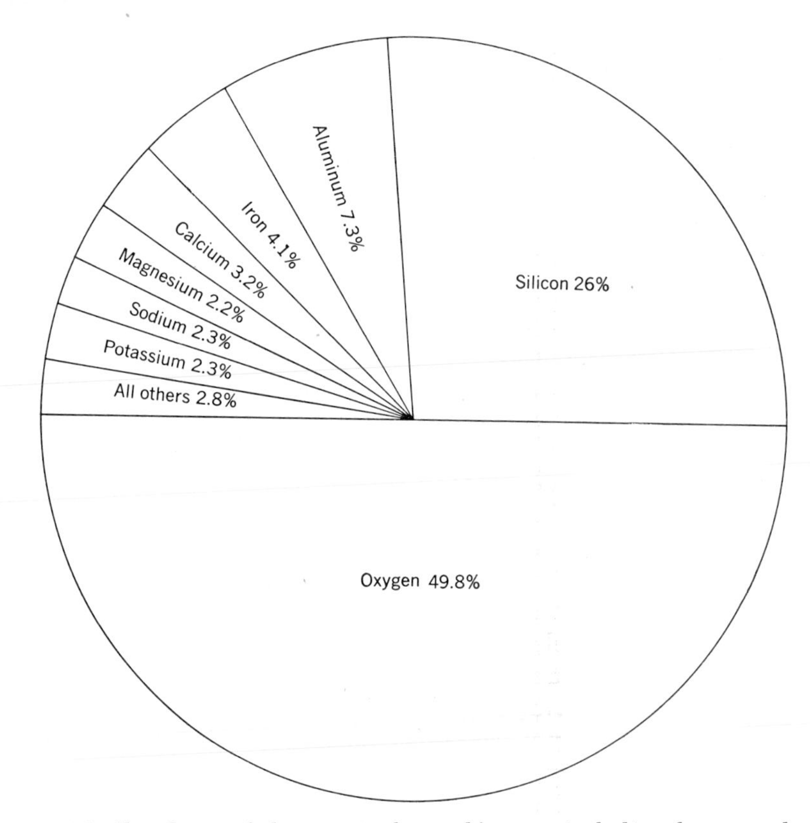

Fig. 10-1. Abundance of elements in the earth's crust, including the atmosphere.

where in its early pages a table or "pie" showing the relative abundance of elements found in the earth's crust, including the air and the sea (Fig. 10-1). There usually follows a class discussion emphasizing that most of these elements are not found "free" in nature but combined with others. These are man's resources. Are they boundless? Are they exhaustible?

[2] A Brownian movement apparatus, which can be used on the stage of a microscope, can be obtained from a supply house (Sec. 18-3).

When discussing the abundance of elements it is interesting to note, for instance, that although aluminum and iron rank third and fourth, they present resource problems to the United States. When we come to the far less abundant elements, we run into some serious shortages in our country. (As a matter of fact, the United States is self-sufficient in only two metals, magnesium and molybdenum.)

Later in the course, as individual elements are studied, students might be referred to the summary of Volume I of *Resources for Freedom* (Sec. 19-2*f*), *Minerals Yearbook, 1953* (Sec. 19-6*d*), or to *America's Needs and Resources* (Sec. 19-2*n*).

Perhaps some of your students would be interested in making a collection of as many of the natural elements (or their ores) as they can find. They might add notations on the abundance of these elements and indicate the ones that are serious resource problems.

States of Matter. You may want to use water as an illustration of matter in its three states. From the conservation point of view, you might stress water's role in each of its states. Draw from your students that as liquid, in the form of seas, lakes, streams, ponds, ground water, etc., it is the prime essential of life on earth. As a vapor, it moves over the surface of the earth, finally returning to us in liquid form. As ice, it offers a protective covering to lakes and ponds, so that aquatic life may flourish even in the coldest weather. Because water expands as it freezes, it is able to split up rocks into whose fissures it has run. What has this weathering of rocks to do with soil making (Sec. 7-2)?

A film that is particularly helpful when studying the states of matter is *Molecular Theory of Matter* (Encyclopaedia Britannica Films).

CHEMICAL CHANGE

10-4. The Nature of Burning: An Inductive Sequence[3]

The relationships between burning and conservation are many. Fuels —coal, oil, gas—must be burned in order to supply us with the energy we want. Often, we burn them wastefully. (Incomplete combustion is a great waster of fuel as well as a smoke nuisance.) Forest fires, too, are a serious conservation problem. Your students will need to know something about the nature of burning to understand how to manage and protect our combustible resources.

[3] This sequence, instituted at the Fieldston School in New York City by Augustus Klock, is used in the chemistry course in the following way: All students perform each of the experiments individually. After an experiment is written up and reviewed by the teacher, there is a general class discussion in which results are compared and conclusions drawn on the basis of the pooled evidence. Only after the nature of burning is revealed through the laboratory work do students refer to a text for further enrichment.

The following series of experiments presents an "inductive sequence" of laboratory experiences, by which students discover or confirm, step by step, the nature of burning:

What Changes Are Produced When a Metal Burns in Air? (Before starting this experiment students should be familiar with a bunsen burner and should have seen that a deposit of soot on a porcelain dish may be burned away in a nonluminous flame.)

1. Hold a piece of magnesium ribbon by means of a forceps in the nonluminous flame until it catches fire. Note that it makes a blinding light (which is the evidence of an exothermic reaction) and forms a white ash.

2. Repeat, using a piece of copper wire, holding it in the hottest part of the flame for about a minute. Note the black and brittle coating and the rose red one underneath. Could the black coating possibly be soot?

3. Repeat with a piece of platinum wire. There is no change.

The students learn that when metals burn, new substances with new properties are formed. By definition, this means chemical change. They learn, in addition, that burning is not necessarily accompanied by a flame and that not all metals burn in air.

Is There a Change of Weight When a Substance Burns?

1. Weigh a coil of no. 36 copper wire (approximately 2 grams) accurately on a hornpan balance. Heat the coil intensely in a weighed porcelain crucible and cover (Fig. 10-2*a*). Lift the cover from time to time. After heating for about 18 minutes, reweigh the crucible, cover, and copper. The students note that there is a gain in weight. They may conclude that since the crucible and cover did not change, something from the air with which the metal was in contact is probably responsible.

2. (Optional) Repeat the experiment using granulated tin. Stir from time to time with a heavy iron wire.

What Substance from the Air Is Responsible for Burning?

1. *Decomposing the Product Formed by Burning a Metal* (optional). If the black substance formed by burning copper decomposed completely on being heated in a bunsen flame, we should be able to find direct evidence as to the cause of the gain in weight of the copper in the last experiments; but it does not do so. Fortunately, however, the product of burning another metal (mercury) in air (Lavoisier's experiment) easily decomposes at a temperature slightly higher than that at which it forms. This product is a red powder.

Heat about 1 gram of this red powder in a Pyrex test tube, collect the evolved gas in a test tube by water displacement, and identify it as oxygen. Continued heating makes the red powder disappear and in its place are small droplets of a silvery liquid condensed on the cool upper portion of the test tube. Mercury! Always with each group of students there is the thrill of discovery.

Students are now ready for these and other questions: If the red powder was formed by burning mercury in air, with what did the mercury combine when it burned? From where did the mercury get this substance? If the copper and tin behave in burning as mercury does,

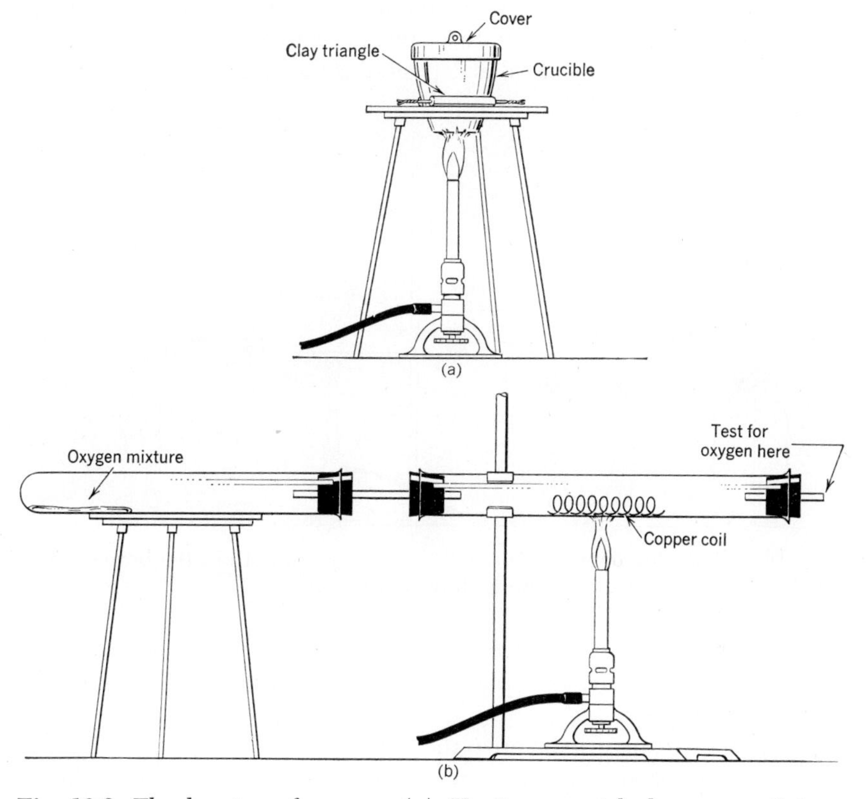

Fig. 10-2. The burning of copper. (*a*) Heating a weighed copper coil in a weighed crucible; (*b*) burning copper in pure oxygen. Compare its appearance when burned in air.

with what must they have combined when they were burned in air?

2. *What Happens When Copper Is Burned in Oxygen?* (This is usually done at the end of an experiment on the preparation and properties of oxygen.) Place a copper coil in a combustion tube (Fig. 10-2*b*). Heat the "oxygen mixture" of potassium chlorate and manganese dioxide. Heat the copper coil intensely for a few minutes after the combustion tube is filled with pure oxygen. (Test at *X* to make sure.) When cool, examine the copper wire. Since the results are identical with the heating of the copper in the air, only "more so," the student has evidence (one added

proof, if he has done part 3), that when a metal burns it combines with oxygen from the air.

What Happens When Burnt Copper Is Heated in Pure Hydrogen? (Optional. This might be done at the end of an experiment dealing with the preparation and properties of hydrogen.) Pass a slow stream of dry hydrogen over the copper oxide (Fig. 10-3). When you are *sure* the hydrogen is pure (it should burn quietly, not explosively, when a collected test tube of the gas is tested), put the burner under the boat and heat intensely. The shiny metallic deposit plus the formation of water adds

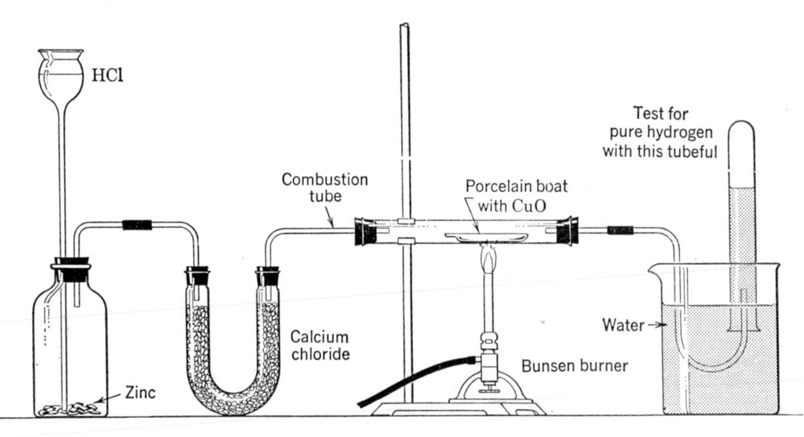

Fig. 10-3. Reducing copper oxide with hydrogen. Do not put the burner under the boat until you are sure the hydrogen is pure.

another link to the chain of evidence as to the nature of burning: the product of the burning of copper plus hydrogen yields water (hydrogen *oxide*) plus copper.

Now students may summarize the evidence, gradually accumulated in all these experiments, to prove what happens when a substance burns. Some students might go further to show step by step how a "phlogistonist" would have explained the same series of experiments (gain of weight: property of "levity," phlogiston weighing less than nothing; reduction: calx (CuO) plus phlogiston (H_2) yields the original metal!). Students will also become aware of the fact that the accumulating weight of evidence must finally sound the death knell for a mistaken theory. At the same time they will be gaining some understanding of why it is that theories take so long to die.

Draw attention to the fact that in the course of a few weeks students have shared in the great years of discovery of Priestley and Lavoisier. These men have "come alive" as the class relived their great moments in history.

When this long chain of experiments is started, some of the students may have no notion as to the nature of burning, others may come as "phlogistonists," while still others may know the answer already without fully understanding it. At the end, however, all will have had a living experience in one of the important methods of science.

10-5. What Conditions Are Needed for Burning?

The prevention and control of forest fires are two vital problems in conservation.

Understanding of the nature of burning, factors that affect the rate of combustion, and methods of preventing further oxidation will give your students the necessary background in science. All these principles will then find application when it comes to the education of students in the prevention and control of the needless fires that continue to destroy several of our most valuable resources.

Fires Need Fuel. Try burning various substances, some combustibles (a wood splint, a piece of charcoal, a few drops of kerosene) and some noncombustibles (water, iron, aluminum, asbestos fiber).

Fuels Must Be Raised to Kindling Temperature. Put a match under a piece of paper, a log, a lump of coal. Only the paper catches fire, for different substances combust at different temperatures. This will lead to a definition of kindling temperature—the lowest temperature at which a given material catches fire and continues to burn.

Make some fine wood shavings and ignite them with a match. Compare this with the attempt to make a log burn by applying a match. Your students should now see that a substance may have different kindling temperatures, depending upon its state of subdivision.

Strike a large match and watch it burn. The head of the match is made of some material with a low kindling temperature. Discuss with your students how, when the head is scratched, the friction develops enough heat to kindle the match tip. How does the rest of the match stick catch fire?

Have your students lay a small fire of paper, twigs, kindling, and a log. They are now ready to explain why a single match stick can set fire to the entire mass.

Fires Need Air. Place a piece of lighted paper or a lighted candle under an inverted drinking glass. Notice that the fire goes out before all the substance is consumed. Ask your class why this happens.

10-6. Spontaneous Combustion

A Demonstration. There are several ways of demonstrating spontaneous combustion. (This experiment is dangerous and must be done with the utmost care.) Drop a tiny piece of white phosphorus, no bigger than a pinhead, in several cubic centimeters of carbon disulfide in a small vial. Keep tightly stoppered away from flame! Put a few drops of this solution on a piece of filter paper resting on a tripod. In a minute or two the paper will burst into flame.

Or you may place a piece of white phosphorus the size of a pinhead on an asbestos pad. The white fumes indicate that oxidation is taking place. Cover the phosphorus with a little powdered bone black and soon the phosphorus will catch fire.

Students are now ready to find out why spontaneous combustion takes place, where it occurs, and what precautions are necessary to prevent it.

A Strange Fire. A curious kind of spontaneous combustion occurred a few years ago in the Ohio Valley floods. The lower parts of haystacks were drenched with water; as the flood receded, some of the haystacks, to the puzzlement of the farmers, burst into flame. Can your students figure this out? The explanation lies in the fact that during respiration of living plant cells, food material slowly oxidizes and heat is given off (Sec. 3-13). This process is aided by the presence of water. The hay itself also slowly oxidized, giving off heat—and the cycle was well on its vicious way.

It has been estimated that at least 8 per cent of our total annual fire loss is the result of spontaneous combustion of all types. These fires are almost always preventable.

10-7. Explosions

Making a "Safe" One. Take a tin can with a lid (a baking powder can is excellent for the purpose). Puncture a hole in the top of the lid and another near the base of the can. Admit ordinary illuminating gas through the bottom hole, until the can is *well filled* (Fig. 10-4). Allow time for filling and cautiously check the odor of the gas coming from the hole in the lid. Ignite the gas at the top of the can. It burns with a tall, luminous flame. Now remove the gas inlet and turn off the gas. The flame becomes smaller and less luminous until it seems to disappear —when all of a sudden—pop! The lid flies off with a bang. This is a dramatic demonstration, filled with suspense, to which students always respond. Why didn't it explode right

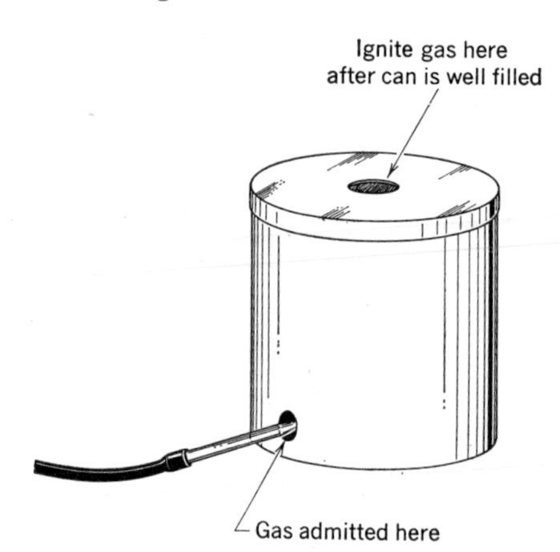

Fig. 10-4. A "safe" explosion, using a tin can with cover and illuminating gas.

away, if it was going to explode? Why did the flame become nonluminous? Why did it seem to disappear just before the explosion? What made it explode? These are all questions leading into a discussion of the nature of explosions. (To use this experiment to illustrate what takes place in an internal combustion engine, see Sec. 15-9.)

Dangers of Explosive Mixtures. Understanding the nature of explosions from an "explosive mixture," students may consider some of the common resulting accidents. An entire hospital room has exploded as the spark from a disconnected plug set fire to the mixture of air and the gas used as an anesthetic (ether, for example). Chemistry students might write and balance the equation for the burning of ether:

$$(C_2H_5)_2O + 6O_2 \rightarrow 4CO_2 + 5H_2O$$

(Notice that the reaction produces gases that expand enormously from the heat produced by the reaction.)

Discuss with your students the hazards of explosions in the home. Household accidents include the explosion of gas when mixed with air in an oven; gasoline, ether, some dry-cleaning fluids, turpentine, fingernail polish remover, certain paints giving off heavy vapors that explode when mixed with air. Knowing these facts should make students more aware of the danger. A pilot light on a stove, a dying ember in the fireplace may set off the blaze that is liable to end in destruction and tragedy.

Students should also be aware that, when working on a car, one may through carelessness set off a gas-air explosion, which may destroy both car and mechanic.

A Homemade Dust Explosion. Use a "press-on" covered can, a funnel containing a teaspoonful of lycopodium powder (an easily flammable dust), a piece of rubber tubing, and a candle as shown in Fig. 10-5*a*.

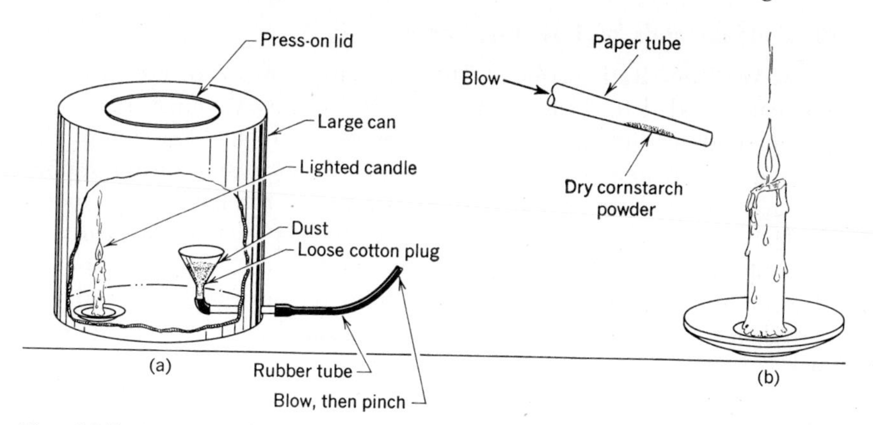

Fig. 10-5. Dust explosions in the laboratory. (*a*) Exploding lycopodium powder; (*b*) igniting cornstarch powder.

Light the candle, press the cover on, blow once through the rubber to scatter the dust inside the can, and (important!) be sure to pinch the tube immediately, to prevent backfire. There should at once be a miniature dust explosion.

Other kinds of dust might be tried, such as starch or wood dust. An electric sparking device might take the place of the candle.

Or you might try this technique: Dry some cornstarch by warming it for a few minutes over a candle flame. Then put ¼ teaspoon of the dry powder into a rolled paper tube (Fig. 10-5*b*). With a single puff, blow the cornstarch powder into the candle flame and watch the starch ignite.

A Real-life Dust Explosion. In dust explosions, the large amount of surface of the substance exposed to the air is the cause of serious explosions. Dust of flour, starch, paper, or other easily burnable substances may be floating around the air of a mill or factory. Although the mixture would not ordinarily burn at low temperature, a spark from a match or cigarette may set off a disaster. Dust from spices, cork, hard rubber, and even dry milk has been reported as causing this kind of explosion.

10-8. Fire Hazards in the Home

Danger Spots and Safety Measures. Protecting our homes against fire is a conservation measure in every sense of the word. If one of your students has a good-sized doll house, this might be set up before the class, the danger spots marked, and remedies suggested.

The remedies should include fire stops made of concrete or of specially treated fire-resistant wood (Sec. 9-11); proper electrical wiring; the safe disposal of trash; the ready availability of fire extinguishers; an emergency fire escape; chimneys and flues kept in repair; the protection of open fireplaces by screens and of stoves by metal or asbestos board.

10-9. Fundamentals of Fire Fighting

How Are Fires Extinguished? The elimination of one of the three requirements needed to create a fire (Sec. 10-5) will extinguish it.

All methods of fire fighting have to make use of at least one of the following: (1) Remove the combustible material; (2) shut off the supply of oxygen; (3) cool the burning substance below the kindling temperature. Have your students illustrate each of these principles in turn.

1. Shut off the gas and a lighted burner will go out. Separate glowing embers, remove all burnable materials from the surroundings, and you have taken the first steps in putting out a campfire. What are the next steps?

2. Your students will recall what happens when an inverted tumbler is placed over a lighted candle (Sec. 10-5). Ignite a small fire in an iron

pan and cover it with a loose-fitting lid. In both these cases the fire goes out for lack of oxygen.

3. Blow out a candle. The cool moving air does the trick.

Extinguish a small fire with dry sand. Draw from your students that the substance is cooled below its kindling point and the sand blankets the fire, thus smothering it. (An ordinary blanket is often part of laboratory equipment, in order to smother a fire quickly.)

Put out a small fire by pouring water on it. Can your students see that water, too, has a double action? It cools the burning material, and the steam produced tends to blanket the fire. In general, dousing a small fire with water is the simplest method of putting it out. As a matter of fact, water is usually the most important means of fighting many kinds of fires, large or small.

Is Water Ever Harmful for Putting Out a Fire? *An Oil Fire.* Using a large porcelain or ironware dish, pour in a very little oil or fat and ignite it. Pour a stream of water from a wash bottle on the fire. The water displaces the oil, which is lighter, and this spreads the flames. Use care, demonstrator!

A Magnesium Fire. Burn a piece of magnesium ribbon held in a forceps. The brilliance and intensity of its burning will be evident.

Add a little water to some magnesium powder in a test tube and heat it gradually. Watch for bubbling. Test for hydrogen.

Make a wad of magnesium ribbons. Ignite in a safe place and spray cautiously with water. Use care, for when water strikes burning magnesium, hydrogen is liberated and the burning is intensified.

The above experiments are particularly interesting in connection with the magnesium fire in the Connecticut Valley. It was during the 1955 floods that a magnesium factory burned with explosive fury, causing additional disaster in the town of Putnam. From the Metal Selling Corporation of Putnam, Connecticut, comes this description of what happened to their magnesium plant:

> Most of the magnesium fuel was in ingot form, stored in a large timber structure. The building ignited from causes not definitely determined, but electrical failure brought on by flooding is most probable. The fire burned for hours out of control; the pile of magnesium finally started to burn; and molten magnesium ran onto the flood waters, throwing itself about and burning violently.

No one is quite sure how the fire started. The flood was probably not responsible for that, since magnesium reacts with water only at elevated temperature. We do know, however, that water, particularly in small amounts, not only is ineffectual in putting out a magnesium fire but will actually produce an "explosive" condition by liberating hydrogen. What application has this to the putting out of fires from incendiary bombs, which are usually made of magnesium?

10-10. Fire Extinguishers

The Carbon Dioxide Extinguisher. Into a large test tube students may put a few grams of sodium bicarbonate. Then they may add a few cubic centimeters of dilute hydrochloric acid and bubble the evolving gas through limewater in another test tube. The milkiness of the limewater identifies the carbon dioxide.

If a lighted splint is put in the carbon dioxide as it is generated, the flame is immediately snuffed out. Another more striking way of illustrating the same point is to put some lighted candles on an inclined trough (Fig. 10-6) and pour carbon dioxide down from the top of the trough. As the gas reaches each candle, the flame is extinguished.

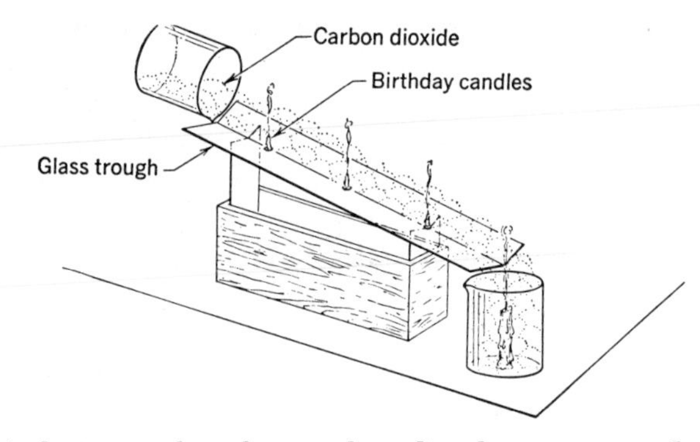

Fig. 10-6. A device to show how carbon dioxide puts out a flame. The gas, being heavier than air, pours down and puts out the flames.

A Homemade Extinguisher. Students may make their own extinguishers in this way: Using a quart milk bottle, fit it with a rubber stopper and a glass nozzle. Dissolve 2 tablespoons of sodium bicarbonate in a glass of water and put the solution in the bottle. Suspend a small vial of *dilute* acid from the stopper. Cover the bottle with a wire mesh for protection. Stopper the bottle and use wire or cord to tie the stopper to the bottle. When the bottle is inverted (this should be done over the sink), the contents of the bottle of acid will react with the bicarbonate and the evolving carbon dioxide will force a spray of water out through the nozzle.

If a small fire is lighted in an iron pan in the sink, your students should be able to smother the flame with their extinguishers. This is due to the combined action of the water, which lowers the temperature of the fuel below its kindling point, and the carbon dioxide, which blankets the fire by keeping out the oxygen.

Acid and Soda Type, Commercial Fire Extinguishers. Several commercial fire extinguishers work on the principle discussed above. The acid used is concentrated sulfuric. When the fire extinguisher is turned over, the acid and soda are mixed to produce a spray of water and carbon dioxide. Demonstrate this to your class.

Foamite Type, Commercial Fire Extinguishers. Other fire extinguishers generate the gas by similar action but enclose it in a stiff foam. This type is particularly useful in putting out stubborn fires, such as oil conflagrations, which water cannot extinguish.

Explicit directions on building a laboratory fire extinguisher of the Foamite type are given in Fred T. Weisbruch, *Lecture Demonstration Experiments in High School Chemistry* (Educational Publishers, Inc., St. Louis, 1951).

Liquid Carbon Dioxide Extinguisher. In order to understand the principle of a liquid carbon dioxide extinguisher, try some of the following procedures:

Ask your students to wet their hands and allow them to dry naturally. Do they notice the cooling effect? Why does one feel cooler in a wet bathing suit than in a dry one?

On a large, flat cork sprinkle a drop of water. On the water place a thin watch glass which has a few cubic centimeters of carbon disulfide or ether in it. Blow some compressed air across it (Fig. 10-7). The drop

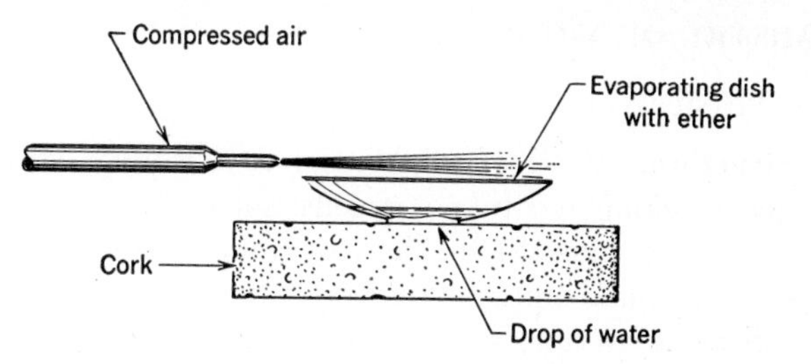

Fig. 10-7. An experiment to show the cooling effect of evaporation. The drop of water freezes and "cements" the glass to the cork.

of water, in freezing, should bind the glass and cork together for a few moments.

If you can obtain a tank of liquid carbon dioxide, place it over a desk or table and tilt it downward. Surround the opening with several heavy cloth bags, one inside the other. Carefully open the valve. As soon as this is done, the liquid carbon dioxide vaporizes and rushes out of the opening. This sudden evaporation of part of the carbon dioxide cools the remaining liquid to a white solid or "snow." (This is so cold that a sludge of the snow mixed with ether will freeze mercury solid.)

If you cannot get a tank of liquid carbon dioxide, obtain some "dry ice" and show students how it sublimes, passing directly from the solid to the gaseous state.

Your class is now ready to study a liquid carbon dioxide fire extinguisher. When the valve is opened, the escaping liquid evaporates, forming carbon dioxide snow, thus showering the fire with an extremely cold blanket of nonflammable gas. Discuss with your students the additional advantages, namely, that no liquid mess is left once the fire is put out, because the solid carbon dioxide sublimes. Furthermore, the carbon dioxide is able to penetrate obstructions without damaging equipment, thus making it one of the most rapid and efficient of fire-fighting substances.

The Carbon Tetrachloride Extinguisher. Pour 1 milliliter of gasoline or benzine into a Pyrex crystallizing dish. Ignite the liquid with a match. When the liquid is burning, pour a test tube of water into the dish. Note that the water has no effect on the flame. Now pour a test tube of carbon tetrachloride into the dish. The flame is immediately extinguished. CAUTION: Vapors of carbon tetrachloride are highly toxic. Be sure to have proper ventilation.

The Pyrene fire extinguisher is mainly carbon tetrachloride, which cools and smothers burning fuels unaffected by water. Demonstrate to the class the method of operating this extinguisher.

THE CHEMISTRY OF WOOD

10-11. Some Physical Properties

Cellular Structure. Wood of all kinds has a cellular structure (Fig. 10-8) arranged in elongated tubes or cells, some of which serve to conduct water from the roots to the leaves, some to store away digested foods, and some to build up a tough body structure.

Drive a nail or screw into a piece of wood. This is possible because the vacant cell cavities allow the cell wall to expand so that the nail or screw can easily be forced into the wood. Discuss with students how this makes it possible for pieces of wood to be fastened together without difficulty, affording a variety of possibilities in construction.

Have any of your students done wood carvings? What makes it possible to whittle wood with a penknife? Wood is easily worked because so much of the volume of the wood is composed of cell cavities.

Students might weigh a dry piece of wood, then soak it in water and weigh it again. Elicit from students that wood is light when dry because the empty cell spaces are filled with air, not with water.

As a person holds a stick of wood in a fire, he may note that heat is not conducted rapidly from the heated end to his hand. The cell pores of the wood, acting as dead-air spaces, make lumber a good insulator of heat and sound.

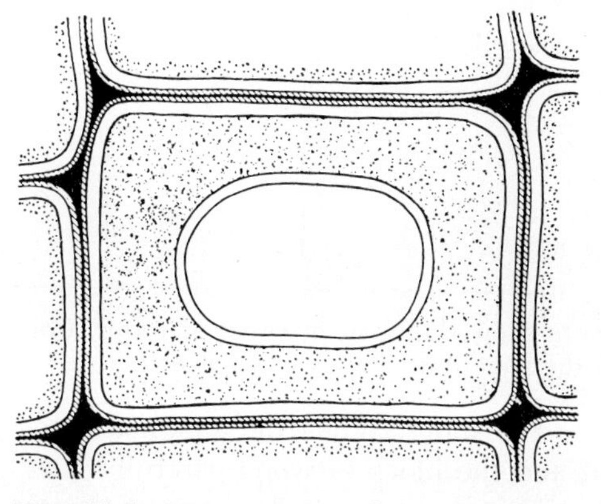

Fig. 10-8. Cross section of a wood fiber.

Students may get samples of various kinds of wood and compare their ability to resist denting, scratching, or cutting. Students may discover that the difference between hardwood and softwood lies in the degree of compactness, or closeness, of the cells. Have students find out about the relative durability, price, and use of the hardwoods and softwoods.

Tear a piece of facial tissue or a paper napkin. Have students note the tiny softwood fibers along the torn edge.

Ask students to cut a small twig and pound it with a mallet. They will notice how the woody fibers separate, as in the first step in making wood pulp.

Density. Most wood is light enough to float, but there is great variation in the densities of various kinds. Poplar, for instance, weighs 0.39 grams per cubic centimeter, while lignum vitae with a density of 1.33 grams per cubic centimeters is so heavy that it sinks in water.

Students may weigh rectangular blocks of wood, and by careful measurement of length, width, and thickness, calculate their volume. Dividing the weight in grams by the volume in cubic centimeters will give the density of the wood.

Flotation. The floating of wood will raise questions about the buoyant effect of water. Students might compare the weight of a floating block of wood with the weight of the water displaced by it and thus have evidence of the fact that a floating body displaces a weight of fluid equal to its own weight.

To perform this experiment, students may weigh a block of wood in air. Then they may arrange an overflow can (a can with a spout) and catch bucket as in Fig. 10-9. The overflow can should be filled until the

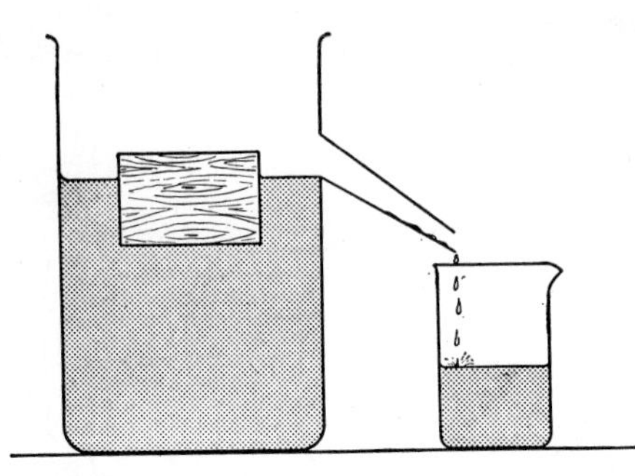

Fig. 10-9. Device to show the buoyant effect of water. Compare the weight of wood in air with the weight of the water displaced.

water runs out at the spout. When the weighed catch bucket is placed under the spout and the block of wood carefully lowered into the overflow can, the water that is displaced will run into the bucket and may be weighed. Students may then compare the weight of the wood in air with the weight of the water displaced.

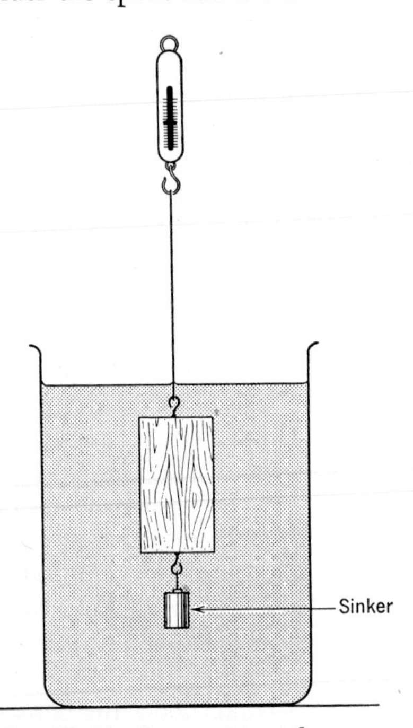

Fig. 10-10. Determining the specific gravity of a solid lighter than water.

Specific Gravity. One of the important characteristics of a substance is its specific gravity, its relative weight as compared to the weight of an equal bulk of water.

Practical use is made of the fact that the specific gravity of almost all kinds of wood is less than 1. Wherever possible, logs are transported from forest to lumber mill by floating them on bodies of water. What effect has this practice on transportation costs?

Here is a method of determining the specific gravity of solids lighter than water. This makes a good student experiment in physics.

Weigh a sample of wood in air (*a*). Then weigh a sinker under water and add this to the weight of the wood in air (*b*). Now, as in Fig. 10-10, weigh both the sinker and the block of wood submerged in water (*c*).

To calculate the lifting or buoyant effect of the water on the piece of wood, subtract (*c*) from (*b*). This will be equal to the weight of the water displaced by the fully submerged wood (*d*). If the weight of the wood in air (*a*) is divided by the weight of the water displaced by the completely submerged wood (*d*), the specific gravity of the wood can be obtained.

If regular (rectangular or cubic) blocks of wood are available, then your students might use this simple procedure: Float the block of wood in water. Measure the length under water (*a*) and the whole length above and below water (*b*). The specific gravity may be obtained by dividing (*a*) by (*b*). Can students figure out why this is so? To determine the specific gravity of a substance heavier than water, see Sec. 13-5.

10-12. Destructive Distillation of Wood

Students might do these experiments individually or as class demonstrations.

Charcoal: The Primitive Way. Cover a small cube of wood in a crucible with sand so that the crucible is level full. Heat until no more fumes (the nature of which will be revealed in the next paragraph) are given off. If a flame breaks out on the surface of the sand, let it burn and note its color. Cool and examine the product. Identify it. (Physically: black, crumbly; makes a black mark on paper. Chemically: burn in a bottle containing limewater. Limewater turns milky on shaking.)

Charcoal Plus By-products: The Modern Way. Heat 15 cubic centimeters of sawdust in a thick-walled Pyrex test tube (preferably one that has been used) until there is an appreciable deposit of liquid in *B* (Fig. 10-11). Allow the air to bubble out of the system and then collect and

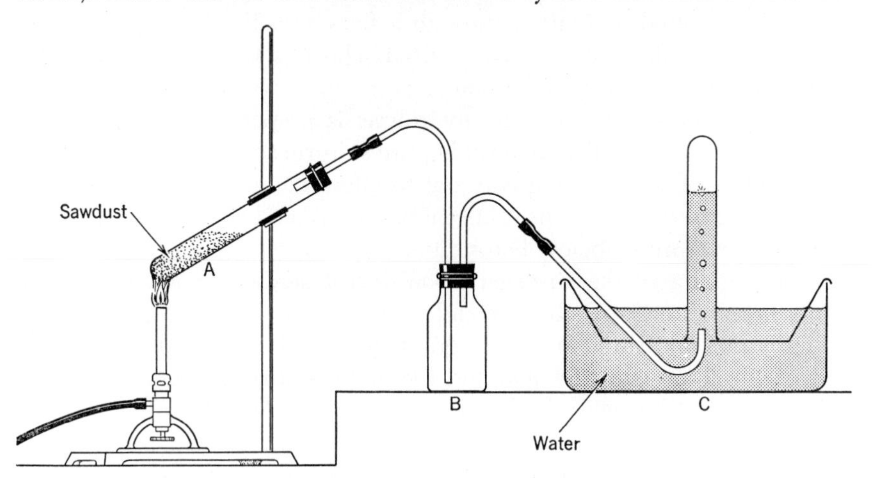

Fig. 10-11. Destructive distillation of wood. There are new products in *A*, *B*, and *C* after the sawdust is heated. What are they?

test the gas in test tube *C*. Note the blue color of the flame as the gas burns. Test the brown, viscous liquid in *B* with litmus paper. It will prove to be acid. The residue left in *A* is black.

The student is now ready to study references (found in chemistry texts) on the commercial process of destructive distillation of wood, the various products formed, and their uses. Next, he will be ready to define destructive distillation. He will be able to differentiate between this process and that of fractional distillation (Sec. 8-16).

At this point, there might be a discussion of how primitive people prepare charcoal as compared with the modern industrial method in which the valuable by-products are saved. The conservation principle implied is clear.

10-13. Wood: Of What Is It Made?

Although cellulose is the main constituent of wood, lignin is the chief "impurity" that must be removed to obtain pure cellulose. The two procedures described here and in Sec. 10-15, Wood Extractives, were sent to us from the Forest Products Laboratory at Madison, Wisconsin. These experiments are not to be found in high school chemistry manuals or textbooks and should provide a stimulating project for your advanced chemistry students.

Lignin. *Isolation of Lignin.* Lignin is a noncarbohydrate constituent of wood and is not hydrolized by acids. (Your students should learn what organic hydrolysis is by referring to a chemistry text.) Lignin is left as a residue when finely divided wood is treated with 70 to 72 per cent sulfuric acid for 2 to 3 hours, followed by adding water and heating to a boil for 3 to 4 hours.

Wood is ground and sifted through a fine-meshed window screen, or sawdust from a fine-toothed saw is sifted. This fine wood dust is allowed to dry in the air for at least 24 hours.

Sulfuric acid solution for the hydrolysis is prepared by pouring 100 milliliters of concentrated chemically pure sulfuric acid (98 per cent) into 60 milliliters of water, using care not to allow the acid to spatter or the mixture to boil due to the heat of reaction. This acid solution is cooled to room temperature or below before use.

Then 2 grams of the air-dried wood dust described above are placed in a 100 milliliter Pyrex beaker and 25 milliliters of the cooled sulfuric acid solution measured out in a graduate. To the wood dust are first added 10 milliliters of the acid and the mixture stirred with a short stirring rod until it becomes thick. The remainder of the acid is then added, a small amount at a time with stirring. The mixture is stirred frequently for 2 hours and then poured into 900 milliliters of water in a 2-liter flask. (The experiment may be interrupted until a later period at this stage.)

The contents of the flask are boiled gently for 3 to 4 hours and then allowed to settle, after which the lignin is filtered off through a weighed filter paper. The filtrate is saved for experiments on sugars (Sec. 10-15). The precipitate is washed with hot water until the filtrate is free from acid, as shown by litmus paper. The filter paper with the precipitate (lignin) is dried in an oven at 100°C for 2 to 3 hours and then weighed. The percentage of lignin may then be calculated.

Uses of Lignin. Uses for lignin and methods of extracting it are on the frontier of research in the timber industry. Much still needs to be explored and understood. There are now some limited uses for lignin in skin lotions, road binders, bacteriacides. Your students might consult the USDA Yearbook *Trees* (1949) to find still other uses—a "dispersing agent for Portland cement, in the negative plates of storage batteries, and for the production of vanillin and tannins." If a lignin plastic were made practicable, it might drastically alter the entire future of wood and plastic industries.

Your students might discuss the significance, from a conservation point of view, of adding a new fiber to industry in addition to utilizing a voluminous and cheap by-product of another industry. Conservation, far from being fixed or static, is a constantly changing frontier for thought and action.

Cellulose. *Isolation of Cellulose.* Cellulose in wood is resistant to the action of chlorine dioxide and sodium chlorite so long as lignin is present. Lignin is readily oxidized and converted to soluble products. This action is the basis of one method for isolating cellulose from wood.

As described in the isolation of lignin, 5 grams of wood dust are placed in a 250-milliliter Erlenmeyer flask and extracted with 100 milliliters of methyl alcohol overnight to remove extractives. The methanol is decanted off and 160 milliliters of hot water poured over the wood dust. Then 1 gram of sodium chlorite is introduced and the flask shaken till the chlorite dissolves; then 10 drops of glacial acetic acid are added. The mixture is heated on a steam bath at 70 to 80°C and rotated gently at intervals. (This oxidizes and dissolves the lignin.) After 1 hour, 1½ grams of sodium chlorite and 10 drops of glacial acetic acid are added. If after another hour the product (cellulose) is not white, the addition of sodium chlorite and 10 drops of acetic acid is repeated. When the product is white, it is washed onto a filter paper and rinsed with warm water. The cellulose residue and filter paper are dried in the air for 24 hours. The weight of the cellulose divided by the weight of the wood dust used shows the cellulose content of wood.

Uses of Cellulose. Your students will learn that most paper is composed of wood fibers or cellulose. This substance, too, is the base of 70 per cent of the better plastics, as well as rayon (Fig. 10-12). Wood itself is still

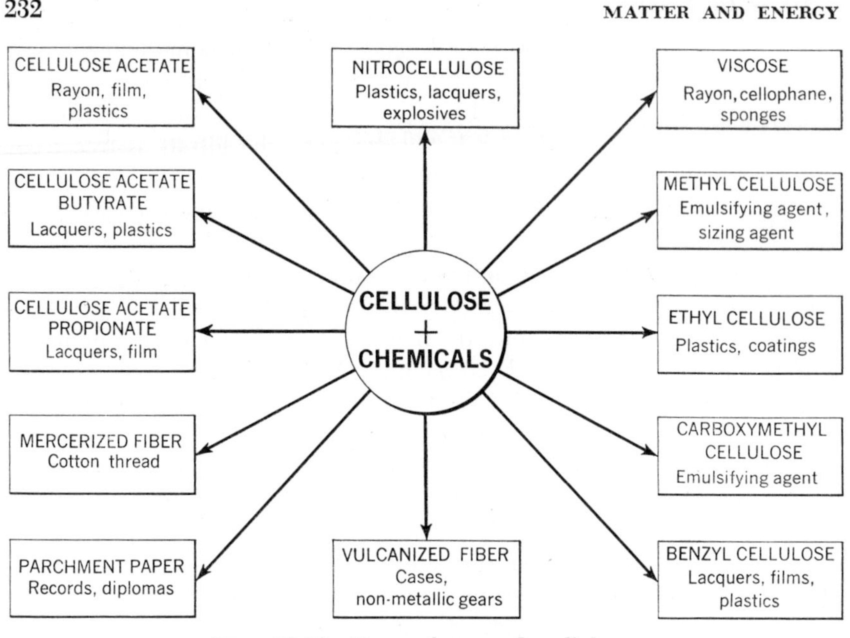

Fig. 10-12. Uses of treated cellulose.

one of our most important construction materials. Are there any sources of cellulose besides wood?

Minerals. Students may weigh a wooden block, burn it completely, and weigh the ash. In addition to lignin and cellulose, wood contains a small percentage of minerals (usually about 1 part in 100 by weight). These minerals are found in the ashes remaining when the wood is burned. How did the tree build up cellulose? From where did the minerals come? Here is an opportunity to point up, once again, what are the "raw materials" needed for healthy plant growth.

10-14. From Wood to Paper

A Project in Paper Making. Here is a simple technique, which at the same time is historically interesting. Nearly every town has a greenhouse which contains some growing papyrus. Students may peel off the outside layers and cut the pith into very thin strips. These should be dampened and laid crisscross under a heavy weight. In the morning, when the weight is lifted, the papyrus will be matted into a primitive kind of paper.

Here is a rather ambitious project suggested by the American Cyanamid Company:

A convenient weight of paper for demonstration purposes is about 4 to 5 grams per 100 square inches. If no slush pulp is available, you can prepare your own by defibering non-wet-strength facial tissue or napkins or toilet tissue. A Waring blender or Hamilton-Beach milkshake stirrer is preferred for defibering. Lacking these, an electric or hand egg beater may be used to defiber the pulp. First soak the 4 to 5 grams of paper in water, then dilute it to about 500 milliliters and stir until all fibers are separated. If hand or electric egg beaters are used, they must be stopped frequently to clean off pieces of paper, which will tend to wrap around the blades. With an electric egg beater, the preferred procedure is to pour the water into the mixing bowl and add the paper a little at a time while the beater is running.

After the pulp is prepared, the sheets can be formed on a Büchner funnel. The preferred procedure is to cut a disk of fine-meshed screen wire (60 to 100 mesh) that will just fit inside the Büchner funnel. Place the funnel on a suction flask and apply vacuum. Hold a screen flat on the surface of the Büchner funnel with the fingertips of the left hand and pour the stock slurry into the screen slurry with the right hand. As soon as the vacuum is built up enough to hold the screen flat, remove the left hand and pour the remainder of the stock rapidly into the Büchner funnel. Maintain vacuum until all the free water has been drained from the sheet. Then disconnect the vacuum and insert the Büchner funnel over a dry blotter. Blow the screen with its sheet of wet paper from the Büchner funnel onto the dry blotter and press it lightly with the palm of the hand. Then strip the screen from the wet sheet, which will adhere to the blotter. Place another blotter on top of the wet sheet and press the sandwich, at first gently and then firmly with the palm and heel of the hand. The paper may be dried conveniently without wrinkles by transferring it to another dry blotter and pressing it with a hot electric iron.

Novel water-marked sheets may be prepared by soldering fine wire (24 gage or smaller) to the screen. The wire may be shaped to form any desired design. A sheet formed on a screen with this fine wire soldered to it will give a clear water mark of the pattern.

The stock may be treated prior to sheet formation with a wide variety of chemicals to produce useful modifications of the properties of the finished paper.

Wet-strength resins may be added to the stock (about 3 per cent of fiber weight). When they are used, a small amount of an acid or an acid salt should be added to the stock after the resin. In general a pH of about 4.5 is desired. Alum (aluminum sulfate) is an acidic salt widely used in the paper industry to furnish the low pH and aluminum ions which are required for sizing paper. About 3 per cent of the dry fiber weight of aluminum sulfate, $Al_2(SO_4)_3 \cdot 18H_2O$, is ample to provide the proper pH. The sheet is then formed in the manner described above. Wet strength is not developed until after the sheet has been thoroughly dried with the hot iron.

Sizing of paper can be accomplished by adding about 3 per cent of resin size (based on dry fiber) to the fiber followed by 3 per cent alum. Here again the sizing is not developed until after the sheet is dried.

10-15. Wood Extractives

In addition to lignin and cellulosic materials, wood contains extractives. Some of these are water-soluble, while others dissolve in organic solvents.

Water-soluble Extractives. Many types of wood such as oak, chestnut, and sumac contain tannin materials. The tannins are even more abundant in the bark of the trees. Place some oak or chestnut wood or bark sawdust in water and allow it to stand overnight or until the next class period. The water will have become brown. The addition of a few drops of ferric chloride to the solution causes it to turn black, indicating the presence of tannin.

Oils in Wood. Almost all pines and other cone-bearing trees produce oily substances. Turpentine, which is found principally in southern pine, is the most important commercial product.

The extraction is carried out most readily in some type of extraction apparatus such as the Soxhlet extractor[4] or other extraction tube where a small amount of hot solvent may be used to extract resinous and oily materials.

The wood most suitable for this experiment is southern yellow pine or western ponderosa pine stump wood of the type used for solvent extraction of oleoresins. This wood contains up to 30 per cent extractives. Other pine woods contain 3 to 6 per cent extractives.

Put pine wood (ground, shredded, or sawdust) into an extraction thimble, and place it in a Soxhlet or other extraction tube. Attach a condenser with cooling water to the extraction tube so as to provide reflux of the solvent over the wood. Place a mixture of 1 part methyl alcohol and 1 part benzol in a flask and attach to the bottom of the extractor. Heat the flask by an electric hot plate or steam bath so that it boils gently. (Avoid the use of a free flame because the vapor of alcohol and benzol is very flammable.) Extract for 4 to 6 hours. Remove the flask and boil off the solvent at low heat on an electric plate or steam bath. The residue in the flask is the oily material or oleoresins of the wood.

Sugars from Wood. When wood is treated with strong sulfuric acid at room temperature or with dilute acid at elevated temperature and under pressure, the cellulose and hemicellulose of wood are hydrolyzed to simple sugars.

The filtrate from the isolation of lignin from wood (Sec. 10-13) con-

[4] The Soxhlet extractor, extraction tube, and paper extraction thimbles may be found in most laboratory supply catalogues (Sec. 18-3).

tains sugars. Carefully neutralize this solution with 10 per cent aqueous sodium hydroxide solution, using litmus paper to determine the neutral point. The presence of sugar in this solution may be determined by the use of Fehling's solution (Sec. 18-1*k*).

Furfural from Wood. Wood contains pentosans, which on hydrolysis are converted to pentoses (five-carbon sugars). These pentoses are readily converted to furfural by heat in the presence of acid.

Place 5 grams of sawdust from hardwood (such as oak or maple) in a 100-milliliter flask; add to this 10 milliliter of dilute hydrochloric acid (1 part of concentrated hydrochloric acid and 2 parts of water). Heat the mixture gently over a flame. Hold a piece of filter paper, which has been dipped in a solution of 1 part of aniline in 2 parts of glacial acetic acid, over the mouth of the flask. A crimson color on the filter paper indicates the presence of furfural. Repeat the test using ground corncob or wheat bran.

Furfural, as your students may discover, is an important raw material in the commercial manufacture of many plastics.

This might be a time when you would want to discuss "substitution" products and their role in wise resource use. Is better use being made of wood when, instead of being used for lumber, it is converted to a plastic? There are no easy answers to questions like this, but your students may gain awareness of some of the many factors involved.

11

Water and Weather

Water is essential to all living things; without it they perish. Water is not, however, always in the right place, in the right amount, at the right time.

To begin to find a solution to the problem of adequate water supply —a problem of increasing urgency to many if not all communities—the students need an understanding of the water cycle with its never-ending pattern of precipitation and evaporation. They need to know something too of the curious properties of water, so intimately associated with weather and climate and so closely linked to life on earth.

This chapter helps students to analyze the water cycle through experience. There are direct experiences also with water's physical behavior and its effects on weather and climate.

THE WATER CYCLE

There are many concepts in the sciences that can be developed through experience to give students a perception of the cycle of evaporation and precipitation—the water cycle.

11-1. Evaporation

Water Evaporates. Wet down a blackboard with a sponge. Have the students watch, then ask where the water has gone.

How Fast? Wet two pieces of filter paper. Place one over a radiator or other source of heat. Place the other in a cool part of the room. Which dries faster?

Wet two pieces of filter paper. Hang one so that wind will blow on it or place it in front of a fan. Hang the other so that as little wind as possible will hit it. Which dries faster? Repeat under different conditions, i.e., in a sunny place, a shady place, a damp place, a dry place, etc.

Place equal amounts of water in a shallow dish and in a narrow tumbler. From which vessel will the water evaporate faster?

Take two flasks with equal amounts of water and attach one to a vacuum pump. What happens to the rate of evaporation?

These or similar activities will demonstrate that heat, breeze, a wide surface, and decreased pressure above the liquid all serve to speed up evaporation.

At this point, students may be interested in discovering what happens to the water that has evaporated. In order to find out, they will need to know something about air and its behavior.

11-2. Air Motion

Warm Air Expands. What happens when air is warmed (Fig. 11-1)? Method *c* is particularly interesting for physics and chemistry students.

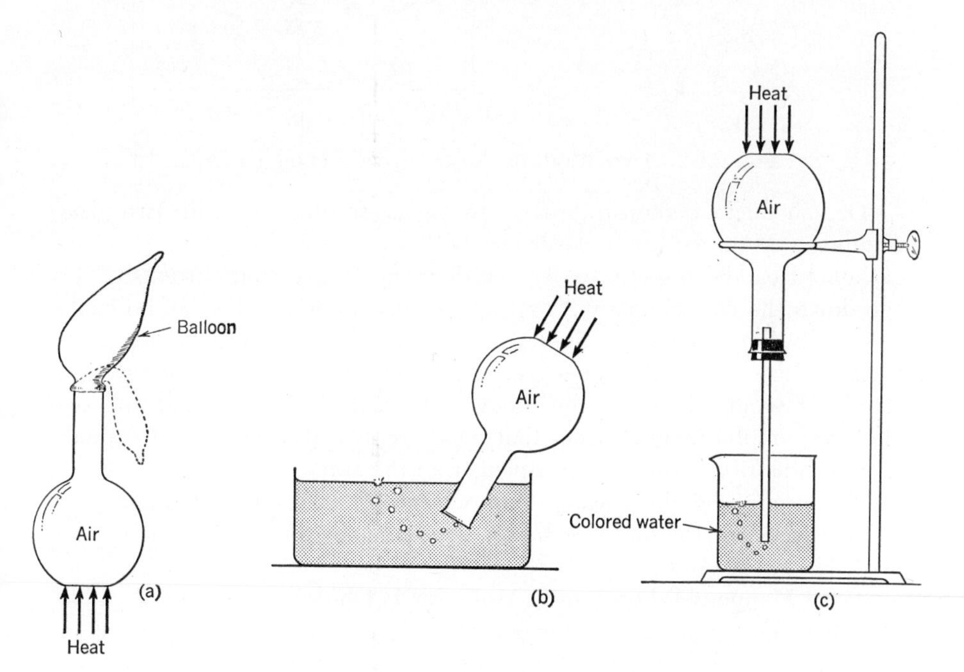

Fig. 11-1. Ways of showing what happens when air is warmed.

Heat the flask and allow a few air bubbles to escape. Now cool the flask and notice the colored water rise in the glass tube. Heat once more and see the liquid level in the tube go down. The discussion of all that has happened leads to consideration of air pressure (Sec. 11-6). This in turn leads to consideration of equilibrium, which should eventuate in an understanding of what takes place when the temperature of a gas changes and the pressure remains constant (Charles' law).

Air Currents and Wind. Use a pinwheel and a source of heat (Fig. 11-2*a*). A convection current is set up if there is a difference of temperature between any two parts of a fluid (air, in this case).

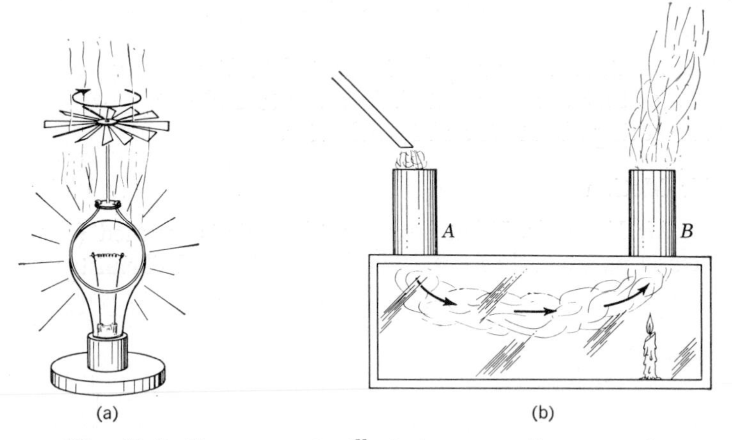

Fig. 11-2. Two ways to illustrate convection currents.

Or you might demonstrate this: In a glass-fronted box with two glass chimneys or tin cans with cover and bottom removed (Fig. 11-2*b*), place a lighted candle directly under one of them. Convection currents of air go down the cool chimney *A* and up the warm one *B*. This can be made visible by applying some lighted touch paper[1] or cigarette smoke at *A*.

From this demonstration experiment you may want to proceed to a study of winds. This may be followed by a discussion of land and sea breezes, emphasizing the fact that winds represent a tendency to equalize and distribute the heat received from the sun.

If you are near the seashore, temperature readings of sea and sand at various times of the day may be recorded and the direction of the breeze noted.

What Happens When Warm, Moist Air Is Chilled? *Contact with Cold Surfaces.* Heat a dish of water gently. Hold over it a cold, dry funnel or glass square and note how the moisture from the air condenses on the cool surface.

(Your students may think of other illustrations: the "sweating" of a glass of ice water on a warm, humid day; the droplets of moisture visible as they breathe out on a cold day.)

[1] Filter paper soaked in potassium nitrate solution and dried.

What happens when warm, moist air near the ground is chilled at night?

Meeting of Warm and Cold Air Masses. Arrange a covered jar containing a damp blotting paper so that it is inverted over a hot water bottle containing *warm* water. Put another hot water bottle containing *cold* water on top of the jar. (Coffee cans might be used instead of hot water bottles.) After about an hour there should be a cloud of condensed vapor inside the jar near the cold bottle (Fig. 11-3). Students may now

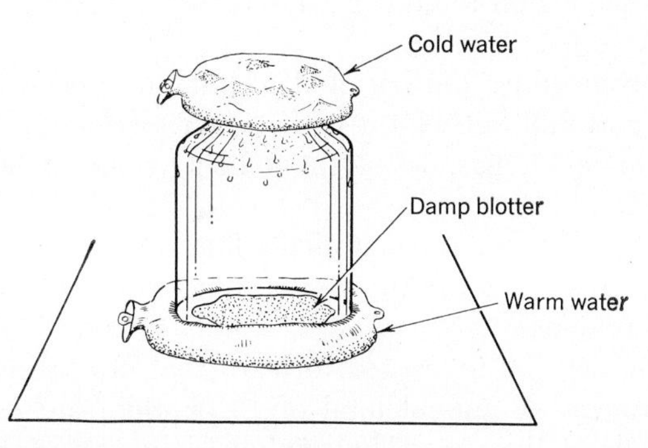

Fig. 11-3. When warm air meets cold air. Notice the condensed moisture in the upper part of the jar.

see that a "warm front" near the lower part of the jar rose to meet the "cold front" above it. Droplets of moisture condensed where the humid, warm air met the cooler air.

Cooling by Expansion. No doubt your students have noticed in pumping up a bicycle tire or a football that the tire or ball becomes hot as well as the barrel of the pump. Have they also noticed that if they press the needle valve to allow air to escape, the expanding air is quite cool?

Allow a very small amount of smoke from a burning match (to serve as nuclei for condensation) to enter a liter flask. Add a few milliliters of alcohol to the flask, stopper it at once, and shake well. As the alcohol vaporizes, the pressure inside the flask increases. Turn on a lantern projector and hold the flask in its beam. Now remove the stopper. The gases, rushing out with a noise, are cooled by expansion and the flask becomes filled with a dense fog.

Here is a variation that might be tried: Rinse a gallon jug with water, shake a little dust or smoke into the jug, and insert a one-holed stopper with a glass tube. Connect this to a pressure pump. As air is pumped in, watch the inside of the jug. Continue until the stopper is forced out and note what happens in the jug as a result.

You will find some interesting additional experiments on cooling by expansion (carbon dioxide snow and the effect of nuclei on condensation) in *Demonstration Experiments in Physics* by R. M. Sutton (McGraw-Hill Book Company, Inc., New York, 1938).

11-3. Rainfall

Your students might discuss the effect of geography on rainfall. On the West Coast, for instance, the cooling by expansion of the moist ocean air as it rises over the Cascade Mountains causes rain and hence rich, fertile valleys along the coast. However, the heating by compression of the air as it descends on the other side creates dry and desert regions in Nevada and Arizona.

Study the geography, "the lay of the land," in your own region with your students and find out why it is that your section of the country has the kind of climate it has. Is anything being done in your vicinity to increase rainfall?

Too Little, Too Much. Have students find out about the variation in rainfall in our country and in the world. What is meant by humid, semi-arid, and arid regions?

Your students will be interested to learn that, for ordinary farming, a region should have an annual total of 18 or more inches properly distributed throughout the year. The rainfall is therefore intimately linked with productivity of the soil, and water must be provided by means of irrigation of some kind where the rainfall is insufficient.

Can there be too much rainfall? Your class will have illustrations and stories of devastating floods which were unleashed by unusual and excessive rainfall. What can man do to decrease the danger of floods (Sec. 7-12)?

How Much Do We Have? It has been estimated by the U.S. Geologic Survey that about 1½ million billion gallons of water fall on our United States every year. The number doesn't mean much, does it? But it's a lot of water! It is, as your students have learned, very unevenly distributed, but the average calculated amount is 30 inches per year.

What Becomes of It? What happens to all this precipitation? As students search for an answer they will become aware that much of it returns to the air by evaporation and by the transpiration of plants. Then there is the portion that runs over the surface of the ground, eventually reaching the sea, as well as the amounts that remain stored on the surface in lakes and reservoirs. Finally, there is the portion that soaks into the soil and is absorbed into the underground reservoir or water table.

This might be the time to begin a discussion of the importance of water storage, both surface and underground, in meeting a community's growing needs for water.

Many interesting statistics may be gleaned from a small, pamphlet of the U.S. Soil Conservation Service, *Water Facts* (PA–337).

Measuring Rainfall. Rain is measured in terms of depth of the sheet or layer it would make if none drained off or were otherwise lost. In America this is noted in inches to the nearest hundredth.

A Rainfall Gauge. A juice can or similar container may be set in some open area and anchored so that it will not blow over. Use a thin ruler to read the depth of the rainfall. Take the reading right after the rain stops or water may be lost by evaporation. Readings may be taken for several months during various seasons.

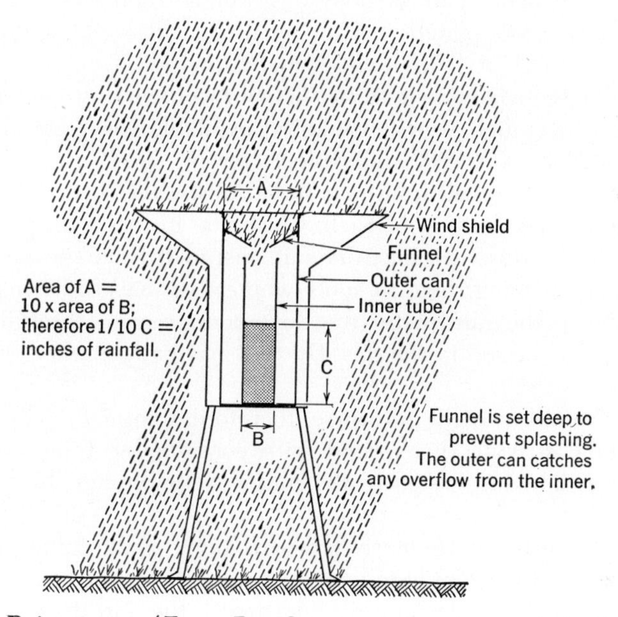

Fig. 11-4. Rain gauge. (*From Boy Scouts of America merit badge booklet, Weather.*)

More accurate measurements can be made by collecting rain from a larger area in a narrow vessel (Fig. 11-4). (Snowfall is measured both by actual average depth, as it lies upon the ground, and by the reading after being collected and melted in a rain gauge. The first can be roughly figured at about ten times the second.)

If your class has a chance to examine a professional rain gauge, study its mechanism. It may be the kind that is connected to an electrically operated recorder. (Each time 0.01 inch of rain collects in the bucket inside, it tips and thus closes a circuit for an instant.)

If possible pay a visit to your local weather bureau with your class. This can make a fine excursion and a good learning experience, which may stimulate some of your students to set up their own weather stations and to become life-long weather observers.

The Meaning of "One Inch of Rain." There are some interesting calculations that your students might make in order to broaden their concept of the meaning of "one inch of rain." For instance, after ascertaining from an appropriate table that an acre of ground contains 43,560 square feet, it can be calculated that a rainfall of an inch over an acre of ground would mean a total of 6,272,640 cubic inches of water. This is equivalent to 3,630 cubic feet. Students might go on to calculate the weight of this amount of water (1 cubic foot of water weighs 62.4 pounds). How many gallons does this weight represent? (1 gallon of water weighs 8.345 pounds.) How many barrels? (45 gallons to the barrel.)

If water is collected in cisterns in your community, students might figure out how much water would be available for their cistern if a 1-inch rainfall fell on 3,000 square feet of roof.

The Striking Force of Splashing Raindrops. Take several pie tins and punch holes in the bottom of each. Cover the insides with paper towels and then fill the tins with fine, dry soil. Just as it begins to rain take the tins outdoors, placing them in spots where they have differing amounts of exposure to the rain. After the downpour is over, carefully observe the surfaces of the soil in the tins. Do they have any marked differences? If so, why?

(A raindrop has weight, of course; therefore it normally picks up speed while falling, striking the ground with considerable force and hurling soil particles into suspension in the runoff. Your physics students, knowing that kinetic energy is represented by mv^2, will note the effect not only of the size but particularly of the velocity of the falling raindrop.)

The Size of Raindrops. Students may dust sheets of filter paper with a water-soluble dye (like Tintex) and expose them to the rain for a few seconds. On striking the paper, the drops cause spots which are recorded by the dye. (This method,[2] devised by J. Wiesner in Germany in 1895, has been used with slight modifications by a number of European investigators since that time.)

Students might allow raindrops to fall into a layer of loose flour,[3] 1 inch deep and with a smooth surface, contained in a shallow tin receptacle about 4 inches in diameter. The container should be exposed to rain for about 4 seconds. The dough pellets that are produced should be allowed to remain in the flour until they are dry and hard. They may then be passed through screens for separation into size groups. The size of the raindrops can also be determined by allowing drops of measured

[2] See *Raindrops and Erosion,* USDA Circular 895, for this reference and much other interesting material.

[3] This method was devised by W. A. Bentley of the U.S. Weather Bureau in 1902 and described in *Weather Review,* October, 1904.

size to fall into the same flour, making note of the size of the dough balls formed.

One of your students might report on the "raindrop spectrometer," an automatic device for recording the sizes of drops above 0.01 inch in diameter.

Snow as a Crop. Your students may be interested in learning about the new science of snow surveying, by which snow scientists are able to estimate with amazing accuracy the water content of the mountain snow packs (Fig. 11-5). These surveys make possible the Soil Conservation Service's Water Supply Forecast, each April 1, which helps farmers and industries of the West to save millions of dollars.

If you live in a region of plentiful snowfall, your students might try this experiment: Fill three equal-sized boxes with snow. Over one sprinkle

Fig. 11-5. Snow surveying in Ketchum, Idaho. One surveyor attaches scales to a ski pole while the other prepares to measure snow with a sampling tube. (*U.S. Soil Conservation Service photo.*)

a coating of carbon black, cover another with sawdust, and leave the third uncovered. Place all the boxes close together out of doors, and note the rates of melting of the snow. (Box 1 should melt first and box 2 last.)

Experiments like this, conducted by the U.S. Forest Service in 1956, indicate that in the snow fields well above the timber line it may be possible to speed up the snow's rate of melt in a drought year and hold it back in a wet year.

11-4. Humidity

Detecting Moisture in the Air. Here is a rough method: Water vapor changes the color of cobalt chloride—blue when dry, pink or grayish-white when moist. Soak some blotting paper or unglazed white paper in a strong solution of cobaltous chloride and then dry it in an oven until it turns blue. (The paper may be stored in a glass jar with a tight top that contains a drying agent like fused calcium chloride.) Students may hang the paper up and watch it turn pink as moisture is absorbed from the air. One can time the speed with which the paper turns color on days that vary greatly in humidity.

Students might use this same moisture-detecting device to show that the moisture content of air in different parts of an area may vary widely and that variations are related to differences in plant and animal life. (Clothespins or Scotch tape will be useful in holding the paper in place.) Several different areas might be selected for making tests—a lawn, underneath trees or shrubbery, a bare spot on the playground, a hollow log. How long does it take for the paper to change color? What about the variations in plant and animal life as the conditions of moisture change? What might happen to the living things in a humid, moist area if a relatively dry condition were to set in?

Saturated Air. Put a little water in a test tube or bottle, and cork it tightly. Notice that the water level remains constant, because the air above it quickly becomes "saturated" with moisture for that particular temperature. Equilibrium sets in, for no moisture can escape from the system. Next, place a little water in a thin-walled flask and cork it. Place it in the sun or in an oven until it becomes warm and then cool it. The walls of the flask become dim because of drops of water that the air could no longer hold at the lower temperature.

Dew Point. When your students first notice dew forming on the grass toward the end of the day, they might record the temperature.

To find the dew point, they may place some water in a shiny metal container, add small pieces of ice gradually, and stir the mixture gently with a thermometer. Finally, water droplets form on the outside of the can. This temperature should be recorded; it is the dew point.

Physics students can do a more careful and accurate determination of dew point. For laboratory instructions, consult N. Henry Black, *New Laboratory Experiments in Practical Physics* (The Macmillan Company, New York, 1949, page 127), or a similar manual.

Determination of dew point is of particular interest to farmers because frost in late spring or early fall may injure or ruin certain crops. If the dew point is above 40°F, the temperature will seldom fall to freezing during the night. Further cooling is retarded, once the dew point is reached, by the heat of vaporization set free when dew forms.

Relative Humidity from Dew Point. Knowing the dew point, we may compute the relative humidity of the air, i.e., the ratio between the density of moisture actually in the air and the density of moisture that would be present if the air were completely saturated. Students will need to use a humidity table for this calculation.

Table 11-1. Weight of Water Vapor in Saturated Air

Temperature, °F	Weight in grains* per cubic foot	Temperature, °C	Weight in grains per cubic meter
−20°	0.21	−30°	0.44
0	0.54	−20°	1.04
+20	1.30	−10°	2.28
40	2.86	0	4.87
50	4.09	+10	9.36
60	5.76	20	17.15
70	7.99	30	30.08
80	10.95	40	50.67

* One pound (Avoirdupois) is equal to 7,000 grains.

For example, if the temperature is 50°F and the dew point 40°F, then, using the humidity table, we find that a cubic foot of saturated air contains 4.09 grains of water at 50°F and 2.86 grains at 40°F (Table 11-1). Therefore, air is 2.86/4.09 or about 70 per cent saturated.

You might want to point out an important application of dew point and relative humidity determinations. In certain forests of California, for instance, the dew point is watched closely and when the relative humidity is very low, "no smoking" signs are put up and sections of woodland may even be closed as precaution against forest fires.

Relative Humidity by Instrument. If your laboratory has any humidity-measuring instruments, such as the hair hydrometer or the psychrometer, have your students learn to use them.

Youngsters may make their own sling psychrometers by mounting two identical thermometers as in Fig. 11-6. The instrument may be swung hard for a few minutes by the strong string or rope, instead of using a fan or the wind. After reading the temperature on both thermometers, consult a table of relative humidity, to be found in many general science and physics texts.

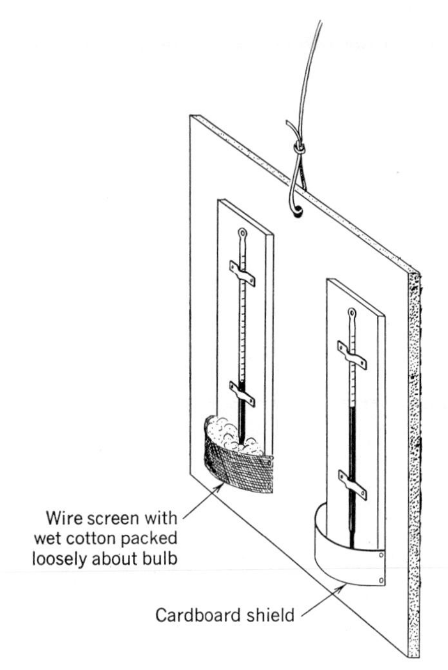

Fig. 11-6. A homemade sling psychrometer. (*From Cornell Rural Leaflet, vol. 45, no. 1.*)

11-5. Distillation: The Hydrologic Cycle

Simple Condensation. Boil a kettle of water and as the hot steam comes out of the spout, condense it on a flat plate of glass.

Distillation with a Condenser. In setting up a distilling apparatus (Fig. 11-7*a*), you may accomplish cooling in several ways, depending on your equipment:

1. Immerse the condenser flask in the sink with water.
2. Allow water from the faucet to run over a clamped condenser flask.
3. Use a standard Liebig condenser with faucet and sink.

The liquid to be condensed may simply be colored water, or more advanced chemistry students might proceed as follows:

Ask them to make up a sample of impure water in a beaker by adding to 100 milliliters of water ½ gram of solid calcium sulfate, 3 drops of concentrated ammonium hydroxide, ½ gram of powdered clay, and enough methyl orange to give the liquid a decided color. This sample of water contains all the types of chemical impurities present in natural waters: the calcium sulfate, being partly soluble, represents the *dissolved solids;* the ammonia water supplies a *"volatile" dissolved gas;* the powdered clay corresponds to a *suspended undissolved solid;* and the methyl orange represents *organic coloring matter.*

Students may then distill off 30 cubic centimeters for the first fraction, and 30 more for the second fraction. The third portion, or residue, remains in the distilling flask.

Your students will need to know at this point tests for a sulfate (Sec. 7-11) and for a hydroxide (Sec. 7-8). They may test each of the two distillates and the residue for ammonium hydroxide and sulfate. Ask them to observe each also for clearness or turbidity and for the presence or absence of color. When all results are recorded, your students will be in a position to answer questions like the following:

1. What impurities are found in each of the distillates? Explain why.
2. What impurities are left in the residue? Why?
3. Which of these three portions is the purest? Why?

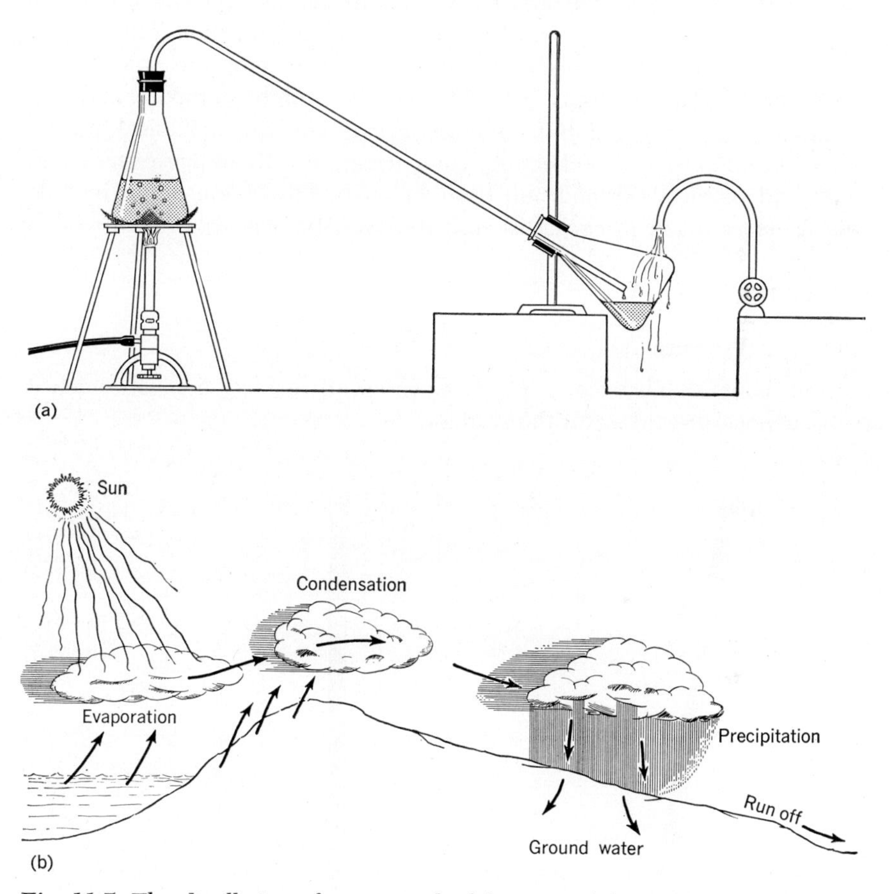

Fig. 11-7. The distillation of water in the laboratory (*a*) may be used to illustrate the hydrologic cycle (*b*).

4. How could sea water be purified?
5. How could water that contains a "volatile" gas in solution be purified?
6. Why must one filter the residue prior to making the test for a sulfate?

This experiment, or one like it, which you and your classes have been

performing for years, is really a splendid illustration of the hydrologic cycle. True, you are using a bunsen burner instead of heat from the sun, but the water is evaporating as it is warmed and condensing as it cools, just as it does in nature (Fig. 11-7*b*). You may want to use this as an opportunity to review the basic facts about the water cycle.

You may want to consider also what happens as rain water is intercepted by the earth. This will lead to a discussion of runoff and storage.

Some Projects: Students might make a drawing of the water cycle and explain how it works. In addition, they might compare maps of farm, forest, and population areas with a rainfall map. Other students might be interested in collecting, comparing, and discussing experiences with and pictures of flood and drought areas. Discussion might include the water problem in each case and the probable causes.

WEATHER

11-6. Air Pressure

A Barometer. That air exerts pressure on all surfaces against which it rests is not self-evident to the student.

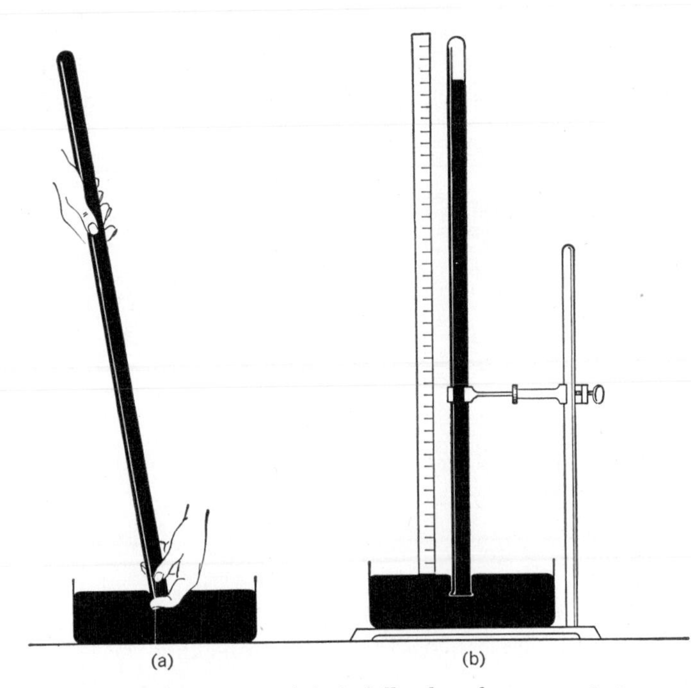

Fig. 11-8. Making a barometer. (*a*) A full tube of mercury is inverted into a dish of mercury; (*b*) the finished barometer. Why does the mercury level indicate air pressure?

A simple barometer such as Torricelli made may be easily constructed. Use barometer tubing about 3 feet long. Seal and anneal one end. Fill the tube completely with mercury, using a medicine dropper for the last few drops. Holding your thumb over the end of the tube, turn the tube upside down in a dish of mercury, and attach the tube to a ring stand (Fig. 11-8).

Why does the mercury drop to a certain level? Measure that level with a yardstick. What is there in the tube above the mercury level? What holds the mercury up in the tube?

You can mark the level of the mercury in the tube with a small rubber band or marking crayon. Watch the level as it varies from day to day and discuss the "rising" and "falling" barometer and its relationship to the weather.

Students may demonstrate and give reports on the aneroid barometer, the altimeter, and the barograph.

Correlation between Pressure and Weather Conditions.[4] Have students take the outdoor temperature each day for a week at the same

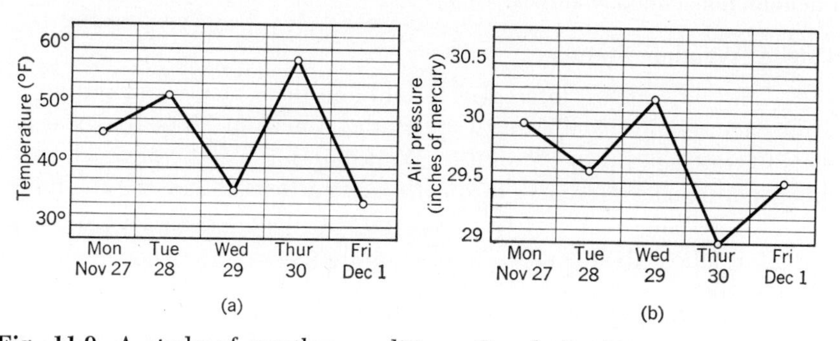

Fig. 11-9. A study of weather conditions. Correlation between temperature and atmospheric pressure. (*a*) Thermogram; (*b*) barogram.

time, also a reading of the barometer. (If no barometer is available, the pressure figure may be obtained from the daily newspaper or radio account.) Make two charts (perhaps large ones for bulletin board display) plotting the days of the week against temperature on one graph and against pressure on the other.

The charts shown in Fig. 11-9 were made by grade 8*b* students in Providence, Rhode Island. Fortunately the record was made during a week when weather phenomena over Providence afforded a striking example. A strong cyclone developed over the Gulf of Mexico and then moved over the Providence region, bringing unusually warm weather and low pres-

[4] This technique is supplied by Dr. J. G. Jensen, Department of Natural Resources, Oregon State College, Corvallis, Ore.

sure. The pupils were not long in discovering the correlation. As they put it, "Why, they are all opposite."

Try it with your class. A more extensive correlation can be made if records of sky conditions, rain, sun, and wind are also kept during the same period.

11-7. Some Simple Weather Experiments

Dr. Vincent Schaefer of cloud-seeding fame, now director of research of the Munitalp Foundation, Inc., has described in a series of articles in the 1955 issues of *Weatherwise* (American Meteorological Society, 3 Joy St., Boston 8, Mass.), experiments that any teen-age boy or girl can do. These experiments are designed to further a proper understanding of the changes that occur in the weather. He shows how it is possible to prepare a tiny sample of the atmosphere in a "cold box" so that some of its properties can be observed and physical and chemical changes actually produced. These experiments are not only spectacular, but they answer many questions about atmospheric reactions that combine to produce the phenomenon called weather.

11-8. A Weather Station

If your students are interested in building instruments and setting up a weather station, have them write to the American Meteorological Society for the list of projects entitled *Workshop for Weathermen*. This will give them specific references to *Weatherwise* articles describing the building of every conceivable weather instrument. *Weatherwise* can also supply information about model weather station kits.

11-9. Man Theorizes about the Weather

Is Our Weather Changing? Many weathermen think our weather really is changing and even dare to forecast "continued warm" for at least the next hundred years. They have based this prediction on the following kinds of evidence:

1. Annual weather temperatures have risen in various places.
2. There are many cities which have suffered in recent summers from damaging heat waves.
3. There are longer growing periods on northern prairies.
4. There is a northward march of fish, birds, and vegetation.
5. There is a growing frequency of tropical-type hurricanes along the eastern coast line.

Your students could begin making and recording observations of their own. They might consult older people and records on long-term observations. Your ablest students might be interested in learning how to use the simple moving average method in a variation study. Have them look up this method in a book on statistics such as William A. Neiswanger, *Elementary Statistical Methods* (The Macmillan Company, New York, 1956).

Prediction of a Coming Ice Age. Students might bring to class a report of the theory of ice ages, put forward by two scientists distinguished in the fields of geology and meteorology, Drs. Maurice Ewing and William Dunn. These scientists believe that the warm up we are now experiencing will result in the melting of the ice sheet over the Arctic Ocean. This, in turn, will mean an increase in snowfall in the north, causing glaciers to grow once more. The theory presupposes that the oceans work as a "thermostat" to keep the earth alternating between glacial ice ages and interglacial periods such as today.

A simple account of this theory and the evidence adduced to support it may be found in the The Coming Ice Age, by Betty Friedan, in *Harper's Magazine,* September, 1958.

Tackling the Hurricane. Research scientists are beginning to learn enough about hurricanes, those 100,000-cubic-mile caldrons of air, water, and heat, so that better forecasting may be expected. Perhaps someday there may even be hurricane control. Your students might discuss what such control could mean in terms of conservation of life and property.

The "heat engine" of the hurricane, as described by Robert H. Simpson, head of the Weather Bureau's hurricane research, is illustrated in Fig. 11-10. Water vapor, condensing to steam in a ring around the eye,

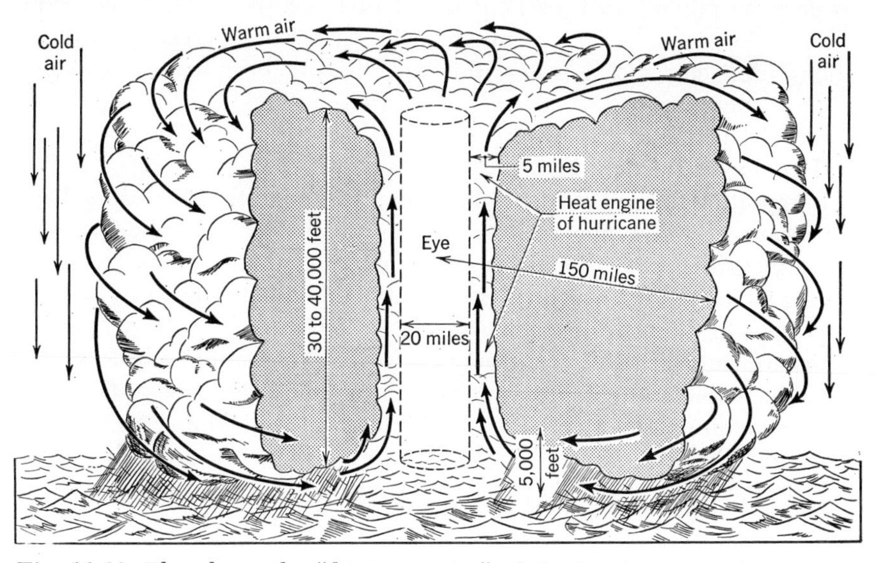

Fig. 11-10. This shows the "driving engine" of the hurricane, which occupies only 1 per cent of the volume of the storm. (*From the New York Herald Tribune.*)

heats the air, which rises. Rising air pushes the atmosphere out at the top and in ever-widening spirals. When spirals strike the cold atmosphere beyond the core, they sink. This pushes the air toward the eye and starts the spiral winds going at lower levels.

11-10. Man Changes the Weather

He Makes Rain. Can we do anything about too little precipitation? Can we "make" it rain? This is a question that will naturally arise when you are discussing rainfall.

Since dust or other particles are necessary as condensation nuclei (Sec. 11-2), scientists began using various substances, dry ice and silver iodide among others, to seed clouds. Your students may want to know what these other agents are, how the cloud seeding is done, and where it has been tried. (An excellent pamphlet can be obtained from the United Nations entitled *Rainmaking: A Study of Experiments* (1954).

How successful have experiments in cloud seeding been? Oregon State College at Corvallis has done some interesting research on the value of artificial rain making in that area. Students might write for information.

A member of your class might try to obtain a copy of a report submitted by President Eisenhower's Committee on Weather Control in February, 1956. This is the first scientific appraisal of man-made rain to be undertaken in our country. The report states that it is feasible to increase rainfall by 9 to 17 per cent or more. The 9 to 17 per cent increase in precipitation was obtained in studies of cloud-seeding operations in Pacific Coast states, this area having been chosen because cloud-seeding operations there are carried out on a relatively "permanent" basis, but this does not mean that rain-increasing operations will be successful only in that area.

In reporting to the President, the committee found that "cloud-seeding, by means of the commercial technique which involves releasing into the atmosphere silver iodide smoke from ground generators produces results which are not spectacular or breathtaking, but which can be very important to the water economy of the nation."

Experiments also indicate it may be feasible to control hailstorms and possibly "inhibit" lightning squalls and "modify" tornadoes, the top-level committee reported. The inhibiting of the lightning would cut down one of the principal causes of forest fires. Such developments hold tremendous economic possibilities, but all of this is in the future. The committee urged that its research work be continued and that other agencies devote much more scientific study to weather control.

Could indiscriminate cloud seeding, instead of promoting rain, actually be the cause of drought? Such was a debate in which weathermen were engaged as they studied a report made to the National Academy of Sciences early in 1957 by Dr. Ross Gunn of the U.S. Weather Bureau. Dr. Gunn's findings seemed to indicate that the cleaner air is, the better are the chances of rain from warm and supercooled clouds.

One of your students might bring in a report describing Dr. Gunn's experiments, and the class might follow the scientific "debate" in the current scientific press. How are such debates finally settled?

It will become apparent to your students, as they gather evidence on artificial rain making, that it is still in the experimental stage. That is why the immediate benefits of water storage should not be overlooked. In Indiana, for example, it is estimated that 13 inches of their 39-inch annual rainfall is lost to runoff. If 4 inches of the water lost could be stored on the surface or underground, there would be a sufficient quantity for any of the foreseeable needs of irrigation.

11-11. New Tools for Studying Weather

A MACHINE FORECASTS WEATHER[5]

> Washington, January 24, 1956. Scientists have proved that an electronic brain can forecast certain aspects of weather as accurately as the weather man—and faster. This machine has for months been issuing regular predictions of winds and pressures at three altitudes over continental United States.
>
> Although the mathematical possibility of predicting weather by machine has existed for many years, it was not until the post–World War II development of high-speed electronic calculators that experiments became practical. Now it is being done, and the achievement promises to revolutionize weather predictions.

Have your students watch developments of the Joint Numerical Weather Prediction Unit, as it is called. Machine forecasting is a joint effort of Air Force, Navy, and Weather Bureau.

A Homemade Electric Brain Machine. Several of your students may become fascinated with the idea of an electric brain machine. There exist several "do it yourself" opportunities for them.

"Geniac" is a low-cost kit and text combination. With this 400-component construction kit your students can create any of thirty-three brain machines including logic, arithmetical, and game-playing circuits. Each geniac comes as a self-contained course in computer design and the instructions are simple enough so that teen-agers can design factoring machines, puzzle-solving circuits, etc. Circuits operate on one flashlight battery, and use ingeniously designed parts. No soldering is required, and very little wiring. For further details write to Science Kits, Dept. SN-29, Oliver Garfield Company, 126 Lexington Ave., New York.

[5] *New York Herald Tribune.*

Your students may also obtain information and diagram for a "Do-it-yourself Computer" from the Research Laboratory of the General Electric Company, Schenectady, N.Y.

A Satellite to Study Weather. Your students will be interested in following the progress of each man-made satellite as it yields data (Fig. 11-11) that will add to man's knowledge of air density, temperature, pressure, meteorites, solar ultraviolet radiation, cosmic ray densities, and even aid in making geodetic determinations and studies of the earth's crust.

Some of your students will be curious to know "how it works." You

Fig. 11-11. The "weather eye" collects data. Two of these instruments, weighing less than 4 ounces each, were mounted in Vanguard II satellite to record radiation emitted from the earth's cloud layer for long-range weather forecasting. Left to right: retaining ring, detector-mounting wafer, spacer, solar battery, and a second spacer. (*Perkins-Elmer Corp., Norwalk, Conn.*)

might refer them to a general science or physics textbook. In *You and Science* by Paul F. Brandwein, L. G. Hollingworth, A. D. Beck, and A. E. Burgess (Harcourt, Brace and Company, Inc., New York, 1955), the chapter, Space: Our New Frontier, describes some interesting experiments your students might try out and demonstrate.

WATER AND CLIMATE

11-12. Water: What It Is

Bring to class a jar of water. What actually is water? How does it behave under varying conditions? Does its behavior affect our climate? These and other questions can be elicited from your students as you begin the discussion.

Pulling Water Apart. In order to find out of what elements water is composed, suggest tearing it apart. Explain that this can be accomplished

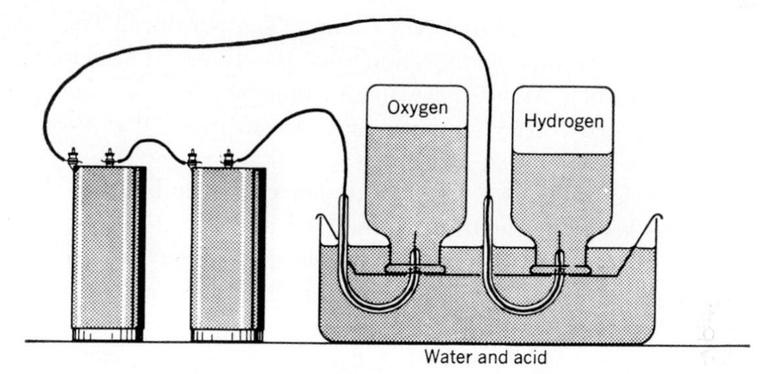

Fig. 11-12. Apparatus for breaking water into hydrogen and oxygen.

by means of electricity. Before electrolyzing water, however, be sure your students are familiar with the gases oxygen and hydrogen and how they are identified by the glowing splint and "pop" tests.

The simplest kind of homemade electrolysis apparatus can be used (Fig. 11-12). Explain that the water will need to be acidified with a little sulfuric acid to carry the current. As the gases are collected they can be identified by appropriate tests. At this point some student may ask, "Can water be made by uniting the two gases?"

Making Water from Its Constituents. Collect a test tube each of hydrogen and oxygen by water displacement. Put them mouth-to-mouth for a minute so that they will diffuse. Now someone may cautiously bring a lighted taper to either tube. There should be a loud explosion accompanied by a cloud of steam as the hydrogen and oxygen combine to form water. (To refine this experiment, the gases could be dried before starting, then collected over mercury, so that the droplets of moisture after the explosion would be conclusive evidence.)

11-13. Water: How It Behaves and How Its Behavior Affects Climate

Water into Steam and Steam into Water. Heat a little water in a beaker. Insert a thermometer. Continue heating until the water boils. Record the temperature. Heat until the water disappears. Hold a glass plate over the steam and notice the drops of water condensing on the cool surface.

Water into Ice and Ice into Water. Set a test tube of water in a beaker that contains a freezing mixture of crushed ice and rock salt. Insert a thermometer in the test tube. Observe the freezing and record the freezing point of the water. Remove the test tube from the freezing mixture and note the melting and warming of the water as it stands in the room.

Can Water Soak Up Heat and Not Change Temperature? Try keeping a thermometer in boiling water (don't let the thermometer touch the bottom of the vessel). Allow the water to boil more rapidly by increasing the heat under it. Your students may be surprised that there is no difference in the temperature reading.

Next, take a large bucket filled with ice cubes and water. Place it over a fire and keep the mixture well stirred and agitated. The temperature will read 0°C, no matter how hot the fire, as long as any ice remains unmelted. This will lead naturally to a more complete discussion of changes of state with their accompanying energy changes.

Your students are now aware that heat needs to be added to ice in order to melt it, or to hot water in order to boil it. Point out that when water freezes or steam condenses, this energy is released again as heat. Your physics students could make quantitative measurements of the heat of melting ice and the heat of condensation of steam.[6]

What effect would the freezing and thawing of lakes have on the surrounding atmosphere?

Specific Heat of Water. Take two test tubes, one containing sand or dry, sandy soil and the other filled with water. Keep the weights equal. Heat them both in a beaker of water. Bring to a boil and keep the test tubes immersed for half an hour. Then place the test tubes on a cake of paraffin wax (Fig. 11-13). The test tube of water should melt the most wax and sink the deepest. This indicates that water is able to soak up heat more readily than sand and that it has more heat to give up when it encounters a cooler environment.

[6] See a manual such as N. H. Black, *New Laboratory Experiments in Practical Physics,* The Macmillan Company, New York, 1949, pp. 121, 124.

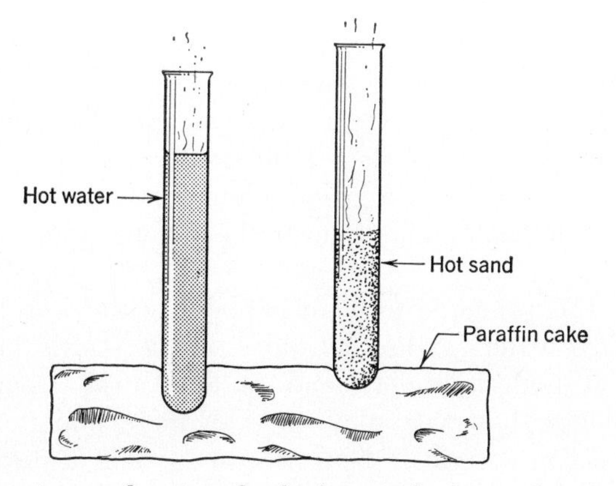

Fig. 11-13. Experiment showing the high specific heat of water as compared to that of sand.

Because of its high specific heat, water does not become as warm as land in summer nor as cold in winter. How does this tend to prevent extremes of temperature in nearby land areas?

The waters of the earth, due to their vastness and high specific heat, act as a gigantic reservoir for storing excess warmth in summer and gradually releasing it in the cold winter weather.

The Temperature of Water and Living Things. Do the kind and abundance of living things that inhabit the water vary with temperature? Students will know something about the differences in aquatic life in cold, temperate, and tropical waters. A member of your class might keep tropical fish as a hobby and could plan a demonstration and discussion with his classmates.

The Varying Density of Water. Fill a tall glass cylinder nearly full of cracked ice and let it stand until some of the ice has melted. Take the temperature of the water near the top, the middle, and the bottom of the jar. (A thermometer may be suspended by a string to reach the bottom of the jar.) The temperature at the bottom should be higher than 0°C, for water's maximum density is at 4°C, as you will recall.

Students might think about this peculiar property of water—the fact that at the bottom of an ice-covered lake the temperature will be a few degrees above freezing. Might this have an effect on the living things in a lake in the cold of winter?

Or you might try this experiment: Into a 500-milliliter round-bottomed flask fit a one-holed stopper into which has been inserted a 4-millimeter glass tube about 1 foot long. Fill the flask to the top with distilled water tinted with a little red ink. When the stopper is carefully inserted, the excess water will rise in the tube. Try not to let air bubbles enter the flask. When the flask is gently warmed, the water in the tube will begin to rise because it is expanding. What happens to the density of the water as its temperature rises?

Another way to come to the realization that the density of liquids varies with temperature is this: Chill water and then measure and weigh on a sensitive balance a given volume (50 milliliter, for instance). Do the same with water that is near the boiling point. Compare their weights.

Now apply this principle to what happens in the world's oceans. The warmed surface waters at low latitudes, rising a little higher than the cold waters at high latitudes, tend to flow away from the equator. (Prevailing winds, however, play an even more important part in the formation of ocean currents.) Now you may want to discuss how these currents affect the climate of neighboring land masses. Have findings of the International Geophysical Year thrown any new light on these phenomena?

The Behavior of "Solid Water." In a tall jar of ice water, where does the ice stay? Almost all liquids in solidifying become more dense, but this is not true of solid water or ice. Ask your students what this strange behavior of water means to life on earth.

Since lakes freeze from the top and not from the bottom, the protective covering of ice allows the warmer water underneath to remain liquid. This is what preserves aquatic life during the cold weather.

You might have your students consider for a moment what would happen if ice did not float. They would soon see that our lakes would freeze from the bottom up. Furthermore, since water is a poor conductor of heat, there would be little melting, and each winter would add to our store of frozen liquid until in cooler climates our water would be locked up in the solid state. Think of the poor fish—but hold on a moment—think of us, too. The small amount of thawing in summer would not be sufficient to supply enough moisture to start rainfall. No rainfall—no plant life. No plant life—no animal life. Man becomes extinct!

12
Earth's Envelope of Air

What the air is, two of the great cycles in which air and life are involved, "mining" the air for its useful substances—these are topics selected for development in this chapter.

Air, which seems limitless in quantity, is becoming so poor in quality over some of our industrialized areas that it menaces the well-being and sometimes even the lives of city dwellers. For this reason we have given special emphasis to air pollution and its control.

THE AIR AROUND US

12-1. Air: What Is It?

Oxygen and Nitrogen. Place a very small mound of dry red phosphorus on a flat cork floating in a pan of water. Ignite the phosphorus with a hot wire and quickly place a tumbler or beaker over it as it burns (Fig. 12-1*a*). Your students will note that, when the burning stops, and the apparatus cools for a short time and the fumes dissolve, the water will have risen about one-fifth of the way up the tumbler. Students can deduce that the oxygen in the air has been used up and that it must occupy about one-fifth of the total volume of air (see Sec. 10-4, The Nature of Burning).

Test the residual gas, impure nitrogen, in the tumbler with a lighted splint, and note that it does not support combustion.

Volumetric Composition of Air (Quantitative). This experiment, for a chemistry class, might be done as a demonstration. Enclose about 50 cubic centimeters of air in a 100-cubic centimeter graduate half filled with water and inverted over water in a large battery jar. Hold the graduate so that the water level in it is the same as that in the battery jar outside (why?), and read accurately the volume of enclosed air. Ask students to record the barometer reading and the room temperature, making sure that the temperature of the water in the battery jar is the same as that of the room. Students may then reduce the observed volume to "standard conditions." (This is a good opportunity to use knowledge of the gas laws.)

Securely fasten a piece of white phosphorus, about ½ to ¾ inches in diameter (never to be touched with bare fingers), to the end of a special phosphorus spoon (a metal cup with a prong in the center) or else a wire and thrust it into the *upper half* of the enclosed air

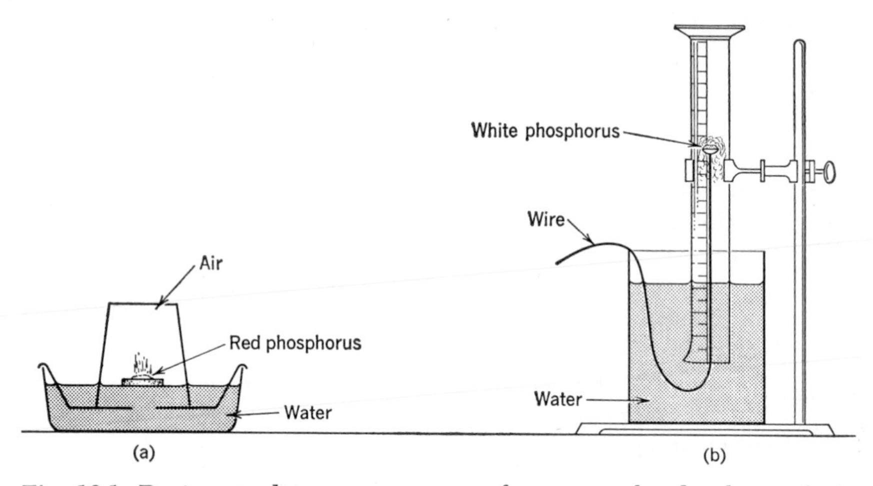

Fig. 12-1. Devices used to remove oxygen from an enclosed volume of air. (*a*) A qualitative experiment. Why does the water finally rise in the tumbler? (*b*) A quantitative experiment. How much gas remains after 24 hours? What is it? How may the volumetric composition of the air be determined?

(Fig. 12-1*b*). Have students observe what goes on in the graduate immediately after inserting the phosphorus, and elicit from them that the phosphorus is oxidizing and the finely divided, white product is drifting down into the water. Chemistry students will be interested in tracing the course of the phosphorus pentoxide to its final solution in the water as phosphoric acid.

After the apparatus has been standing for at least 24 hours, students may note the change in the water level, remove the phosphorus spoon; and read the volume of the gas remaining in the graduate. A lighted splint thrust into it will be extinguished. What is the gas? After reading pressure and temperature, students may reduce the volume to that of a dry gas under standard conditions. They are then ready to calculate the percentage of oxygen and nitrogen in the air.

Here is an opportunity to emphasize the roles played by these gases in making life possible on earth. Oxygen is needed by all living things for respiration (Sec. 3-13). Atmospheric nitrogen, inert gas that it is, not only dilutes the oxygen but also plays a vital part in the nitrogen cycle (Sec. 12-3).

The Rare and Inert Gases. Fit a portable light socket with an argon bulb. Attach the socket to the 110 a-c outlet and show the glow given by argon gas.

Exhibit neon sign tubes and if possible show the glow discharge from various other such demonstration tubes. These tubes, containing

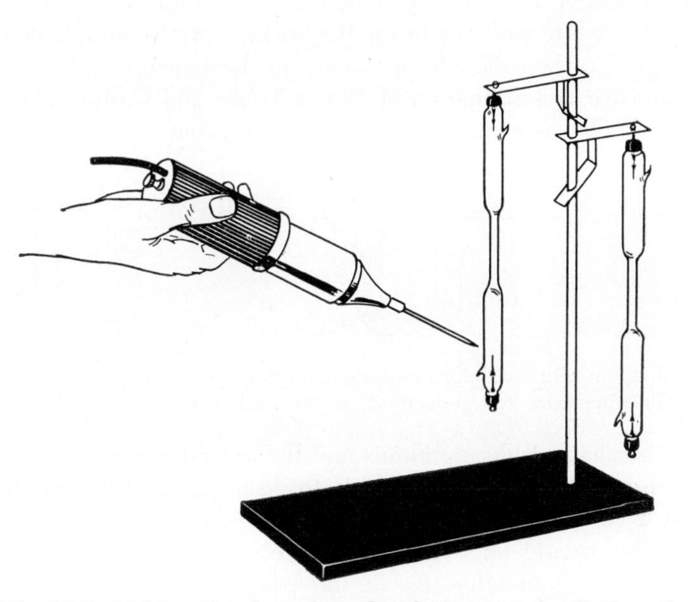

Fig. 12-2. Making Geissler tubes glow by means of a Tesla coil.

helium, argon, neon, etc., can be obtained from most chemical supply houses (Sec. 18-3). It is best to use a Tesla coil when operating the tubes. They may be arranged on a wooden frame or clamped on a ring stand. Connect the Tesla coil to the a-c outlet and bring the tip of the coil near (but not touching) the tubes (Fig. 12-2). They will glow brightly in a darkened room as the coil is passed in the vicinity of the tubes.

What are the other inert gases of the air? What are their uses? Have a student report on the discovery of the inert gases of the atmosphere.

Water Vapor. Place a few pellets of sodium hydroxide on a watch glass. After about 15 minutes students may note the moisture from the atmosphere that has formed on the pellets. Or expose some lumps of fused calcium chloride to moist air for 24 hours. Students will notice how wet they become.

At all times, water vapor may be found in the air in varying amounts, depending on the season, the temperature, and other weather conditions.

If you wish, discuss with your students the importance to life of water in the atmosphere. Rain and snow come from it; the life of plants and animals, including man, cannot go on without rain and snow. In addition, our bodily comfort depends to a great extent on the amount of moisture in the air.

Carbon Dioxide. Place a little limewater in a large watch glass and allow the solution to remain on the lecture table until the end of the period, or longer if necessary. Careful observation will show the formation of a white precipitate on the surface of the liquid, due to the action of the carbon dioxide in the air on the limewater.

Quantitative Determination of Water Vapor and Carbon Dioxide. By passing a known volume of air through two tubes (Fig. 12-3), the first

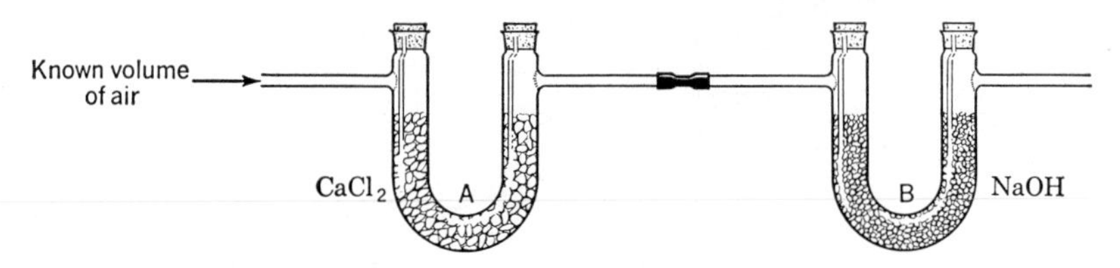

Fig. 12-3. Quantitative determination of water vapor and carbon dioxide in the air. The moisture is removed at *A*, the carbon dioxide at *B*.

filled with calcium chloride lumps and the second with sodium or potassium hydroxide pellets, it is possible to do a quantitative determination of the carbon dioxide and water vapor in the air sample. The tubes and contents should be weighed separately at the beginning of the experiment, and again after the air has passed through the system. The increase in weights will give the moisture and carbon dioxide, respectively, in the given sample of air.

12-2. The Carbon Cycle

How Carbon Dioxide Is Added to the Air. These experiments might be planned as a series of student demonstrations.

By means of a straw or glass tube, a student may blow his breath through limewater. Its cloudiness indicates that he is breathing out carbon dioxide. Do all animals give out carbon dioxide in breathing?

Another student might burn several wooden splints in a bottle that contains a little limewater. After removing the splints he should shake the bottle. What happens? A third student might repeat the experiment with charcoal. Still another might collect a bottle of illuminating gas by water displacement and repeat the experiment.

What kinds of fuels produce carbon dioxide when burning?

If you wish, discuss with your students how, in addition to the respiration of animals and the combustion of carbonaceous fuels, the eruption of volcanoes and the natural processes of decay and fermentation are adding carbon dioxide to the air (Fig. 12-4).

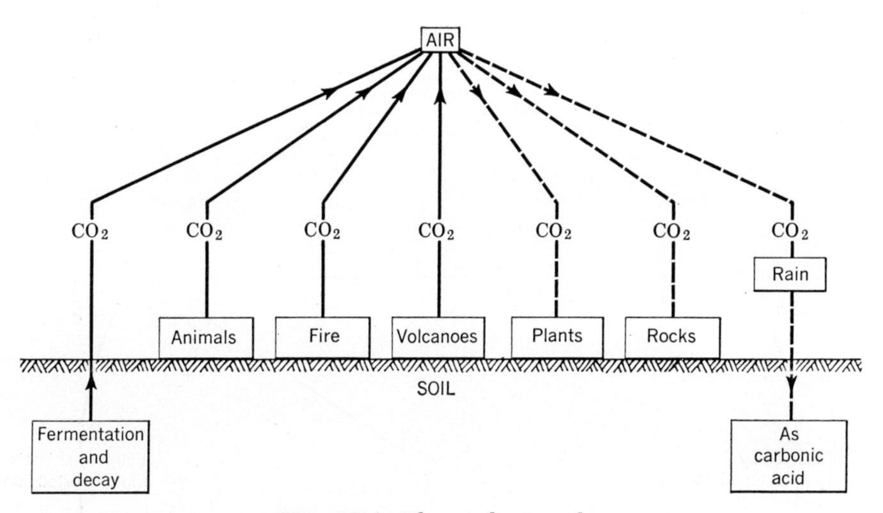

Fig. 12-4. The carbon cycle.

How Carbon Dioxide Is Withdrawn from the Air. You may wish to have students discuss how plants withdraw carbon dioxide from the air (Sec. 3-7). Students might prepare charts showing the close interrelationship of plants and animals: plants absorbing carbon dioxide and releasing oxygen; animals inhaling oxygen and exhaling carbon dioxide.

Students may recall, too, how carbon dioxide attacks limestone rock (Sec. 6-1), forming soluble bicarbonate that is washed away by streams and rivers to the ocean.

You might want to discuss, too, how the shell and coral manufactured by the creatures of the sea represent trapped carbon dioxide, once free in the air. Deposits of limestone and similar rock made from the dead bodies of marine animals cover hundreds of thousands of miles of the earth's surface.

The Ocean: A Carbon Dioxide Regulator. If students live near the sea they might collect some sea water, heat it gently in a test tube, and test the evolving gas for carbon dioxide (Fig. 7-6).

Sea water contains from eighteen to twenty-seven times as much carbon dioxide as does the air. Most of this gas is produced by living creatures of the sea. Ocean water is thus a vast reservoir that helps add carbon dioxide to the air and thus aids in maintaining a level of carbon dioxide concentration.

12-3. The Nitrogen Cycle

Tracing Its Course. Students might recall the experiments on nitrogen and nitrogen-fixing bacteria (Sec. 8-8).

Your class may trace the course of nitrogen from the air, through the legumes, through animals, back to the soil and the air (Fig. 12-5).

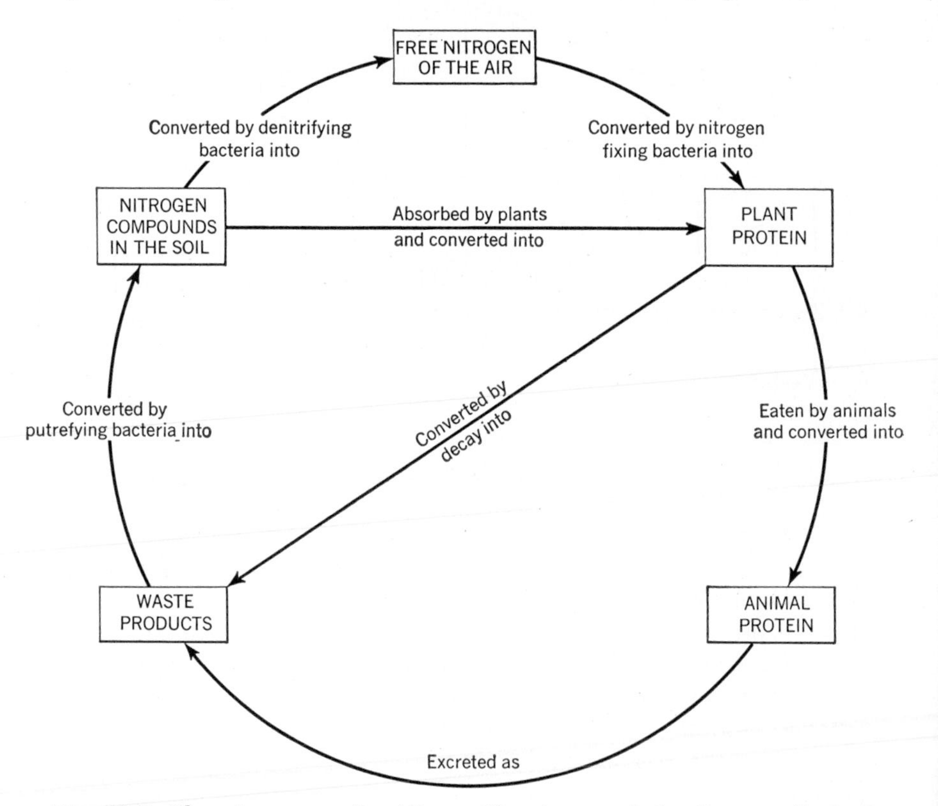

Fig. 12-5. The nitrogen cycle. (*From Chemistry and the Farmer, E. I. du Pont de Nemours & Co.*)

Students might bring in reports of the various kinds of bacteria involved in the nitrogen cycle—nitrogen-fixing, nitrifying, denitrifying. What is the role of each? What would happen to living things if there were no bacteria of decay or soil fungi? Students might explain how the materials that compose living things have been used over and over again since the beginning of life on earth.

12-4. Mining the Air for Its Resources

The air that envelops the earth is indeed a mine of riches. To separate the mixture of gases of which it is composed we must first liquefy the air.

Making Liquid Air. Pump up a bicycle tire and have a student note the heat evolved. Now allow the air to escape from the valve and note the cooling effect on a finger held at the opening. This will help your students to understand the principle on which liquid air machines operate, namely, the cooling effect produced when a highly compressed gas is allowed to expand freely. A physics or chemistry textbook can supply details.

Separating Oxygen and Nitrogen. Place small beakers of alcohol and of water on a hot plate. Students may note that the alcohol vaporizes or boils off while much of the water still remains. The same is true for a mixture of alcohol and water or mixtures of other liquids. Students might look up the boiling points of oxygen and nitrogen. Which gas will come off first from liquid air? What are the chief uses of oxygen and nitrogen?

Separating the Rare Gases. How are the rare gases separated from air? After looking up the boiling points of these gases, students may figure out in what order they would be fractionally distilled from liquid air. What are the commercial uses of the rare gases? Are any of them obtained from any source other than from the air? (Helium is found in connection with natural gas.)

THE AIR WE BREATH: A STUDY IN POLLUTION

12-5. What Is Happening to Our Air?

Your students are already aware that air is needed by all living things. Ask your class to imagine what would happen to life on earth if the supply of air were seriously altered or damaged.

Just as America has encountered conservation problems of water, soil, forests, wildlife, minerals, so also are we experiencing a new and alarming natural resource problem—the disagreeable and dangerous pollution of the air supply over our large metropolitan centers.

Because of the increasing importance of air pollution in our urban life, we are giving a rather fuller treatment to this section. Experimental material on air pollution is not yet readily available in school textbooks.

Special thanks for the various air-testing techniques described in this chapter go to former Commissioner L. Greenburg and Dr. M. Jacobs of the Department of Air Pollution Control of New York City, Dr. A. J. Haagen-Smit of the California Institute of Technology, and Dr. L. H. Rogers of the Air Pollution Foundation of Los Angeles.

"Things of Science" has an air-pollution packet (unit 197) which you may find helpful. It may be obtained from Science Service, 1719 N St., N.W., Washington, D.C.

Factors Contributing to Air Pollution. When large numbers of people are crowded into small areas as in our big cities, there is usually a fertile field for the development of a major problem in air pollution. When no control has been exercised over sources of air pollution for years and years, then air pollution becomes a startling reality. You might want to show a film such as *The City That Disappears* (Stanford Research Institute, Menlo Park, Calif.). The magnitude of a large city's problem is not hard to understand when we realize what are its inescapable needs.

The Need for Heat. Each and every building in a northern city requires a heating installation. When improperly operated, each of these units of heating equipment is a potential smoke producer.

Drop a few lumps of calcium carbide into a narrow-mouthed gas-collecting bottle one-quarter full of water. Ignite the acetylene gas generated in the bottle. Students will notice the thick black smoke, due to the incomplete burning of the gas. A small acetylene light, as in a miner's hat, will burn without smoking because of the presence of sufficient air.

Using a bunsen burner, close the air holes to produce a luminous flame. Hold the bottom of a porcelain dish in the flame and show students the black deposit that collects on it. The incomplete burning of the hydrocarbon is the cause of the soot formation (Fig. 12-6*a*).

Now change the flame to nonluminous and hold the sooty portion of the dish in the hottest part of the flame. Students will see that the carbon is burned off (Fig. 12-6*b*).

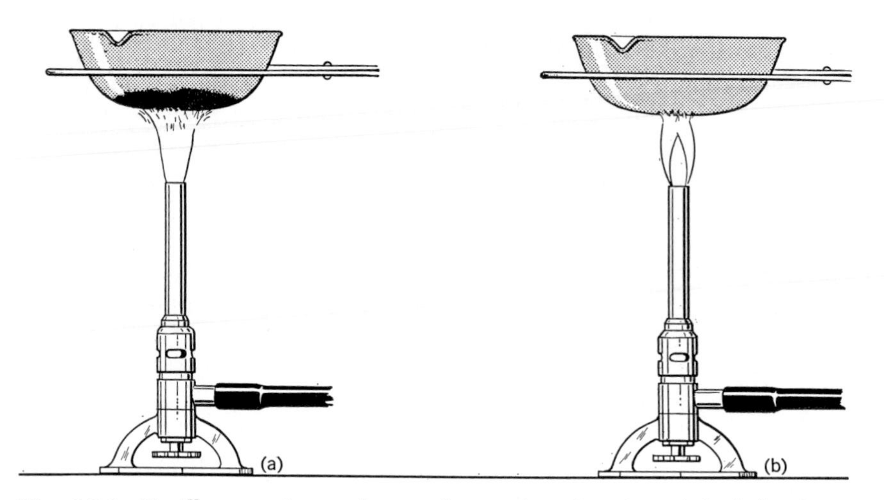

Fig. 12-6. To illustrate incomplete and complete burning. (*a*) A luminous flame deposits soot; (*b*) a nonluminous flame burns it off.

Smoke formation from fuels is the result of incomplete combustion; the carbon, instead of burning to carbon dioxide, is deposited as soot. Proper combustion of fuels containing carbon can help cut down the smoke nuisance. One way to obtain almost complete combustion is to pulverize coal and blow it into a properly constructed furnace. Might students visit such an installation?

The Need to Dispose of Refuse and Garbage. Apartment houses in large cities often have their own incinerators to burn refuse and garbage for easy removal by sanitation crews. There is, as yet, no completely satisfactory design for incinerators from the viewpoint of smoke prevention. Each is a potential "smoker."

The Need for Transportation. Autos, buses, and trucks pour their gasoline- and diesel-engine exhausts into the air. Ships and locomotives also contribute to the load of air pollution.

The Need for Industry. Industry provides us with jobs, manufactures the things we buy, supplies us with power and electricity. Most of the factories, large or small, within many cities' limits must operate heating, process, and refuse-disposal equipment. Many of these installations produce smoke, fumes, and odors.

Why Control Air Pollution? The air upon which our life depends is becoming more and more polluted and has indeed in certain dramatic instances such as Donora, Pennsylvania, and London, England, been the cause of thousands of deaths. Have students report on these disasters. Fortunately, these instances have been rare, but just ordinary, everyday pollution, particularly in crowded urban and industrial areas, can cause untold if less serious damage.

An Inventory of Harmful Effects. *On Human Life.* Air pollution can induce eye irritation. It reduces the receiving of the healthful ultraviolet rays emitted by the sun. It may cause depression and irritation and may bring on respiratory diseases. It can even kill.

On Vegetation. Vegetation is affected by dirtying and poisoning of plants, or sooting of leaves and clogging of pores. Plants are also damaged by penetration of gaseous pollutants into the leaves. Soils may be adversely affected through solid deposits or gaseous contact with pollutants. Damaged soil may well result in damaged crops and unsightly gardens and lawns.

Students may construct a fumigation box into which one or two pots of plants might be placed (weeds or others) and a stream of sulfur dioxide (made by adding dilute sulfuric acid to sodium bisulfite solution) introduced slowly into the box, for a short period. Considerable care must be exercised that the plants are not overexposed. One or two pots of plants should be retained for controls.

Another method might be to expose a plant to toxic vapor by filling a desiccator with a low concentration of the gas and placing the plant in the desiccator for a short time. Several days may be necessary for the effects to become apparent after exposure.

Small concentrations of sulfur dioxide will produce typical markings on various kinds of plants.[1]

On Weather. Visibility is reduced at airports, harbors, and on roads

Fig. 12-7. Air inspector of the New York City Department of Air Pollution Control checks pollution coming over to Staten Island from a plant in New Jersey. He uses a Ringelmann chart for determining smoke density.

and bridges. How is visibility measured (Fig. 12-7)? Air pollution also has the effect of reducing the hours of daylight.

On Property and Structures. Smoke, smog, and odors tend to depreciate real estate and to drive residents away from certain areas. Dirt in the air means that structures must be more frequently painted or cleaned (see also Sec. 13-18). Lighting costs, too, increase as hours of daylight decrease due to smoke.

On Manufactured Goods. Dirt in the air can adversely affect manu-

[1] For a detailed report see *Proceedings of the Third National Air Pollution Symposium,* Air Pollution Foundation, Los Angeles, 1955, p. 177.

factured products, causing specks in white-paper manufacture, odor pickup in food products, and grit on precision bearing surfaces. Clothing requires additional laundering, thus shortening its life.

Fuel Waste. Air pollution is an index of fuel waste. Smoke or fumes coming from a chimney mean that the combustion or process equipment is inefficient, needlessly consuming millions of dollars worth of fuel each year. This makes a double-barreled conservation problem.

What Are the Chief Air Pollutants? The most obvious of air pollutants are the dust and smoke that belch from smokestacks of all kinds. Then, too, there are noxious gases, chiefly sulfur dioxide, carbon monoxide, and nitrogen dioxide. Oxidants like ozone are produced in certain of the smogs (Sec. 12-7). In some instances one may find crankcase oil, salt, aldehydes, death-dealing cyanides, fluorides, lead, and hydrocarbons.

12-6. Some Simple Tests for Air Pollution

Measuring Dust Fall. Students may place a clean bucket or other container, one-quarter full of water, in an unprotected outdoor spot, about 3 or 4 feet above the ground. (Antifreeze should be added if the climate is so cold that the water would turn to ice.) The container should be checked at the end of 24 hours and again at the end of a week for evidences of foreign matter. This will be a rough measure of the air pollution in your locality.

The use of a petri dish is an old and useful procedure for measuring dust fall. Bacteria, molds, etc., can be identified by exposure to the air of a sterile agar in a petri dish.

A simple demonstration which is completed in several hours and which may therefore be useful in a classroom is this: Set a suction flask fitted with a Büchner funnel and a moistened coarse filter paper on the window ledge and connect it to a water aspirator. The filter paper will usually collect considerable dust.

An experiment of this kind can then be related to the amount of dust collected by a room air-conditioning filter. Have a student bring in the clogged filter of such a unit. The class could then do some simple calculations on total quantity of air breathed per day by man in normal activity (0.33 cubic feet per minute),[2] the weight of the material collected on the clogged filter, and the total volume pumped by the air-conditioning unit during this time. This could then be related to the amount of dust retained by the lungs during this period.

Examining Air Dust. Suggest to students that they collect some air dust and examine it under a microscope to see how many different substances they can find.

[2] Calculated from data given in L. A. Harding and A. C. Willard, *Heating, Ventilating, and Air Conditioning,* John Wiley & Sons, Inc., New York, 1937.

An Electrostatic Dust Sampler. When dust particles are placed in an electric field they will be moved by an effect similar to that of a magnetic field upon iron filings. The electrostatic precipitator consists, in its simplest form, of a metal tube and a center needle that is insulated from the tube. A constant electrostatic field of 10,000 to 20,000 volts is applied between the needle and the tube by the use of a homemade Van de Graaff generator (Sec. 16-12) or a Wimshurst static machine. The negative pole of the generator is connected to the needle; the positive pole of the generator and the outside tube of the precipitator are both grounded (Fig. 12-8). When the voltage is applied and smoke

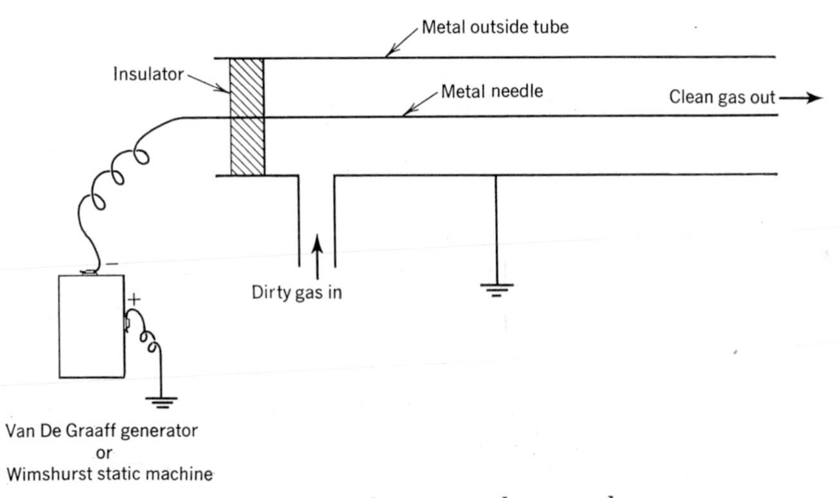

Fig. 12-8. An electrostatic dust sampler.

is blown through the tube, it will be precipitated on the walls of the tube (see also Sec. 12-8).

Measuring the Density of Smoke. Industrial smoke from smokestacks is measured with the aid of a Ringelmann chart. An inspector sights the smoke from his observation post and compares its density with the shades of the chart (Fig. 12-7). Smoke must be of sufficient density when compared with this standard to be in violation of the law. This practice is used in virtually every city in the United States.

If your school is situated in an industrial area, you might possibly obtain a Ringelmann chart from your Air Pollution Control Department. In New York City, for instance, you may obtain a Power's microringelmann by writing to Department of Air Pollution Control, 15 Park Row.

Sulfur Dioxide. Sulfur dioxide in air can be detected by bubbling air through 3 per cent hydrogen peroxide, then making the test for a sulfate. Or, air may be drawn through a very dilute neutral solution of hydrogen peroxide containing an indicator such as a mixture of 0.6 gram bromocresol green and 0.4 gram methyl red in 1 liter of methyl alcohol. When air is drawn through this solution, the indicator will change color, provided sufficient sulfur dioxide is present in the air.

Carbon Monoxide. Draw air through a U.S. Bureau of Standards carbon monoxide detector tube (Fig. 12-9). This tube changes from

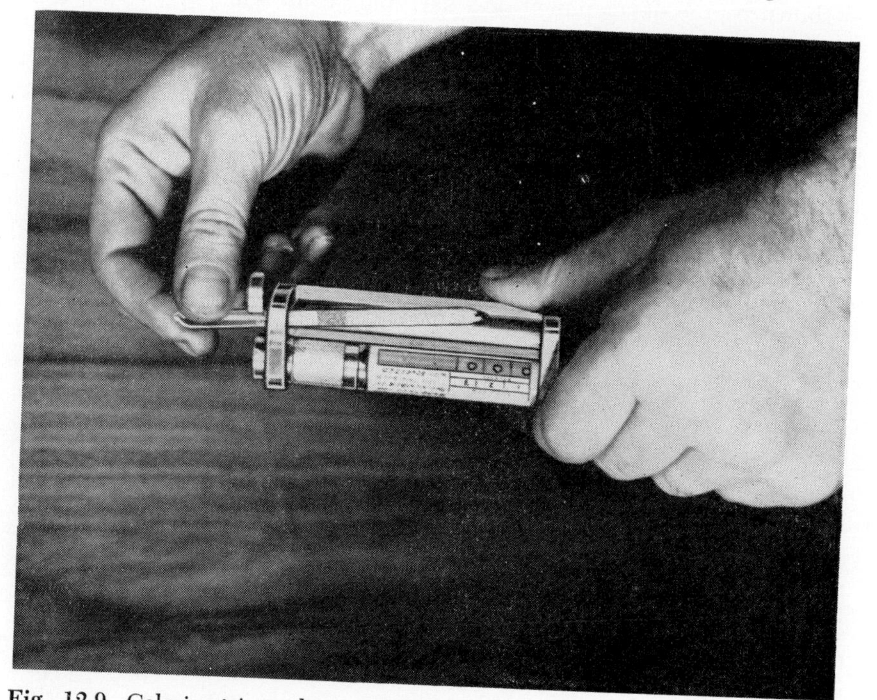

Fig. 12-9. Colorimetric carbon monoxide tester. This tester depends for operation on an indicator tube in which is contained a yellow silica gel impregnated with a complex silico-molybdate compound and catalyzed by means of palladium sulfate.

In use, the sealed ends of a detector tube are broken and the tube inserted in the tester's tube holder. A sample of air is then aspirated through the tube. When the air sample contains carbon monoxide, the yellow silica gel turns to a shade of green, the intensity of which is directly proportional to the concentration of carbon monoxide in the air sample at the time and location of the tests. Mounted directly beside the indicator tube is a revolving color scale. The tester is capable of indicating the presence of carbon monoxide in air from 0.001 to 0.10 per cent by volume.

yellow to various shades of green in the presence of carbon monoxide.

Nitrogen Dioxide. Nitrogen dioxide or nitrites are indicated by the development of red color in the reagent for nitrogen dioxide (Sec. 18-1*q*) when air is bubbled through it. The production of oxides of nitrogen can be shown by bubbling "exhaust" from a combustion motor or a bunsen burner through the reagent solution.

Oxidants. The most peculiar property of a Los Angeles type smog attack (Sec. 12-7) is a strong oxidizing effect. This can be demonstrated with 2 per cent potassium iodide in distilled water. Bubble air rapidly through this solution. An oxidant is indicated when iodine is liberated, as shown by the development of a dark blue color when a few drops of starch solution (1 per cent in distilled water) are added to the test solution. (This may take some time in areas where oxidants are low.)

Other Pollutants. Several other air pollutants are under study at the Boyce Thompson Institute for Plant Research, Yonkers, New York. Your students might write for literature describing the experimental results of exposing plants to the vapors of hydrogen fluoride (an increasingly important industrial chemical) and ethylene (from illuminating gas). Boyce Thompson is also conducting research on the harmful effects on certain plants of the 2,4-D spray as well as mercury vapor poisoning.

12-7. The Story of Smog

What Is Smog? You may want to try this experiment with your students:

Take two very large balloon-type flasks and invert them. Fill one of them with smoke from touch paper or a cigarette. Send a jet of live steam into both flasks. The moisture will condense and run down the sides of the clean flask, while the flask containing the smoke will be filled with a dense fog.

Dust particles in the air form the nuclei around which water droplets condense to form fog. Fog is usually one step in the formation of "smog," a word coined from the two words smoke and fog. Smog is not just smoke or fog. It is composed of many gases from cars, factories, incinerators, and chimneys that react in sunlight, forming some mysterious factors that scientists have not fully identified as yet. These factors are the harmful part of smog. By controlling *all* pollution these harmful substances can be kept down.

Industry is only partly to blame for smog. Scientists believe that certainly in some areas more than half the harmful pollutants come from the activities of ordinary citizens; in other words *we* are probably the biggest makers of smog. The worst offender is the family car. Its unburned fuel, coming from the exhaust pipe, is probably our most pressing air-pollution problem.

The answer is to keep this wasted fuel out of the air. Several likely devices are being tried now, which may cut down smog by stopping this waste. It may, for instance, be possible to perfect devices for removing pollutants at the tailpipe of the engine with a converter or afterburner.

Scientists know also that a device for cleaning the exhaust of automobiles near the car's engine would be valuable in the fight against smog. It has now been discovered that by use of the catalyst vanadium pentoxide 80 per cent of the offensive hydrocarbons in exhaust fumes can be removed.

You might also want to discuss with your class this "quote" from Eugene F. Hill, Manager of the Chemistry Department of the Ford Scientific Laboratory, Dearborn, Michigan: "Since it is a uranium by-product, vanadium pentoxide is in excess supply at a cost which makes an exhaust device look more economically attractive than ever before."

The ordinary citizen does other things besides driving the family car to produce smog. What about the burning of open rubbish in our cities? Or the burning of leaves, which might better be used for compost?

We must be careful also of the kinds of fuel we burn and the ways in which we burn them. Costly? Yes. It is true that Pittsburgh's fuel bill increased when bituminous coal was banned, but the city estimates it saves 25 million dollars in cleaning every year (Fig. 12-10*a* and *b*).

St. Louis and Its Solution of the Smog Problem. It is one thing to ban the smoke nuisance from a city and another to make it economically possible for consumers to foot the bill. This problem was solved in St. Louis, for example, by the discovery of a way to produce smokeless fuel from the inferior Illinois coals, which, though cheap and plentiful, burned with a devastating amount of soot. Extensive research resulted in a method known as the Curran-Knowles process that was able to produce inexpensive and smokeless coke. This coke cost the St. Louis fuel consumer no more and enormously benefited the health and cleanliness of that community.

Los Angeles and Smog. The story of the smog of Los Angeles, why that particular region is subject to this acute problem; how the culprit, ozone, caused by the famed California sunshine acting on gasoline fumes and nitrogen oxides, was tracked down in a brilliant piece of scientific detective work by Professor Haagen-Smit of California Institute of Technology; what the city of Los Angeles is now doing to combat the problem is a fascinating story.

You might want to introduce the topic of smog with this reading selection from an article by Ronald Schiller in the December, 1955, *National Municipal Review.*

> That Los Angeles should have been the first of our large cities to suffer from smog is due to conditions of climate and topography, plus the fact that the city's population has grown so fast that it has outstripped its air supply.
>
> The Los Angeles basin, 60 miles long by 25 miles wide, is hemmed in on three sides by mountains, and the steady pressure of cool air from

Fig. 12-10. Pittsburgh, Pennsylvania, "before and after." (*Above*) 1945—no smoke control; (*below*) 1956—smoke control in effect. (*Courtesy of Allegheny Conference on Community Development, Pittsburgh.*)

the Pacific boxes it on the fourth side. Hot air from the Mojave Desert, flowing westward over the mountains, overrides the cool air, creating an upside-down atmosphere called a "temperature inversion."

When the lid provided by this inversion drops below 1500 feet, preventing the incoming air from escaping over the mountains, the valley becomes a gigantic stagnant receptacle into which are poured the discharges from millions of chimneys, 15,000 industrial stacks, 1,500,000 home incinerators, and 2,500,000 automobile and truck exhausts.

Nighttime provides only temporary relief. Gentle offshore breezes waft the polluted air out to sea, but it drifts back next morning. Each day adds more airborne waste, so that the longer the inversion exists the worse the pollution becomes. The inversion occurs some 250 days each year.

When smog first appeared in Los Angeles in 1943 no one knew what caused it. At first it was thought to come from the sulfur fumes from the city's huge oil refineries. The oil companies installed six million dollars worth of sulfur-recovery equipment but the smog grew worse.

The mystery was solved in 1950 by Dr. A. J. Haagen-Smit. It had been long known that automobile tires in Southern California did not last as long as tires elsewhere. It was discovered that the cause of the cracking of the tires was ozone. Haagen-Smit suspected that ozone might have something to do with smog, too.

He knew that ozone could be created in a laboratory by subjecting air containing traces of hydrocarbons and nitrogen oxides to strong light. He decided that ozone in Los Angeles air was caused in part by the celebrated California sunshine working on the hydrocarbons which emanated from gasoline in the air. Most of this gasoline comes from exhausts of cars and trucks. Since seven per cent of the gasoline that passes through the average automobile engine escapes through the exhaust unburned, 400,000 gallons of gasoline are being sprayed into the Los Angeles air every day! Nitrogen oxides also are spewed into the air by automobile exhausts and industrial stacks as well as back-yard incinerators.

All the requirements for ozone were thus present in the Los Angeles atmosphere. But with what did it combine to form smog? How about the excess gasoline that had not gone into making ozone? In his laboratory Haagen-Smit poured some gasoline into a beaker, piped ozone over it —and instantly the room was filled with smog, the identical eye-irritating, throat rasping, acrid smog that the Angelenos had been breathing for years.

When the villain[3] in the case was identified, the city took steps to

[3] Dr. Haagen-Smit has modified this appellation in the following way: "I would prefer to speak of a conspiracy of 'villains,' and identify them as hydrocarbons, oxides of nitrogen, ozone and their reaction products. In the formation of L.A. type smog, oxides of nitrogen come first, because they are emitted in all burning processes. With hydrocarbons, oxides of nitrogen react to form ozone in a photochemical reaction. Neither oxides of nitrogen nor ozone are eye-irritating at the concentration

come to grips with it. Now all day long at smog monitoring stations throughout the Los Angeles area, technicians carefully watch their instruments, sending hourly reports to Air Pollution Control headquarters. Summaries are relayed to keep the populace informed.

But identifying the villain is only part of the story. Stopping pollution at its source still seems the prime necessity. It will take bold civic planning and millions of dollars to clear the Los Angeles skies and those of other cities that are fast developing similar problems. Ultimately all cities must realize that air supply, like water supply, has limits, and that they cannot go on forever discharging more and more into their skies without serious consequences to their citizens.

Research goes on apace. Your students may bring to class newspaper and magazine reports on new findings.

Ozone: One of the "Villains." A simple and not too dangerous ozonizer, a form of Cottrell precipitator (Sec. 12-8), can be made by connecting a

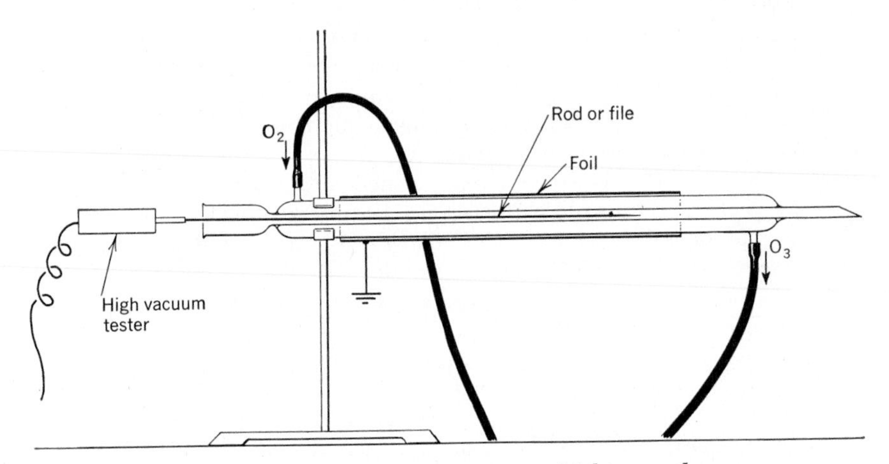

Fig. 12-11. An air ozonizer using a Liebig condenser.

metal rod or round file mounted in the center of a Liebig condenser to a source of high-voltage alternating current (Fig. 12-11). The outside of the condenser is wrapped with tin or copper foil and grounded. Oxygen is passed through the cooling jacket of the condenser instead of water. For best results a condenser should be selected in which the space be-

found in L.A. atmosphere, but the presence of both leads to eye irritation and plant damage because of the simultaneous presence of hydrocarbons."

Dr. W. L. Faith, Managing Director of the Air Pollution Foundation of California, added this statement (in July, 1958): "The big point that we make of all this is that both hydrocarbons (probably certain olefins) and oxides of nitrogen are present, chiefly in automobile exhaust, and therefore the exhaust must be controlled before smog can be banished."

tween the outer jacket and the inner tube is held to a minimum. For a safe source of alternating high voltage, commercial high-vacuum testers such as described in the catalogue of Central Scientific Co. (Sec. 18-3) might be useful.

Producing an Aerosol. An "aerosol" is a minute particle of matter, solid or liquid, so small that it can remain suspended in the air almost indefinitely. In smog, aerosols (which include smoke, dust, mists, and fumes) diffuse light and reduce visibility.

It might be possible to show the typical aerosol formation with gasoline by using the ozone maker described above. Fill a flask with ozone. A drop of gasoline placed in the flask should cause the formation of considerable haze.

A simpler method of showing aerosol formation is to open simultaneously bottles of concentrated ammonium hydroxide and of concentrated hydrochloric acid standing side by side. Almost instantaneously a dense white aerosol of ammonium chloride is formed.

Ozone Detection: Its Cracking Effect on Rubber. The cracking effect of ozone on rubber under tension can be demonstrated by suspending a bent piece of rubber in a flask containing ozone, or by passing ozonized air from the ozone maker (Fig. 12-11) over a bent rubber strip.

If no ozone is available and you live in a region of smog of the Los Angeles type, a cumulative test can be made by hanging a bent loop of rubber outside in a shady spot for about a week and observing the cracks obtained.

Smog's Effect on Plant Growth. The effect of smog on the growth of seedlings might be demonstrated by an interested student. Dr. O. Clifton Taylor, horticulturist at the University of California, Riverside, has shown that smog causes substantial weight losses in grapefruit and lemon seedlings.

12-8. Cleaning Air

Dry Cyclones. This process consists in using revolving jets of air to remove small particles.

Liquid Spray Cleaners. In this method small particles and fumes are washed out of air. The difficulty of removing some effluents by water washes may be shown by blowing cigarette smoke through water.

Charcoal Filters. The efficient action of activated carbon filters can be shown by passing air through a filter of this kind and comparing the results of the tests for solids and gases described in this chapter on filtered and unfiltered air.

Dust Chambers

1. By whirling clouds of fine clay or silica-gel particles, one is able to pick up acids and harmful liquids in smoke.

2. High-frequency sound waves can shake the soot out of smoke.

3. Settling chambers slow the speed of smoke until the heavier particles settle out.

4. Electrostatic precipitators cause smoke particles to coalesce and settle on a charged plate.

The "Oxycat." An "oxycat" invented by E. J. Houdry consists of a catalyst of aluminum and platinum alloys honeycombed in rows and layers inside industrial smokestacks. The noxious solvents are turned back into carbon dioxide and water. This process creates additional heat that can be piped back for useful purposes.

How Dust Particles Are Precipitated. Many manufacturing plants formerly expelled large volumes of smoke, dust, and acid mists from

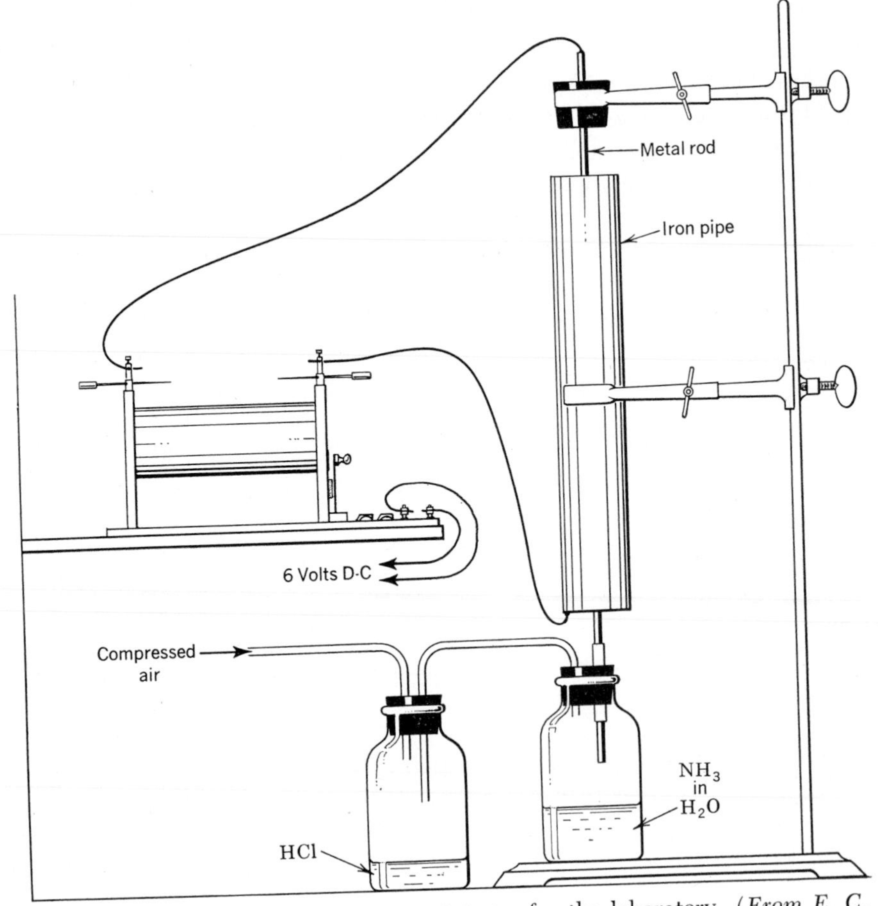

Fig. 12-12. A demonstration dust precipitator for the laboratory. (*From E. C. Weaver and L. S. Foster, Chemistry for Our Times, McGraw-Hill Book Company, Inc., New York, 1954.*)

factory stacks. These expelled products blighted and often poisoned the countryside.

Dr. Frederick G. Cottrell (1877–1948), an American chemist, solved the problem by precipitating the colloidal dust with electricity of high voltage. By using the Cottrell method of coagulation of smoke, smelters and factories have become better neighbors; purer and cleaner chemical products can be made; potash is recovered from the stacks of cement kilns; zinc oxide is salvaged from brass foundries; precious metals are no longer lost from refineries. Small precipitators can be used to keep down household and office dust.

The Cottrell process has not only helped to solve the smoke problem but has actually turned wastes and nuisances into a source of profit. This is indeed both wise and profitable from a resource point of view.

The Cottrell Precipitator: Laboratory Model. Set up the apparatus described under an ozone generator (Sec. 12-7). Do not wrap the entire length of the tube in metal foil but leave a little of the tube free so that students may view what happens on the inside. Use a water suction pump or equivalent to pull a slow, steady stream of air filled with cigarette smoke through the glass tube. Complete the circuit and the smoke-filled tube will immediately clear, as a result of precipitation of the colloidal particles of smoke.

A variation of this model, using ammonium chloride as smoke, which is blown into the smokestack by compressed air, is shown in Fig. 12-12.

12-9. How Can Air Pollution Be Attacked?

On These Fronts. No one way, but at least four are needed:

1. Patrolling for air-pollution offenders.
2. Stopping the spread of air pollution.
3. Carrying on practical scientific work on the causes of and the cures for air pollution.
4. Educating the general public on the problem. This means not only fuel dealers, building managers, installers of combustion equipment, architects, engineers, *but all of us.*

Air Pollution and Us. Unfortunately, but quite probably, much of what happened to the clear skies of Los Angeles is happening to the city in which you live. Already there is mounting smog in New York, Detroit, Chicago, Houston, Philadelphia, Louisville, Des Moines, New Orleans, San Diego, Cincinnati, and many others. The chances are that unless something is done, most of our cities will have crossed the smog threshold in a decade or two, and their citizens will be breathing badly polluted air.

Little is known about the tolerance of living things to various degrees of air pollution. Is there, for instance, some connection between air pollution and lung cancer? Far more research is needed. Ordinarily, given enough space, the pollutant becomes dissipated. But there doesn't seem to be enough space any more. Should we permit the atmosphere over our cities to become almost but not quite lethal before action is taken?

Like water, air belongs to all of us. As with water, we can tolerate only limited amounts of pollution in our air. We use our air, particularly in the big cities, as a huge garbage-disposal system, simply by pouring millions of tons of refuse directly into it.

As we now have water commissions and sanitation laws, each city will need to provide itself with air-pollution-control officials and regulations. Adequate funds and powers will also need to be assured. The entire field of air-pollution control is so new and so complicated, it may be that individual cities or even counties will not be able to cope independently with the many problems that need immediate solution. Perhaps an approach must be made similar to that in other fields of resource conservation: creation of an effective organizational pattern for air resource management, and development of vigorous and imaginative air conservation programs.

We must learn to conserve our air, for its pollution is one of the major threats to the future of our cities. In order to survive, cities must have clean air. Though an ounce of prevention may be costly, it is surely worth the far more expensive pound of cure.

13

Our Mineral Resources: Finding and Identifying Them

Earth's mineral wealth is the subject of this chapter. What minerals are, how they were formed, where they are distributed, how ores may be located, what their properties are—these topics are illustrated with appropriate teaching techniques.

Until recent times, we in America have been tempted to take our resources completely for granted. We recognized that we were a nation unusually wealthy in our mineral resources and we could not quite believe that it might ever be possible to exhaust our stores.

Just as we have had to take thought for our renewable resources, our water and soil, our forests and wildlife, so we are beginning to take stock of the nonrenewables—our rocks and mineral ores, both metallic and nonmetallic, and our fossil fuels.

Nonrenewable resources differ in one important respect from the renewables. Once taken from the earth, they cannot, for countless generations, "grow" again. We "harvest" our crops. We "mine" our minerals. In both instances there can and indeed must be wise management.

OUR MINERAL WEALTH

13-1. To Start the Unit

Some of your students may already be interested in mineral and rock collections. These might be brought to class. Or it may be possible to explore a road cut, bank, cliff, excavation, or quarry for specimens. (Permission should be asked when visiting a quarry.)

Minerals, the inorganic chemical elements or compounds found naturally in the earth, have fairly definite and stable properties. Rocks are the large masses of minerals or mineral-like materials that form so important a part of the earth's crust. They include solid bedrock as well as the unconsolidated debris above it.

You may want to spend a little time on the different kinds of rock to be found on earth. Igneous rocks are formed at high temperatures or from molten materials (Sec. 13-2). Sedimentary rocks are formed and moved from place to place by winds, waves, currents, ice, and gravity (Fig. 7-2). Metamorphic rocks are those which have been altered by heat, pressure, or chemical action. Can your students find examples of the various kinds of rock?

For help in testing, identifying, and classifying rocks and minerals you might want to use as a primer the Golden Nature Guide, *Rocks and Minerals* (Sec. 19-6g).

13-2. How Are Minerals Formed?

The Cooling of Melted Earth Materials. Carefully melt some sulfur in an earthenware crucible or porcelain dish, making sure that it does not catch fire. Cool it, and when a crust forms puncture it and pour off some of the liquid. Students may observe the formation of prismatic crystals on the sides of the evaporating dish (Fig. 13-1).

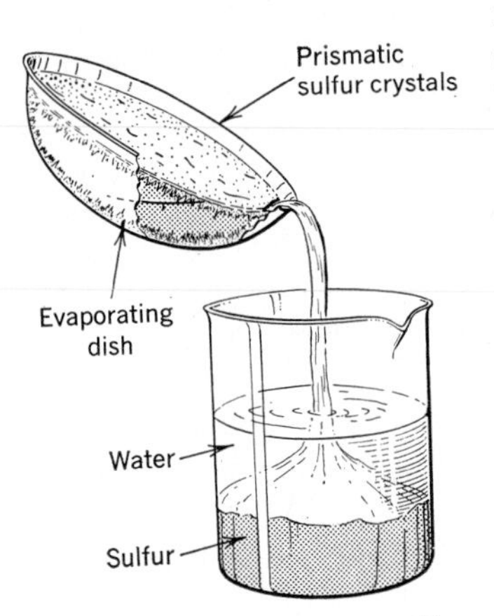

Fig. 13-1. Making sulfur crystals by cooling molten sulfur.

Or this technique might be tried: Melt a thin layer of sulfur on the flat bottom of a crystallizing dish. Then set it on the lantern for vertical projection. In a few seconds, crystals may be seen to branch out from the sides of the dish. Instead of sulfur, melted acetamide may effectively be used to demonstrate crystallization on cooling.

Deposition from Vapors. Heat some flowers of sulfur in a large test tube. Melt and boil the sulfur cautiously. Students may note the deposit of a finely divided yellow powder as the sulfur sublimes on the cool upper portion of the test tube.

Invert a bottle of sulfur dioxide over a bottle of hydrogen sulfide and allow the gases to diffuse for a few minutes. When your students examine the inner walls of the bottles they will find, in addition to a film of moisture, a deposit of finely divided sulfur. It is believed that this is the way sulfur has been formed in volcanic regions.

Deposition from Solutions. Wet a clean lantern-slide cover with a saturated solution of ammonium chloride and warm it over a flame. Then place it in the slide holder of a projection lantern before crystallization starts. Or you might warm a slide and pour on it a solution of salicylic acid. In all these cases crystallization proceeds rapidly, especially if the lantern is warm. The process, of course, may be viewed on the screen.

Growing Crystals. The growing of crystals is an absorbing project that can be done at all levels of science work.

Students may hang a piece of string in a shallow open dish containing a saturated solution of sugar, salt, or copper sulfate. As the crystals grow, students might draw pictures of the crystals and try to identify the crystal systems to which they belong.

In chemistry classes, when studying solutions, solubility curves, etc., students might make up their own solutions for crystal growing. Studying the solubility curve of copper sulfate, for instance (Fig. 13-2), it is seen that about 42 grams of blue vitriol will dissolve in 100 cubic centimeters of water at room temperature. Suppose the student wishes to make up 500 cubic centimeters of stock solution and decides that he will

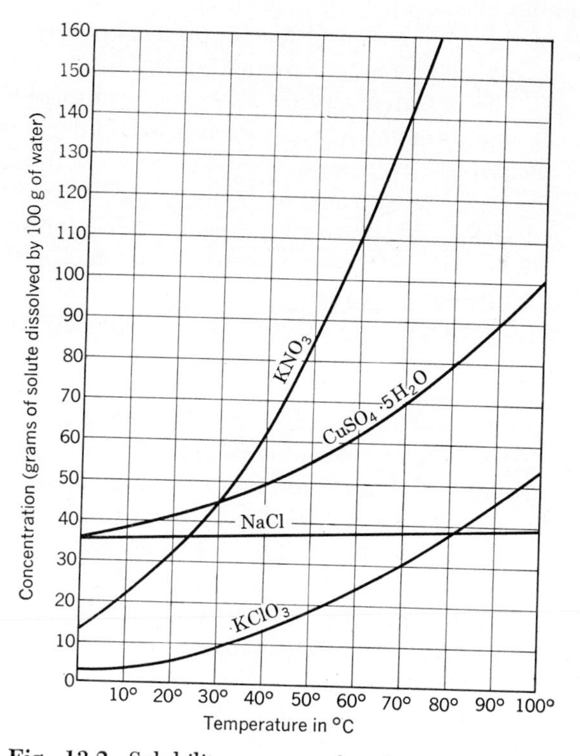

Fig. 13-2. Solubility curves of a few compounds.

need 210 grams of solute. Will that be enough? No, he will need a little more to ensure saturation with slight temperature variations. He will need to crush the powder, heat and stir the solution (why?), and then let it cool to room temperature. Next, he places a little of the solution in a flat-bottomed shallow dish (a crystallizing dish if possible) and leaves it for a day or two. He will usually find some tiny, perfectly shaped crystals. These should be separated out and the other imperfect crystals rejected. Then the "growing" starts in earnest. With two or three seed crystals in the dish, the solution level should be maintained from day to day. The crystals should be turned each day to ensure even growth. In addition, a fine grade of sandpaper may be used to smooth uneven faces.

In one school, crystal growing became quite a hobby in the chemistry class and was passed on from year to year. Students became fascinated and involved as the collection grew. Best results were obtained with copper sulfate, alums of various kinds, potassium dichromate, and potassium ferricyanide. One student, interested in mathematics, made cardboard models of the various crystal forms; another tried to grow model crystals to represent each form; still another grew a potassium alum coating on top of a chrome alum crystal that was efflorescing. Care, patience, and skill were brought to the task and the students enjoyed the continuity of the project, even when they had to leave it. One student, in writing up his report, stressed some of the problems he had encountered and solved in his crystal-growing experience, hoping to help some other student along. His final words were, "Good luck, future crystal grower!"

Crystals from the Sea. Your students may be interested to learn that in studying the earth modern scientists began to work with the deposition of substances from the sea. They learned that when sea water evaporates under natural conditions calcium carbonate is the first solid to separate. As evaporation goes on, gypsum and common salt settle out. Only when the solution is down to 1.54 per cent of its original volume do the potassium and magnesium salts crystallize. This accounts for deposits of these salts in various parts of the world. Students may find out where these deposits are located.

Your students who live near the sea might attempt to do this fractional crystallizing (Sec. 14-13), removing crops of crystals as they form and subjecting them to simple analysis of anions and cations (Sec. 7-11).

Minerals from Plant and Animal Life. Can your students collect samples of stones or minerals that have been formed from the remains of plant and animal life? Most limestones are of marine origin, built up from chemicals supplied by corals, worms, crinoids, mollusks, and algae. Certain samples of coal will also reveal fossils of giant fern.

13-3. Where Are Mineral Ores Found?

Now, you may want to take a look at world geography. Have your students compile a list of the important ores of the world and in what countries they are abundant. The chart shown in Fig. 13-3 will be helpful to

Fig. 13-3. Mineral resources. Self-sufficiency of selected countries in major minerals. (*From F. G. Walton Smith and Henry Chapin, The Sun, The Sea and Tomorrow, Charles Scribner's Sons, New York, 1955.*)

them. This can be brought up to date by consulting the latest *Minerals Yearbook* of the U.S. Bureau of Mines. It is important for students to become aware of the fact that the world situation in regard to minerals is a changing and not a static one.

It will become evident, as your students progress, how particularly rich and blessed our country is in its resources. Yet in late years we have gone from a surplus to a deficit nation in certain raw materials. At the start of the century we produced some 15 per cent more raw materials than we consumed (excluding food); by mid-century we were consuming 10 per cent more materials than we produced.

Your students may be interested in knowing what our present "inventory" is, what our government is doing to enlarge it (Fig. 13-4), what the key commodities are, how the materials problem is really a problem of "costs," and how we may plan for the future. These and many other considerations are covered in *Resources for Freedom*, Summary of Vol. I

Fig. 13-4. In the search for much-needed strategic and critical minerals, Bureau of Mines engineers are engaged in mineral exploratory projects throughout the country. These men are connecting and lowering diamond-drill rods at a manganese deposit in Aroostook County, Maine. (*U.S. Bureau of Mines photo.*)

(Sec. 19-2*f*). Again, it will be necessary to try to bring this material up to date.

13-4. "Prospecting" with Your Class

If your school is located in ore-rich country, then your students can plan to go on field trips which will give them a firsthand view of the way ore is discovered.

If your school is situated so that this kind of field trip is impossible, you can still use ingenuity and go "prospecting." One way that this might be done is for a group of your students to plan a series of demonstrations and talks to illustrate the different methods:

Panning. A student might mix some small pieces of lead shot with some powdered charcoal in a shallow dish or pan. He should then swirl it under running water, allowing the lighter charcoal to run off the top while the heavier lead remains in the dish. The most famous of all prospecting instruments is the miner's pan.

Magnetic Method. Using the iron ore magnetite mixed with gravel and sand, a student may try using a magnet for detection. By means of a compass needle or other magnet, geologists have discovered and mapped the outlines of iron-ore deposits in the Great Lakes district and in other parts of the world.

Gravimeter. When a plumb bob or a pendulum is set up close to a mountainous region, it is deflected from the vertical. This is because the great mass of the mountain exercises gravitational attraction on the pendulum or bob. Similarly, rocks containing minerals (and therefore of high specific gravity) can be detected below the surface by gravity instruments. These instruments are so sensitive that they turn more when near a dense mineral deposit than when close to the surrounding lighter rock. If a gravimeter is available, this might be demonstrated.

Seismograph. This method is more fully described in Sec. 15-9, Prospecting for Petroleum. It is used also to detect the presence of salt domes.

Ultraviolet Detection. Scheelite, an ore of tungsten, and uranium ores are fluorescent and can be made to glow in the dark if placed under an ultraviolet lamp.

Geiger Counter. The presence of uranium ore, which has previously been placed in a pile of rocks, may be detected by means of a Geiger counter.

Geochemical Prospecting. Your students may be interested in following the development of geochemical prospecting for uranium ore. This type of prospecting does not use the Geiger counter for locating deposits deep underground. Instead, small deposits are traced back to the mother lode, much as the gold miners of '49 panned upstream for gold tracings or "colors."

Geochemical prospecting for other ores of heavy metals involves locating traces of ore forming a "halo" in surrounding rock. Figure 13-5 illustrates a test for heavy metals that your students might try if the needed chemicals can be procured. More details of this and other geochemical tests may be found in an article Chemical Prospecting, by

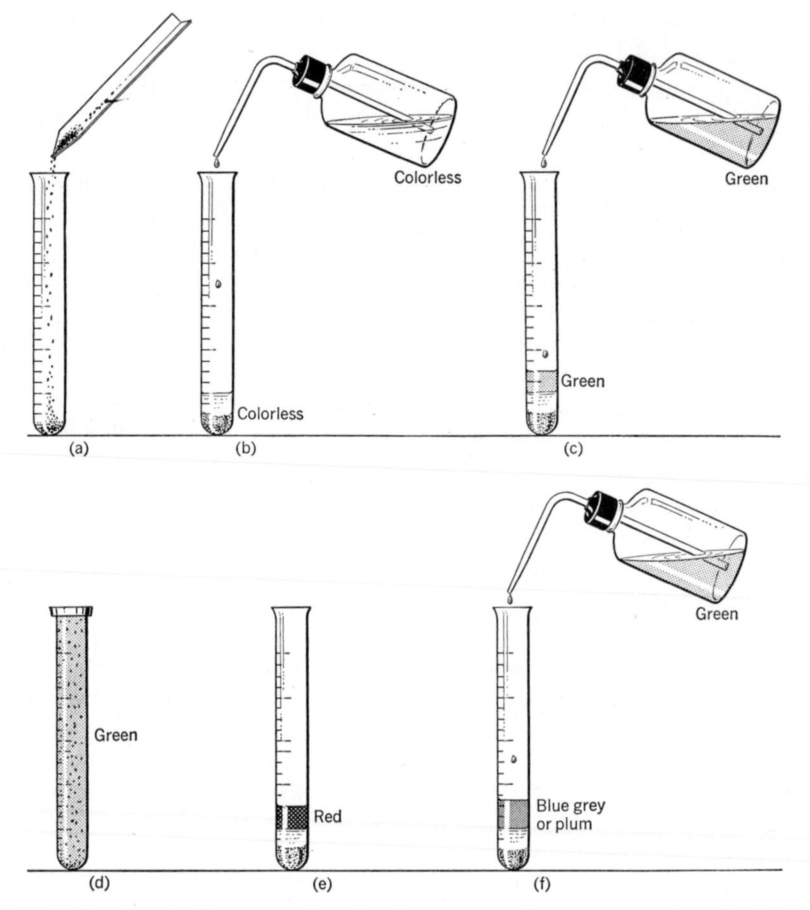

Fig. 13-5. Chemical prospecting for heavy metals—copper, zinc, lead. (*a*) A given amount of stream sediment is placed in a graduated test tube; (*b*) ammonium citrate solution (colorless) is then added to strip the metals from the fine grains of rock and also to maintain the proper acidity; (*c*) a given amount of dithizone (diphenylthiocarbazone) dissolved in xylene (a green solution) is added; it floats on top of the mixture; (*d*) the sample is shaken vigorously for 5 seconds; (*e*) the red color indicates the presence of heavy metals; (*f*) dithizone is then added a drop at a time until the red color of the top layer fades. The total amount of dithizone that must be added to the mixture indicates the amount of the heavy metals present. (*From Scientific American, July, 1957.*)

Harold Bloom and Harold F. Watson in the July, 1957, issue of *Scientific American.*

Prospecting with Plants. If your school is located near any bodies of ore, there is a chance for some interesting research. Professional botanists are busy seeking the correlation between vegetation and ores. It has been known for some time, for instance, that a certain species of violet in Germany is always found near the outcroppings of zinc deposits. It has recently been discovered that over the iron ores in Venezuela the vegetation has a different appearance, with unusual growth forms. This difference can be spotted from the air.

Research in this field is still in its infancy, but its development is of enormous interest to future prospectors. Dr. Richard S. Cowan, Assistant Curator of the New York Botanical Garden, is among others doing pioneer work in this field.

A Method of the Future. A new method of prospecting for hidden mineral deposits may result from discoveries made by scientists at the California Institute of Technology. Studying clues left by nature 250 million years ago, they have found that the location of underground ore is indicated by variations in heavy and light oxygen surrounding the rock. Your students might follow developments in this area and bring reports to class.

13-5. Characteristics of Minerals

Here are a number of ways of identifying minerals by means of their physical and chemical properties:

Hardness. Hardness is the resistance a mineral offers to being scratched. The standard by which minerals are judged is Mohs' scale (Table 13-1).

Table 13-1. The Mohs' Scale of Hardness*

Scale of hardness	*Mineral*	*Scale of hardness*	*Mineral*
1	Talc	6	Orthoclase
2	Gypsum	7	Quartz
3	Calcite	8	Topaz
4	Fluorite	9	Corundum
5	Apatite	10	Diamond

* A mineral softer than 2.5 can be scratched with a fingernail. A copper penny has a hardness of 3 to 3.5. A knife will scratch a mineral with a hardness of 5 to 5.5. A mineral harder than 5.5 will scratch window glass.

Cleavage. Cleavage is the tendency in certain rocks to split and yield a plane surface each time the rock is broken. Your students might illustrate with mica (perfect cleavage in one direction); feldspar (cleavage in two directions); rock salt (cleavage in three directions).

Fracture. Fracture is the characteristic appearance of the surface of a mineral when it breaks in any other direction than along a cleavage plane. Mineralogists use the words splintery, rough, or smooth to describe fracture.

Luster. Luster is the quality of the surface of a mineral in regard to the kind and intensity of the light it reflects. Such words as glassy (quartz or fluorite), metallic (pyrite or galena), earthy (limonite), and pearly (gypsum and barite) are used to describe luster.

Streak. Streak is the color of a mineral's powder. Students may determine streak by rubbing a specimen across a hard white surface like a piece of unglazed porcelain tile. Some minerals have a characteristic streak (hematite's is cherry red); others have none.

Color. Color alone is not a great aid in the identification of most minerals, for so many of them have color varieties. (Students may illustrate this with various samples of quartz.) Color may help, however, when used along with other characteristics.

Fusibility. Using small, thin splinters of the mineral, students may try to melt them in a blowpipe flame (Fig. 13-6). The seven-point fusibility scale is given in Table 13-2.

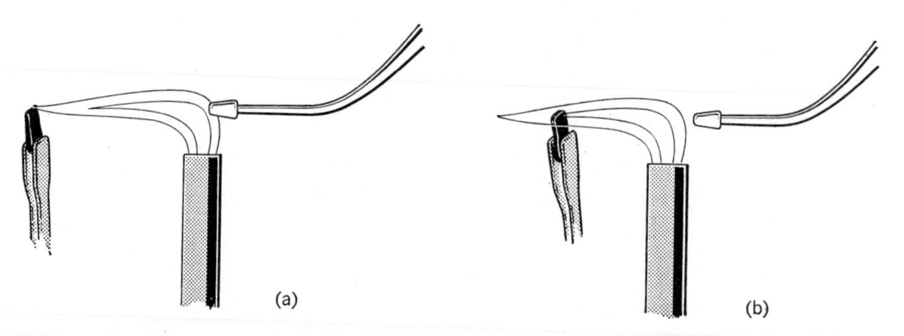

Fig. 13-6. Melting a mineral in a blowpipe flame. (*a*) An oxidizing flame; (*b*) a reducing flame.

Specific Gravity. The determination of the specific gravity of mineral rocks is an interesting experiment in physics. By definition, specific gravity is the weight of a substance compared to the weight of an equal bulk of water.

If your students wish to find the specific gravity of a mineral heavier than water and insoluble in it, there are two methods that may be employed. (For the specific gravity of a substance lighter than water, see Sec. 10-11.)

1. Weigh the mineral in grams. Place the mineral in a graduated

Table 13-2. Fusibility Scale of Minerals

No.	Mineral	Fusibility	Temperature, °C
1	Stibnite	Fuses very easily in candle flame	525
2	Chalcopyrite	A small fragment fuses easily in bunsen-burner flame	800
3	Almandite	Infusible in bunsen-burner flame, fuses easily in blowpipe flame	1050
4	Actinolite	A sharp-pointed splinter fuses easily with blowpipe	1200
5	Orthoclase	The edges of fragments are rounded with difficulty in a blowpipe flame	1300
6	Bronzite	Only the thinnest edges of splinters are rounded with blowpipe	1400
7	Quartz	Infusible in blowpipe flame	1710

cylinder of water and read the level of the water before and after, in cubic centimeters. The difference will represent the volume of the mineral. Since 1 cubic centimeter of water weighs 1 gram, calculate the weight of the water displaced. Then divide the weight of the object by the weight of the equal bulk of water to obtain its specific gravity.

$$\text{Specific gravity} = \frac{\text{weight of object}}{\text{weight of equal volume of water}}$$

2. If your students have studied Archimedes' principle, then they know that the weight of water the mineral displaces is the same as its loss of weight in water. Therefore

$$\text{Specific gravity} = \frac{\text{weight of object}}{\text{loss of weight in water}}$$

Weigh the mineral in and out of water. Find its loss of weight and finally its specific gravity.

Although the specific gravity of some minerals may vary as much as 25 per cent from specimen to specimen, Table 13-3 should prove helpful.

13-6. Soil: Our Most Important "Rock"

This might be a time to review the fact that soil originates from rocks (Sec. 7-2). It is actually the best known and most complex "rock" there is. What other material factors contribute to soil making?

If there is a road cut nearby, perhaps your students can get samples of the bedrock with hammer and cold chisel. They might then try to identify this rock by means of the various tests described in this chapter. The chemical composition of the residual soil depends largely on the rock

Table 13-3. Minerals Arranged According to Increasing Specific Gravity

Mineral	*Specific gravity*	*Mineral*	*Specific gravity*	*Mineral*	*Specific gravity*
Borax	1.7	Wollastonite	2.8	Pyrite	5.02
Sulfur	2.05	Aragonite	2.94	Magnetite	5.18
Halite	2.16	Magnesite	3.0	Zincite	5.68
Gypsum	2.32	Apatite	3.15	Scheelite	5.9
Serpentine	2.50–2.65	Topaz	3.4	Galena	7.4
Orthoclase	2.56	Garnet	3.5	Cinnebar	8.1
Kaolinite	2.6	Azurite	3.77	Copper	8.9
Quartz	2.65	Spinel	3.6–4.1	Silver	10.5
Calcite	2.71	Corundum	4.02	Gold	15–19
Talc	2.75	Chalcopyrite	4.1	Platinum	14–19

from which it comes. Students might see whether they can identify by soil tests (Sec. 7-11) chemicals from the parent rock.

IDENTIFYING METALLIC MINERALS

13-7. Treatment with Acids

A few minerals effervesce when dilute hydrochloric acid is applied, and this makes a useful test (Sec. 7-11). Limestone effervesces vigorously whereas a sample of dolomite effervesces slowly in cold acid. If the acid is heated, however, or the mineral powdered, a vigorous action takes place. Your students may want to identify the gas by passing it through limewater and obtaining the characteristic milkiness imparted by carbon dioxide. Students can also check the difference between limestone and dolomite by identifying the calcium in the limestone.

Some minerals will form colored solutions when treated with nitric acid. For example, put some crushed rock specimens containing copper into a large Pyrex test tube. To this add nitric acid. Does the solution turn blue, indicating copper? Also test crushed rock samples that lack copper, so that students may see the results when this specific metal is absent from rock. Textbooks in mineralogy, metallurgy, or geology describe many tests of this sort.

13-8. Blowpipe Tests

Students may learn to use a blowpipe with a candle, an alcohol lamp, or a gas flame. First have them become familiar with an oxidizing flame, (Fig. 13-6*a*), in which the oxygen is supplied by the oxidized gases as well as the air blown into the flame. Then study a reducing flame (Fig. 13-6*b*), in which hot unburned gases withdraw oxygen from the specimen.

A small hollow is made near the end of a charcoal block and the pow-

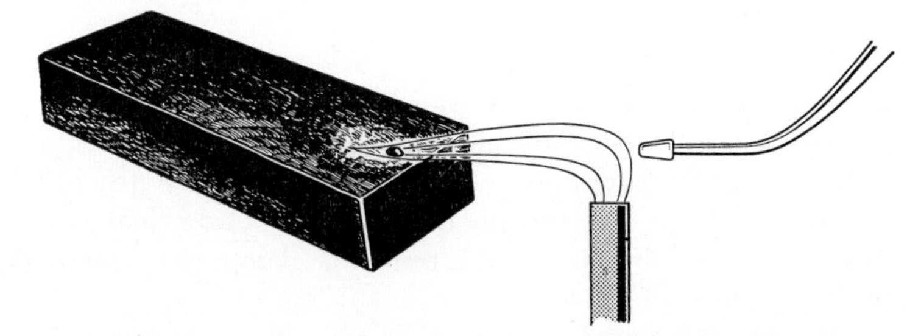

Fig. 13-7. Heating an ore on charcoal with a reducing flame.

dered specimen set in the cavity. Then the blowpipe flame is directed on the specimen, which is heated until changes become visible (Fig. 13-7). These changes may include a fine, colored coating or sublimate, a bead of the metal, or characteristic fumes. Students may be referred to textbooks in mineralogy or metallurgy for identifying the behavior of various minerals.

13-9. Bead Tests

Students may heat a bit of powdered borax in a small loop of platinum wire until a glassy bead is formed. The hot borax (called a flux) is touched to a trace of the powdered mineral and the bead is then heated in an oxidizing flame. The experiment is repeated, but this time a reducing flame is used. In each case, the color of the bead is noted, when hot and when cold. Students may refer to Table 13-4 for identification of the metal.

Table 13-4. Bead Test Colors of Certain Metals

	Oxidizing flame		Reducing flame	
Metal	Hot	Cold	Hot	Cold
Antimony	Yellow	Colorless	Yellow	Colorless
Chromium	Yellow	Green	Green	Green
Cobalt	Blue	Blue	Blue	Blue
Copper	Green	Blue	Colorless	Brown
Iron	Yellow	Green	Green	Green
Manganese	Violet-brown	Violet	Colorless	Colorless
Molybdenum	Yellow	Colorless	Brown	Brown
Nickel	Violet	Brown	Colorless-gray	Colorless-gray
Titanium	Colorless	Colorless-white	Yellowish-gray	Yellow
Tungsten	Yellow	Colorless	Yellow	Brown
Uranium	Yellow	Yellowish-brown	Green	Green
Vanadium	Yellow	Green	Brown	Green

SOURCE: After M. Zim, *Blowpipe Analysis and Tests for Common Minerals*, 1935.

13-10. Tube Tests

These tests consist in heating powdered minerals in open and closed tubes to see what sublimates are deposited in the upper, cooler portion of the tube, and what fumes and odors are given off. A Pyrex test tube with just enough powdered mineral to cover the bottom makes a good closed tube. It is held, by means of a test tube clamp, at a low angle in a bunsen flame (Fig. 13-8*a*).

A piece of glass tubing, about 6 inches long, either straight or bent, is suitable for the open tube. The powdered mineral, placed about an inch

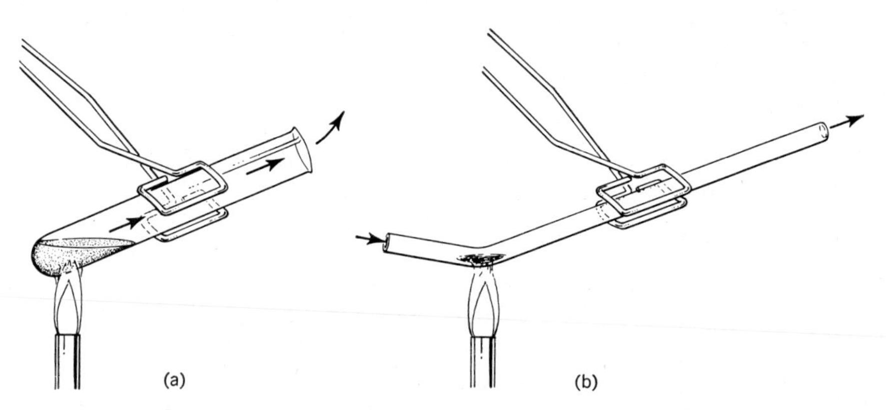

Fig. 13-8. Tube tests. (*a*) A closed tube (Pyrex test tube); (*b*) an open tube (glass tubing).

from the lower end, is heated as in Fig. 13-8*b*. The mineral is oxidized by the air passing over it. Students may observe the sublimates forming at the cool end of the tube.

13-11. Flame Tests and Spectra

No part of a chemistry course is more fascinating than work with flame tests and spectra. The flame coloration of metallic ions as well as the cobalt glass detection of potassium can be accomplished with a minimum of equipment. If, in addition, you have a small, direct-vision spectroscope, it may be shared and the laboratory work so staggered that all your students will have some experience with this instrument (Sec. 7-11, footnote 3).

Flame Coloration. Place on clean watch glasses the chlorides (nitrates or carbonates may be used as substitutes) of the following metallic elements: (*a*) sodium, (*b*) potassium, (*c*) lithium, (*d*) calcium, (*e*) strontium, and (*f*) barium. Moisten each salt with dilute hydrochloric acid. Clean a platinum wire by dipping it alternately in dilute hydrochloric acid (in a test tube or dish) and the bunsen flame until it produces no flame coloration. Then, beginning with sodium chloride, obtain in turn the flame coloration of each of the salts as listed. To do this, dip the platinum wire in the moistened salt and hold it in the front edge of the lowest part of the flame. Be sure to clean the wire carefully each time before starting with the next salt.

Spectra. Mount a direct-vision spectroscope in a burette clamp on a ring stand in a dark room or in any dark part of the laboratory. Direct the spectroscope toward the upper half of the blue flame of a bunsen burner, and have students observe and explain what they see. Students may produce, in turn, the flame coloration of each of the six metallic

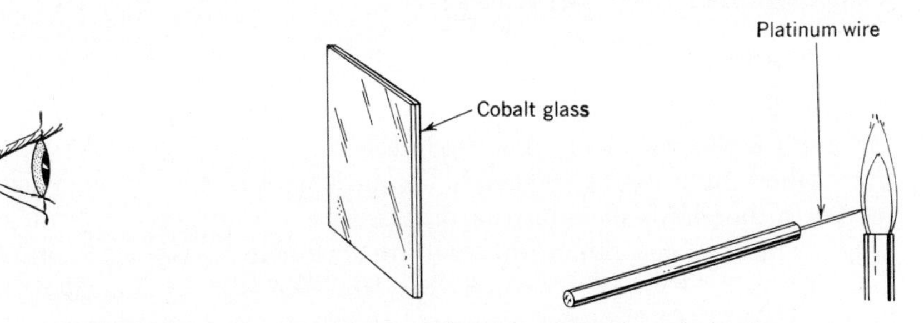

Fig. 13-9. Observing flame coloration through cobalt glass.

elements used above and observe the lines or bands of color that constitute its spectrum. They may then compare the spectrum in each case with that of the same element found in a textbook or wall chart. Sketches of the spectra may be made in color. If your students have taken a course in physics, they may interpret the flame coloration in each case with the aid of the spectrum of the particular element.

Detection of Potassium with Cobalt Glass. Students may observe the flame coloration of each of the above elements through two layers of cobalt glass (Fig. 13-9). They will note how the potassium flame thus observed appears bright lavender, while the other flames are practically blocked out. Students may learn to recognize potassium by this method even when it is mixed with other of the elements. Ask them to interpret the results thus obtained with the cobalt glass, using the spectrum of potassium obtained from a chart. (The small, direct-vision spectroscope seldom reveals the bluish-violet hue in the potassium spectrum.)

Detection of Elements in an Unknown Mixture. Give each student or a student team two "unknowns" composed of a mixture of several different salts. Taking the unknowns one at a time and using all the above procedures, ask your students to determine which of the above six metallic elements are present in the mixture. Ask them to report their findings.

The detection of elements in an unknown mixture is particularly interesting and challenging to students. In one school, three different unknown mixtures are made up and small samples given to individual students in specimen tubes with a code number on a gummed label affixed to each tube. This experiment is followed by another containing unknown mixtures with both positive and negative ions (Sec. 7-11), as well as certain carbohydrates (Sec. 8-14) and sulfur. This gives students an experience in simple qualitative analysis.

SOME NONMETALLIC MINERALS

13-12. Sulfur

Sulfur is one of the most important substances we get from the earth because it is the raw material needed in the manufacture of sulfuric acid, often called the "king of chemicals." Sulfuric acid is used in one way or another in hundreds of industrial processes.

Your students may know that we are fortunate in having enormous sulfur deposits in Louisiana and Texas. How this sulfur is mined by the Frasch process and how it is converted to sulfuric acid are demonstrated in Sec. 14-13.

13-13. Borax

Borax, or sodium tetraborate, once hauled from Death Valley, California, by twenty-mule teams, comes mostly from brines and dry lake beds where ground water has concentrated it. Students might bring in samples of borax and boric acid.

Borax, used in making glass and enamels and in chemical industries, has suddenly found new use, in the form of boranes, as high-energy fuel for modern jet aircraft.

Borax is just one illustration of how an old resource may overnight become a new and more valuable resource.

13-14. Common Salt

Common salt, or sodium chloride, has been an important resource since prehistoric days. Elicit from your students that its chief uses are for nutrition and industry (Sec. 5-14).

All salt deposits are believed to have come originally from the sea (Sec. 13-2). Students might make a solution of rock salt and evaporate it in the sun or over a flame. Might this action account for salt deposits from dried-up seas?

13-15. Fossil Fuels

Coal. Can students justify the statement that coal is the fuel that made the industrial revolution possible?

Coal, formed from the altered remains of plants by a slow series of changes, is classified by moisture content, volatile matter, fixed carbon, and ash (Sec. 15-8). Students might learn the difference between lignite, bituminous, and anthracite coals. Can samples of each be procured?

Where is coal found in America (Fig. 13-10*a*)? Where else in the world? The world's reserves of coal are estimated roughly at 7 trillion tons, with over half of the total reserve in America. Is it at present practicable to mine all these coal deposits? What is a critical factor?

Petroleum. How petroleum is believed to have been formed might be shown through the film *Prospecting for Petroleum* (Shell Oil Company, with distribution centers in San Francisco, Houston, Chicago, and New York).

Petroleum is an example of a resource that was not a resource at all until a century ago. Can students explain this statement?

Where petroleum has been found in the United States is shown in Fig. 13-10*b*. How petroleum is mined and purified and what the situation is in regard to reserves is discussed in detail in Chapter 15.

Before the invention of the automobile, what was the most valuable product of petroleum distillation? What is that product now? What are the uses of petroleum aside from fuel production? Here is another illustration of the changing value of a resource as new uses develop.

Oil Shale. Although deposits of these oil-bearing rocks occur in Colorado, Utah, and Wyoming, they cannot at present compete with our rich oil "pools."

A student might report on the experimental plant for producing oil from oil shale that was in operation during World War II.

Here is an example of a resource held in reserve, ready to be used in time of emergency.

Natural Gas. This gas is often found along with petroleum (Fig. 13-10*c*). A mixture of the lighter chemicals found in petroleum, its chief constituent is methane (Sec. 15-10). Another resource, helium, is sometimes found with natural gas. For what is helium important? Aside from the use of natural gas as a gaseous fuel and sometimes as a liquefied one, natural gas gasoline is an important by-product. Students might note that here is still another source of the presently all-important automotive engine fuel.

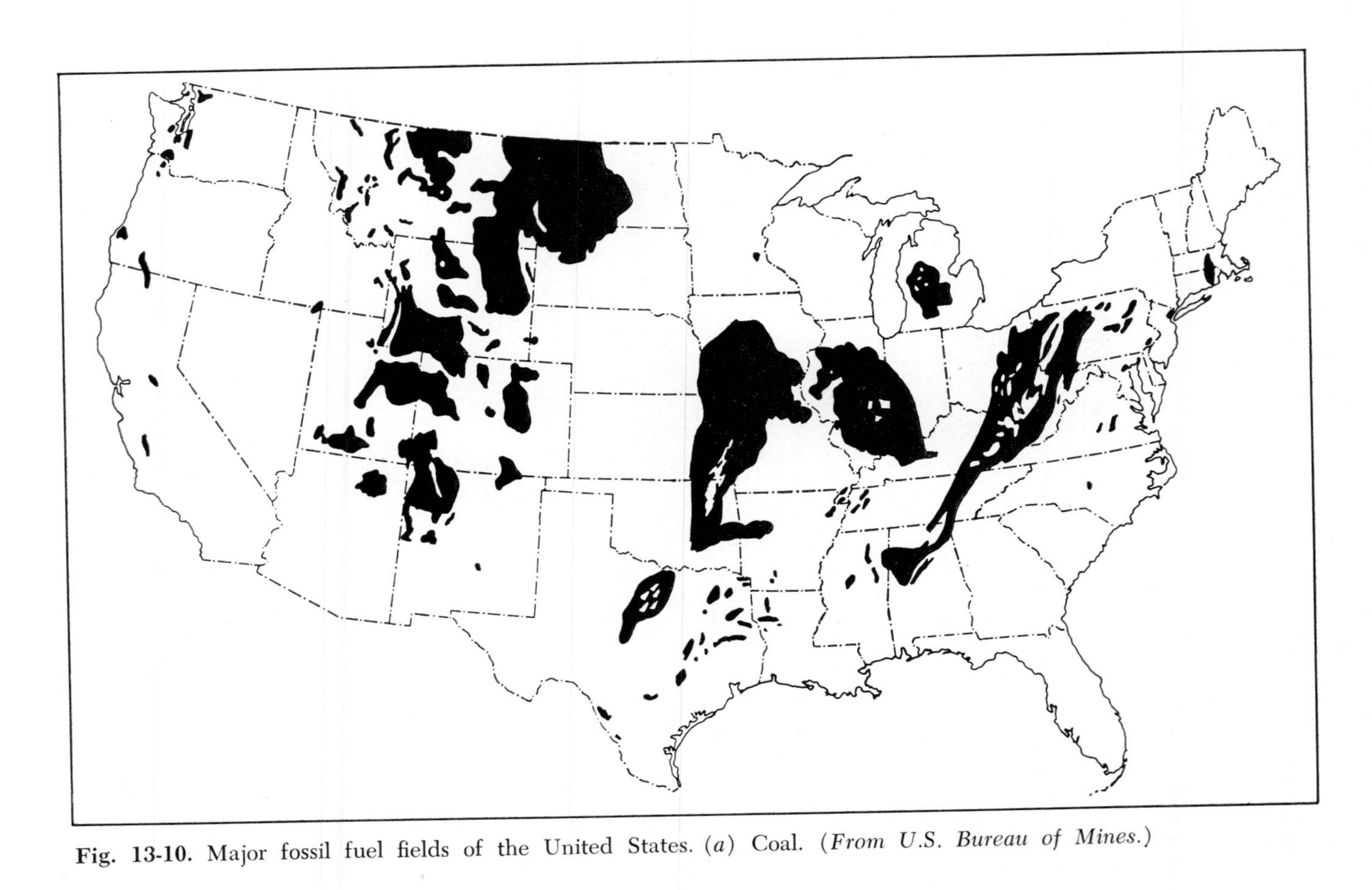

Fig. 13-10. Major fossil fuel fields of the United States. (*a*) Coal. (*From U.S. Bureau of Mines.*)

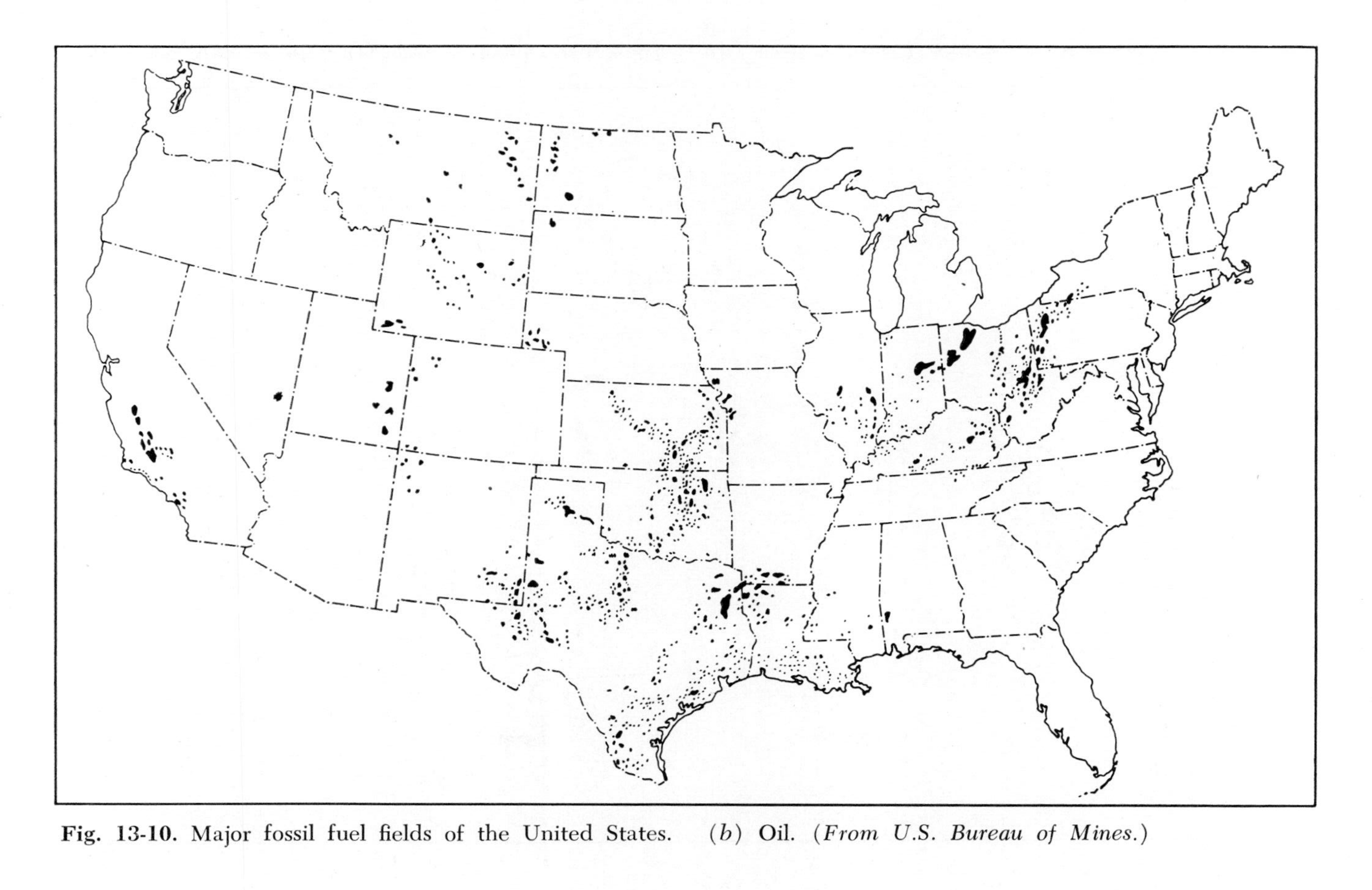

Fig. 13-10. Major fossil fuel fields of the United States. (*b*) Oil. (*From U.S. Bureau of Mines.*)

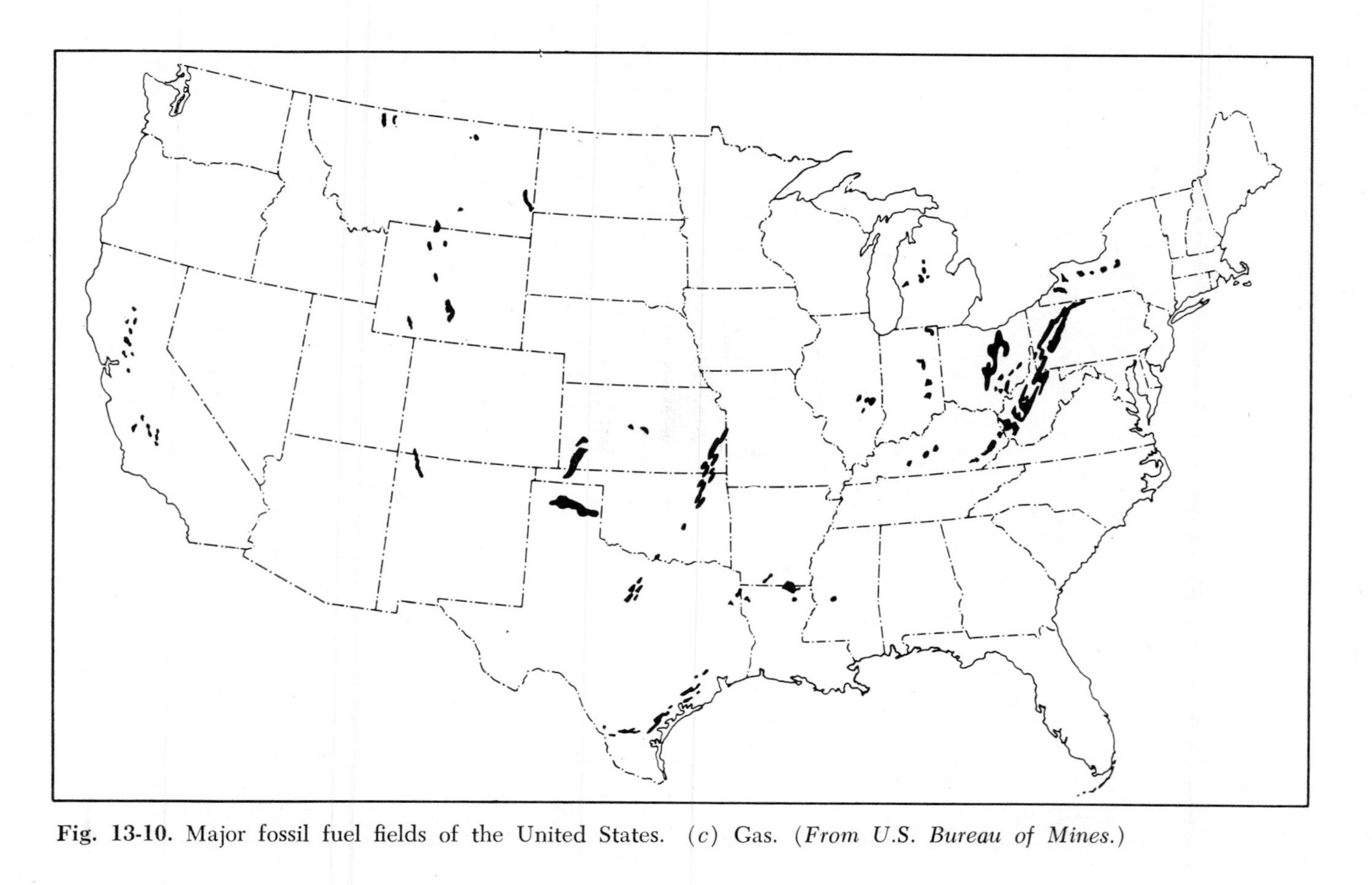

Fig. 13-10. Major fossil fuel fields of the United States. (*c*) Gas. (*From U.S. Bureau of Mines.*)

CONSTRUCTION MATERIALS

Sand, gravel, clays, cements, and building stones are resources with enormous over-all value because of the amounts used for roads, bridges, and buildings.

13-16. Sand, Gravel, Crushed Rock

With what kind of sand are your students familiar—ocean and beach sand, glacial sand, river sand and gravel? Of what are sands made? Students might perform various of the physical and chemical tests described in this chapter on the sand, gravel, and crushed rock available in the vicinity. They may want to try making mortar or cement (Sec. 14-14) if the proper materials are available.

13-17. Clay

Clay used by primitive man for his pottery is still essential in many industries. Your students may know that its most important use is for ceramics of various kinds—from chinaware, to bricks, to drilling mud.

Most if not all of your students will be familiar with the properties of clay, slippery when moist and cohesive when dry. An exhibit of products using clay as a base might be collected and displayed by a student group.

13-18. Building Stones

Your students may be aware that stones and rocks are the oldest building materials known and that they are still much used in modern construction because of their strength and durability. An exhibit of the various kinds of building stones might be displayed by students.

The durability of a particular kind of stone depends on its chemical composition, physical structure, the ease with which it absorbs water, and the kind of atmospheric conditions to which it is exposed.

Effect of Absorbed Water. Recall with your students that absorbed water affects the endurance of rocks or stones because it freezes during cold weather, causing an expansion which weakens and crumbles the rock (Sec. 7-2).

The Barrd test is an interesting way to show the effect of frost on rocks. Into a boiling concentrated solution of sodium sulfate or Glauber's salt, immerse weighed small pieces of rock. Then hang them up to dry for 3 days. As the water evaporates, crystals of the salt are left in the pores of the rock, forcing small bits or sometimes larger sections to drop off. If the rocks are weighed after this treatment, the loss of weight will show the amount of disintegration, which is the same as is normally caused by frost. In general, the greater the loss of weight, the poorer the quality of the stone.

Effect of Acid. Students may pour dilute acid on various kinds of stone and note the action: an intense evolution of carbon dioxide will be given off if there is a large percentage of carbonate rocks in the sample (Sec. 7-11). Outdoors, if water contains dissolved acids, it will bring about rapid decomposition of limestones and marbles.

Effect of Smoke. The atmosphere of a large city with much smoke will contain enough sulfuric acid to affect the endurance of limestone or marble. The ability of a particular kind of stone to withstand the effects of a smoky atmosphere can be tested by soaking a sample for several days in a 1 per cent solution of sulfuric acid. If the stone contains materials likely to be affected by the gases of the atmosphere, the solution will become cloudy. Here is an opportunity to stress one of the damages caused by polluted air (Sec. 12-5).

In concluding this phase of the study of our mineral resources, you may wish to emphasize that the important minerals and construction materials of tomorrow may not necessarily be the ones in use today. Scientists may learn, for instance, how to utilize common, abundant rocks in place of minerals in short supply. In the meantime it behooves us, in the words of Dr. Thomas Nolan, Director of the U.S. Geological Survey, to "use wisely our presently used resources."

14

Our Mineral Resources: Processing and Using them

In this chapter we deal with the way man converts minerals to his own uses. Included are the wresting of a metal from its ore and the making of alloys for special properties and purposes. The story of iron and steel has been chosen because of the importance of these substances to almost every phase of modern life.

Corrosion, one of the chief ways in which metals are wasted and made useless, is given special attention. This is followed by consideration of the methods by which scientists have learned and are still learning to protect metals. This kind of prolonged usefulness is illustrative of a significant conservation measure.

A few nonferrous metals and selected nonmetallic products, important in today's technology, have been chosen for study. Finally, a section is devoted to substitution products with their increasingly important role in today's economy and in the conservation outlook.

FROM ORE TO METAL

14-1. Whatever the Minerals

Whatever the minerals your class is studying, you may want to emphasize these phases of their technology and the resource problems presented:

1. **Abundance of the mineral and where it is found**
2. **How it is mined and processed**
3. **What its most important uses are**
4. **How the product is protected against weathering and corrosion**
5. **How the supply may be renewed by the recovery of scrap**

6. How more abundant materials may be substituted for dwindling supplies

7. How research is improving technology—by more efficient and newer methods, by use of low-grade ores, by recycling, and by finding use for waste products

14-2. Mining an Ore

If your school is near a mine, then a field trip will be the most vivid way of learning how ores are removed from the earth. Strip and open-pit mining present special problems, as will be evidenced by devastated countrysides (Fig. 14-1). A visit to a shaft mine can sometimes be arranged if proper precautions are taken.

How efficient are mining operations? How safe are they? Are the ores being mined still rich or are they low-grade? Has mechanization taken the place of other methods?

If you cannot visit a mine then you might want to show the mining

Fig. 14-1. The once-green valley of an anthracite town now bears gashes and scars of strip mines and culm heaps. (*Picture taken on a field trip to the town of Dupont, Pa., by Fieldston School students and teachers.*)

process in a film like *Lead from Mine to Metal* (U.S. Bureau of Mines; each state has its own distribution center for these films).

14-3. Metallurgy

Preliminary Treatment. Ores, particularly low-grade ones, are found mixed with rock and earthy material called gangue, which is of no value. It is usually economical to concentrate the ore before it is shipped to the smelters where the metal is extracted. One method of concentrating the ore is called the flotation process.

A pinch of red lead in 100 milliliters of water may be shaken in a 125-milliliter flask that has been stoppered. When the mixture has been standing for about half a minute, pour the suspension of fine particles into a 100-milliliter cylinder. To this add about 2 teaspoons of sand and 2 milliliters of oil, then stopper the cylinder and shake it. Students may note that much of the red lead has been adsorbed on the oil and is floating to the top of the cylinder.

Students might bring to class reports on the sintering and pelletizing of ores to prevent waste and to increase efficiency in handling. How important are these treatments as conservation measures?

Extracting the Metal. There are three important methods of extracting a metal from its ore. These are illustrated as follows:

Reducing a Metallic Oxide. To show the reducing action of *carbon*, students might try this experiment. Make a small hole in a charcoal block about 1 centimeter in diameter and 1 centimeter deep. Fill the hole with lead oxide, PbO, and moisten the oxide with a drop of water. Heat the oxide with a blowpipe (Fig. 13-7) until a small globule of metallic lead is formed.

Or mix loosely together in a mortar 4 grams of red lead, Pb_3O_4, with 1 gram of powdered wood charcoal, stirring the two powders briefly to secure a rough, streaky mixture. Put the mixture into an old crucible and heat strongly with the cover off for 15 minutes in the hottest part of a bunsen flame. Cool, and empty the contents of the crucible into an evaporating dish. Swirl the dish and its contents under the running water of a faucet so as to wash the lighter charcoal particles away from the heavier metal particles, as in placer mining. How has the metal been produced?

To illustrate the use of *aluminum* in the reduction of metallic oxides, this makes a striking demonstration: Protect the bottom of an iron pan with a piece of asbestos. Cover this with fine sand, building up the sand around the sides. Into this sand dish put 10 grams of thermit, $Fe_2O_3 + Al$. Make a little depression in the top of this pile of thermit and put into it 1 gram of "ignition" powder, $Na_2O_2 + Al$ or $BaO_2 + Mg$. Into the ignition powder stick a strip of magnesium ribbon (Fig. 14-2). Place the dish and contents on six layers of asbestos in a hood or other safe place. Use caution throughout this experiment. Light the magnesium with a match or bunsen flame. Stand back, as the action is violent. Students

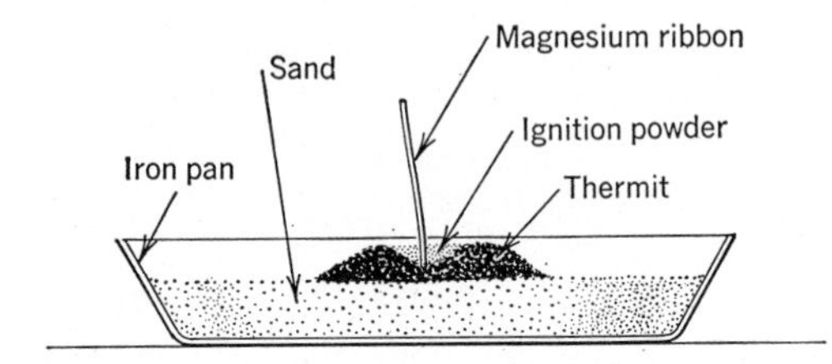

Fig. 14-2. Aluminum as a reducing agent: the thermit reaction.

may explain the use of the substance for igniting the thermit. Ask students to examine the slag and steel button, using a magnet to identify the steel.

This experiment shows what a powerful reducing agent aluminum is. The reaction produces a temperature so high that liquid iron forms. Have your students ascertain that this reaction is useful in welding rails, shafts, etc.

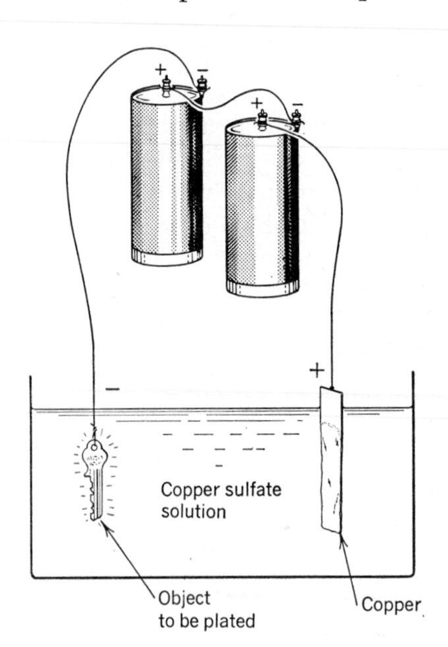

Fig. 14-3. Deposition of copper by electrolysis.

The same reaction enters into the preparation of manganese, titanium, tungsten, molybdenum, chromium, and uranium from their oxides. When a mixture of powdered aluminum and the oxide is ignited the free metal is produced.

Roasting and Reduction. Put a little lead sulfide in a porcelain crucible and mount it on a pipestem triangle. Heat the crucible as hot as possible for a few minutes. Ask students to smell the evolving gas cautiously. Can they identify it? Students may write the equation for the roasting process. It might be interesting to reduce with charcoal the residue left.

Electrolysis. Place a solution of copper sulfate acidified with dilute sulfuric acid in a small glass tank or tumbler. (Various concentrations of copper sulfate solution might be tried.) Using a key as the cathode and a strip of copper for the anode, connect them both to a source of direct current such as two dry cells (Fig. 14-3) or a 110-volt d-c line with a 60-watt lamp in series. When the current has flowed for about 5 minutes it should be shut off and the electrodes removed from the solution. Rinse them and ask your students to examine them carefully, noting the metallic deposit on the cathode. Can they identify the copper? Now your class should be ready to discuss how the copper got there. The copper may be removed from the electrode by reversing the current and making the plated electrode the anode. This might lead to a discussion of the electrolytic refining of copper.

Purification of Extracted Metals. Your students may want to discuss the reasons why metals, when extracted from the ore, need further purification in order to be useful. Why, for instance, is pig iron not suitable for most purposes? How may pig iron be converted into steel?

14-4. Characteristics of Metals[1]

Metallic Luster. Students may examine freshly polished surfaces of various metals like iron and copper and notice their particular luster. Freshly cut sodium has a luster, too. These metals reflect light from a polished surface quite like an ordinary mirror.

Ductility. Samples of copper or iron wire will illustrate that metals can be drawn out into wires.

Malleability. Students may take a piece of lead shot and flatten it with a hammer. Gold, too, is particularly malleable.

Conductivity. Place an iron rod horizontally on a ring clamped to a ring stand, tape a thin sliver of paraffin wax near one end, and heat the other end. The experiment might be repeated using a glass rod in place of the iron rod. Students will note the difference in the time taken to melt the wax.

Students may set up simple experiments to show that various kinds of metallic wires conduct electricity. By using a current-measuring instrument and wires of the same thickness, they may determine which metals are the best conductors.

What about nonmetals? Do they conduct electricity? Students might experiment to find the answer.

Hardness. Each metallic sample to be studied may be scratched with a sharp knife or the mineral hardness test (Sec. 13-5) applied to determine its hardness.

Ease of Melting. Students might hold each sample in turn, by means of a forceps, in the hottest part of a hot flame, perhaps from a Meker

[1] For a pamphlet giving rapid identification or spot testing of some metals and alloys, write to the Development and Research Division, The International Nickel Company, Inc., 67 Wall St., New York.

burner. Have them look up in the appropriate text or handbook the melting points of the various metals.

Cation Formation. Students will recall the deposition of copper from a copper sulfate solution on the cathode of an electrolytic cell (Sec. 14-3). Similarly, such metals as chromium, silver, or nickel may be deposited from water solutions of their compounds.

Metals in solutions form positive ions, or, to express it otherwise, the atoms tend to lose electrons, becoming cations. Students might experiment with various kinds of electroplating. Nickel on copper and copper on nickel may be found in *Test It Yourself* (Sec. 19-2*w*).

Is electroplating ever used in order to cover and protect another metal? Students might scratch a tin can and try to expose the iron underneath. How rapidly will this iron rust when unprotected? In what way is tin plating a conservation measure?

SELECTED METALS AND ALLOYS

14.5. The Story of Iron and Steel

Metallurgy. Some time is spent in most chemistry courses on the metallurgy of iron and the manufacture of steel, because of the importance of this metal to our industrial economy.

In studying the blast furnace in the making of pig iron, these might be some of the leading questions to stimulate thought:

1. What ore of iron is used in the process?
2. What principle is used in the metallurgy?
3. What is the fuel? The reducing agent? What keeps the "blast" going?
4. What other raw material is needed in the operation?
5. What is its purpose? In what form do all the raw materials that enter the furnace leave it? Where do they leave it?
6. Why is most pig iron further purified?
7. How is this accomplished?

You may obtain from United States Steel Corporation, 71 Broadway, New York, a list of their free materials, movies, visual aids, and pamphlets on all phases of the industry. An excellent movie to show is *The Drama of Steel* (U.S. Bureau of Mines).

Our Supply. Have your class learn about the present iron ore situation. What is happening to our high-grade deposits? How much ore do we import? How is research finding answers to the use of lower-grade ore? Have a student report on the story of the development of taconite ores. Have students learn, too, of the technological improvements that are constantly increasing the efficiency of mining and metallurgical processes. Why may these be considered conservation measures?

What are the other raw materials essential to the metallurgy of iron (Fig. 14-4)? Are they in abundant supply? From where do they come? What are some of the factors that determine where ironworks and steel mills are located? These are a few of the many questions that will bring

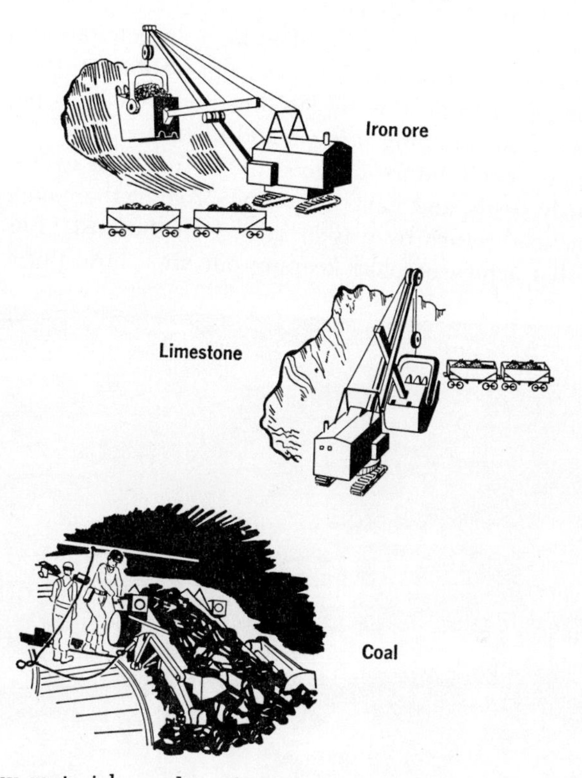

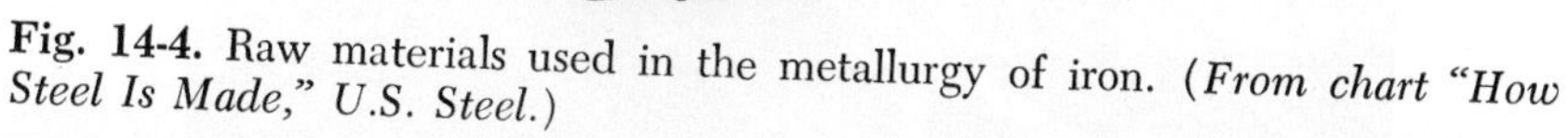

Fig. 14-4. Raw materials used in the metallurgy of iron. (*From chart "How Steel Is Made," U.S. Steel.*)

students face to face with some of the realities of our nonrenewable resource problem.

If you can possibly do so, take your class on a field trip to see one of these gigantic processes in operation.

Field Trip to a Steel Mill. As they go through the plant, ask your students to keep an eye on the conservation measures in practice. This may lead to some interesting findings. Here, for example, is the story of one such visit:

At the Fairless works of the United States Steel Corporation at Morrisville, Pennsylvania, 250 million gallons of water are used every day. Most of this water comes from the Delaware River, and returns to it in as good condition as it left the stream, according to one of the chief engineers.

There are in Pennsylvania anti-stream-pollution laws with which the company must comply. The cooling waters go to "settlers"; the waters from the rolling mills also go to settlers and are also skimmed to remove the oil; water from the tinning process must be chemically treated before being allowed to rejoin the river.

In addition, the company has installed huge "precipitators" (Sec. 12-8), to prevent the flue dust of the furnaces from settling on the countryside. It is not compelled to do this by law but feels that it is being a "good neighbor" to the surrounding farmers and townspeople. U.S. Steel recognizes that these precipitators are good public relations even though they are enormously costly and have not as yet brought the company any appreciable financial return by way of salvage of the dust (Fig. 14-5).

The fact that a measure like keeping our air a little purer is thought

Fig. 14-5. Conservation of raw materials. Experimental sintering machine with storage and preparation facilities for agglomerating fine iron-bearing materials such as ore fines and flue dust. (*U.S. Steel.*)

of in terms of "public relations" is a step forward. When large corporations are willing to spend their money in this way it means that they realize that conservation is responsible citizenship.

Another conservation measure of which U.S. Steel is proud is the amount of tin plate it is able to keep from the scrap heap by new electronic devices. The electronic eye detects imperfections far more accurately than the human, and this has cut down considerably on the amount of electrolytic tin plate to be discarded.

New Iron from Old. You might begin class discussion with these questions: "How many new cars were turned out in our country this year? Where does the steel come from to bring all these cars into being?"

The answer to the second question, students will discover, is a kind of paradox. About half of our new steel is old steel. In the manufacture of steel in the most modern open-hearth furnaces every ton of new pig iron is matched by a ton of scrap. This means we have to dispose of our old cars at a faster and faster rate to provide more and more steel for new cars.

The role of the junk dealer in the salvaging of scrap is becoming an increasingly important one. Magazine articles have appeared (*The New Yorker* of December 10, 1955, for example) describing the fantastic operations involved in reducing old cars to scrap. It is also being discovered that slag dumps themselves contain salvageable amounts of iron; what's more, the slag, after the iron is removed, can be used for fertilizer or roadbed filler.

Conservation is well served by finding uses for formerly useless waste products of industry. When these uses include the salvage of any of our nonrenewable resources, they are particularly valuable.

Can your students find other examples from industry?

14-6. Aluminum: A Light Metal

Some Highlights. When your chemistry class is studying the metallurgy of aluminum there are several points that you may want to stress to bring out the conservation aspects.

First of all, aluminum compounds are abundant and widespread. We have a goodly supply of bauxite, the chief ore of aluminum, in Alabama, Arkansas, and several other states. France, Hungary, Canada, British and Dutch Guiana, and many other regions have ample supplies of bauxite.

On the other hand, the rapidly increasing use of aluminum foil for wrapping foods, for disposable pie plates, etc., is one area in which there is no attempt whatsoever at salvage—probably because it seems unnecessary and too costly at this time.

Since the metallurgy of aluminum is an electrolytic process, a discussion of electrical power sources (Sec. 15-6) might be appropriate. The aluminum industry is one of the largest consumers of electricity, and extraction plants are usually located near a source of current from water power.

Another interesting topic is the increasing use of aluminum and its alloys. Airplanes, for instance, are about 90 per cent aluminum. Iron and steel are beginning to be replaced in home construction and in railroad trains by this light, strong metal and its alloys. These are examples of "substitution" and they may be multiplied as the years go on.

Your class might find it useful to see the movie *This Is Aluminum* (U.S. Bureau of Mines).

Some Properties of Aluminum. Students may secure strips of aluminum metal that have been cut from an old aluminum pan. With tongs, they may hold a strip of the metal in a bunsen flame and note that it melts rather easily. Why should aluminum pans never be allowed to boil dry on the stove?

As a demonstration, add a strip of aluminum to a beaker that is half full of hot sodium hydroxide solution. Note the reaction that occurs. Sodium hydroxide and other strong alkalies attack aluminum. Why should one not use caustic cleaning powders to scour aluminum pans?

Why is it not a good idea to cook "acid" substances like tomatoes or certain fruits in an aluminum pan? Students might try the action of aluminum on acid.

Ask students to devise and set up an experiment to show any difference in the corrosive properties of aluminum, magnesium, and iron. The metals should be allowed to stand for several days in various liquids such as salt water, vinegar, and plain water.

14-7. Newer Metals and Devices

Titanium. Just a few years ago, this metal was a paint pigment, nothing to get excited about. Why all this sudden fuss over it? Titanium has properties that make it unusually useful in a variety of ways. Ask students to bring in a report on its properties. (It is twice as strong as aluminum and 40 per cent lighter than steel. It resists corrosion and offers a fantastically high melting point, well over 3,000°F. These properties, of course, are responsible for its increasing usefulness.)

The story of titanium is an excellent illustration of the development of new resources to meet new needs. Even old needs may be better served by the newer substances. One of the interesting things about the resource picture is that it is never static but constantly shifting as our needs and technology advance.

Some of your students might be interested in telling the story of other of the newer industrial metals—zirconium or germanium, for example.

Semiconductors. Your students, now familiar with some of the important properties of metals and nonmetals, know that in general the metals conduct electricity whereas the nonmetals are nonconductors (Sec. 14-4). Between these lie a class of materials known as semiconductors, typical examples of which are germanium, silicon, lead sulfide, and silicon carbide. These semiconductors are becoming increasingly important both in research and in industrial application.

If an old crystal rectifier is available, it might be shown to the class and its operation demonstrated. In recent years there has been a revival of interest in crystal rectifiers, semiconductors used in the early days of the wireless and later abandoned for radio tubes. This interest was stimulated because of the necessity of microwave detection for radar applications.

The Transistor. It was from a research program directed toward a fundamental understanding of semiconduction that the transistor emerged. These tiny metal junctions are revolutionizing the electronics industry. You might want to have your students bring to class a report on transistors and their application in wrist-watch radios, hearing aids, and pocket radiotelephones, etc. One exciting development is a diffusion transistor, which will permit 2,500 telephone conversations over one wire at once.

The story of semiconductors illustrates strikingly how research directed toward the solving of one problem often opens up new vistas in another field. As far as resources are concerned, it generally means that some little-used substance may suddenly become important. Wise resource use will always need to take into account these demands for new materials to meet the needs of a developing technology.

A student might report on the "supertransistor," called spacistor, which may well revolutionize present electronics devices and techniques, much as transistors did vacuum tubes a few years ago.

Superconducting Metals. Scientists have known for 50 years that at temperatures near absolute zero many metals are superconducting, offering apparently no resistance to the passage of electric current. A student might bring in a report on superconductivity.

The Cryotron. Man's first practical use of this property is the cryotron, far smaller and even more revolutionary than the transistor (Fig. 14-6). The cryotron was first used in the giant "brain" machine built by scientists at Arthur D. Little, Inc., Cambridge, Massachusetts. Your students may want to bring in articles and news clippings about this amazing device, which operates only at temperatures close to absolute zero.

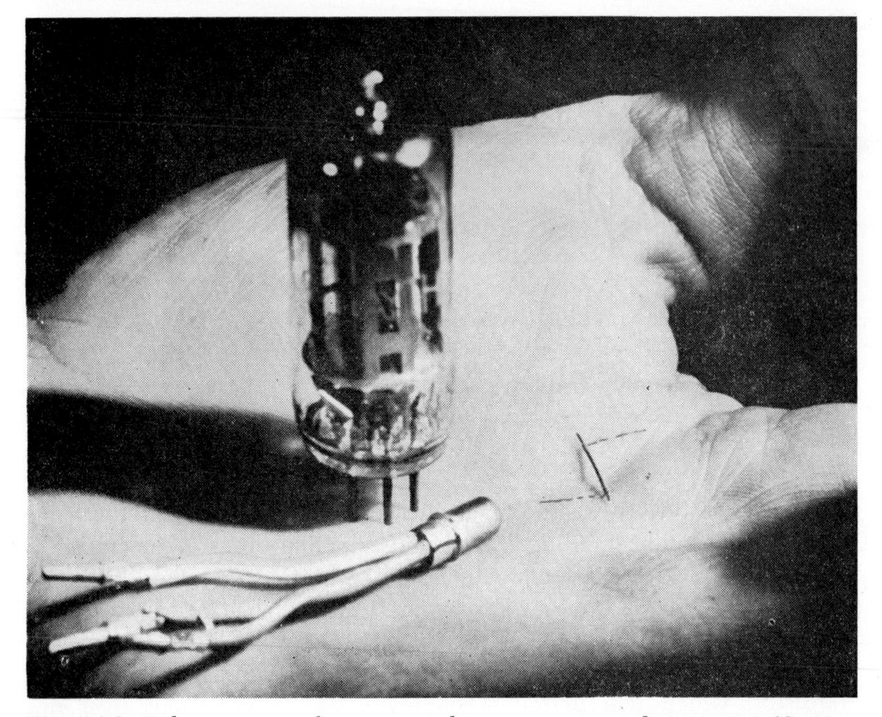

Fig. 14-6. Relative sizes of vacuum tube, transistor, and cryotron. (*Science Service.*)

14-8. Alloys

Need for Alloys. The needs of modern industry necessitate the production of metals with very special properties, thus the preparation of alloys has become one of the most important branches of metallurgy. In addition to the alloys known to the ancients, bronze and brass, there are now over 5,000 metals and alloys of different compositions, each having special properties. Your students might make a collection of the most common alloys used around their homes or a few of the alloys used industrially.

Earth satellites, space vehicles, and long-range missiles have made necessary new metal alloy combinations once considered impossible. Students might for illustration bring in reports of the results of research on "micrometeorite bombardment," conducted by the Air Force's Air Research and Development Command. This laboratory technique produces new alloys by a method similar to meteorite collisions in outer space.

Alloys are particularly interesting from the point of view of conservation. The rusting of iron, for instance, is one of the greatest metal

wasters. Alloy steels, such as chrome-nickel steels, do not rust. Other alloys increase strength or hardness of the product. Can students justify the statement that we live in an age of alloys?

Making the Alloy, Solder. Solder is a familiar alloy, which is used to fasten certain metallic wires together. This can be demonstrated as follows: Place thin sheets of lead and tin (about an inch square) in a heavy porcelain dish on a ring stand. As the metals begin to melt from the heat of a bunsen burner, stir the mixture with an iron wire, a file, or the handle of a spoon. If the ends of two copper wires are twisted together, dipped into the molten mixture, and allowed to cool, they will be so tightly held together by the solder that they cannot be untwisted.

Making a Fusible Alloy, Wood's Metal. The low melting point of this alloy, which is easily prepared in the laboratory, makes it useful for such purposes as plugs in automatic fire-sprinkler systems.

Heat an iron crucible (held by means of a pipestem triangle on the

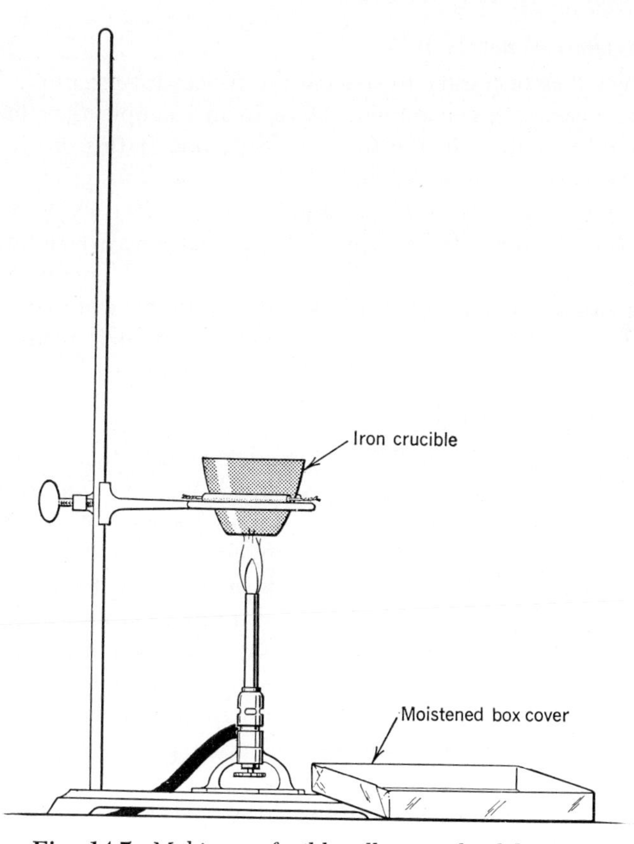

Fig. 14-7. Making a fusible alloy in the laboratory.

ring of a ring stand) in a bunsen, Fisher or Meker burner (Fig. 14-7). Into the hot crucible place a mixture of 5 grams of lead and 2.5 grams of tin. When these are melted, add 10 grams of bismuth and 2.5 grams of cadmium. Stir the mixture with an iron wire until it is completely liquefied. Tilt the moistened cover of a small cardboard box against the base of the ring stand. Using a forceps, carefully pour the molten alloy into the lower edge of the box cover. To solidify the liquid, pour a little water on it.

Students may examine the alloy and compare its appearance with that of the component metals. They might determine its density or specific gravity (Sec. 13-5). Have students drop a piece of the alloy into boiling water. What happens to it? How does the melting point of the alloy (about 60°C) compare with the melting points of its components? In general an alloy has a lower melting point than the metals of which it is composed.

CORROSION: A METAL WASTER

14-9. Corrosion: What Is It?

Sometimes it is necessary to reverse the processes of nature. Ask your students to discuss this statement. Here is an example they might use. Iron is found in nature in the form of oxide ore. If this ore is put into the blast furnace it can be reduced. If the iron thus produced is unprotected it will quickly rust, tending to produce iron oxide again.

The rusting of iron articles represents an enormous waste not only of the articles themselves but of all the materials and energy that went into their production. Surely this waste should be avoided wherever possible. It is for this reason that so much attention is being given to the causes and prevention of rusting or corrosion.

14-10. The Rusting of Iron

Leave some ordinary iron nails exposed to moist air. Ask students to observe their rusting. Or, put a deep scratch in a tin can and ask students to note the rapid corrosion where the tin has been penetrated.

You might have your students set up experiments to test corrosion in both water and air, using various kinds of iron and steel.

(Experiments show that under water all forms of iron—cast, wrought, and steel—rust at the same rate. In air, under identical conditions, steel rusts the fastest of the three; cast iron and wrought iron rust much more slowly.) Ask your students to read up on the latest theories to explain the rusting of iron. Current scientific publications as well as textbooks should be used.

Two-metal Corrosion. Using a cathode of sheet iron, an anode of copper, and a weak electrolyte, set up an electrolytic cell and connect it to a sensitive electrical meter. Have students observe the current flow. The metals should be allowed to remain in the liquid and examined after some hours. The iron should become pitted with corrosion.

Two-metal joints are particularly subject to corrosion, the more active metal being the one that is eaten away. The explanation, which your students may think through, is that in contact with a corroding liquid like salt water a little electric cell is set up. Iron is the cathode, or fuel for the cell. Copper is the anode and is uncorroded. Impure water is the weak electrolyte. Any hydrogen that tends to accumulate and to stop the electrochemical reaction is oxidized to water by oxygen dissolved in the water. Thus the iron pipe rusts.

A lump of charcoal may be placed on a piece of moist iron or steel, and the quickness of rusting noted. Here again there seems to be an electrical process, the carbon acting as anode, the iron as cathode.

Acid Corrosion. Your students may learn by experiment that aluminum, zinc, iron, and tin are easily attacked by dilute acids, liberating hydrogen from the acid. In terms of ions this may be represented as follows:

$$Fe + 2H^+ \rightarrow Fe^{++} + H_2\uparrow$$

Why is this action greatly hastened if oxygen is present? (The oxygen changing the hydrogen to water as fast as it forms is here called a depolarizer.)

Passive Iron. Immerse an iron nail in concentrated nitric acid. The iron is made unreactive or passive. It no longer acts chemically like ordinary iron but more like lead.

Ask students to put the treated iron nail in a solution of copper sulfate. Passive iron should not replace the copper, though ordinary iron will. Iron in the passive state is more resistant to corrosion than ordinary iron. The chromate ion helps to preserve this passive condition. Chlorides destroy the passive state. Students might try this out by immersing one strip of passive iron in sodium chromate and another in sodium chloride solution and then testing the iron for activity.

Other Causes. For other causes of corrosion including concentration effects, stray current corrosion, poorly made alloys, and certain lubricants, your students may be referred to an excellent discussion in *Chemistry for Our Times* by Elbert C. Weaver and Lawrence S. Foster (McGraw-Hill Book Company, Inc., New York, 1954).

14-11. The Protection of Iron from Rusting

With Paint. Students may coat different samples of iron with paint, enamel, and lacquer. Expose them to air and note how they are protected from corrosion.

With a Metallic Coating. *Galvanizing Iron.* Zinc may be melted in an iron dish. Dip the sheet iron that is to be galvanized into dilute hydrochloric acid to remove any coating of oxide. Rinse and dip into the molten zinc. Observe the coating of zinc that forms on the iron.

Plating Iron. This may be done by immersing an iron nail in a concentrated solution of copper nitrate. A displacement reaction will take place, since iron is above copper in the electromotive series.

Another way is to use an iron cathode (an iron key will serve) in a bath of copper sulfate. Turn on the current and electroplate the iron (Fig. 14-3). The coating can be removed by making the iron act as the anode. Figure 14-8 illustrates a research project aimed to improve electroplating operations.

Fig. 14-8. Metals can be conserved by electroplating. Here a continuous electroplating pilot line is operated in order to develop improved methods of depositing metallic coatings on steel coils. (*U.S. Steel.*)

Making an Alloy. Iron may be alloyed with other metals to protect it. Silicon alloys and stainless steel, which contains chromium and nickel, are alloys of iron and steel that do not tarnish. Provide students with samples of ordinary iron and stainless steel and have them try this experiment:

In separate beakers place 100 milliliters of dilute hydrochloric acid. Place a strip of iron in one beaker and a strip of stainless steel of about the same size in the other. Vigorous action with the evolution of hydrogen will take place in the beaker containing the iron. Stainless steel, on the other hand, is not affected.

This technique might be tried instead: On a large piece of stainless steel place small wads of cotton soaked in dilute hydrochloric acid, vinegar, fruit juice, etc. Do the same on a piece of polished ordinary steel. Remove the cotton wads next day and compare the action of the acids on the two pieces of metal.

Other Ways. You may wish to ask your students to do a little research. Can they learn about other ways of protecting iron by thin surface coatings? They might bring in reports on "Russia" iron and "Parkerized" iron.

14-12. Aluminum: Does It Rust?

Ask students to take a strip of aluminum and put it in hot water. Is there any action? It is common knowledge, of course, that hot water does not appreciably attack pots and pans.

Scratch a piece of aluminum with sandpaper while it is under mercury. Keep the surface of the aluminum away from air until you add hot water above the mercury. Now ask students to notice the action of the aluminum with the hot water. There should be vigorous bubbling, with the liberation of hydrogen.

Discuss with your class the difference between the results of these two experiments, and have them discover that aluminum is protected from the corrosive action of the water by a hard, tightly adhering skin, a film of aluminum oxide. Your students will learn that even though aluminum oxidizes, just as iron, the aluminum oxide forms a protective covering and makes unnecessary any additional surface protection.

SELECTED NONMETALLIC PRODUCTS

14-13. Industrial Chemicals

Sulfur. Sulfur is mined by means of the Frasch process, an understanding of which involves a review of some important scientific principles.

Melt some flowers of sulfur in a test tube. Note how quickly and easily it melts. What is its melting point? Could boiling water be used to melt it? Elicit from students the fact that water at sea level boils at 100°C. Someone may suggest that water can be made to boil at a higher temperature if the pressure is increased (Fig. 5-10). This was the way Frasch melted the sulfur below ground. Now students are ready to study details of the Frasch process, including finally the role of the compressed air in bringing the melted sulfur to the surface.

Your students might profit from the movie *Sulfur* (U.S. Bureau of Mines). Several might be interested in making a working model of the mining of sulfur.

The Frasch Process: A Working Model. In order to avoid the danger accompanying great temperature and pressure, paraffin might be used to represent sulfur, dyed to a suitable yellow color by the admixture of some strongly colored yellow candles. Oil-soluble dyes of the type used in preparing these candles would, if available, serve to color ordinary paraffin for this purpose.

A wide-mouthed bottle *D* (Fig. 14-9) filled with lumps of yellow paraffin represents the underground deposit of sulfur. The lower rubber connection is removed from a Liebig condenser of the separable type (*C*). The cork of the wide-mouthed bottle is bored to fit the lower end of the condenser water jacket. Both the inner tube and the water jacket extend into the bottle. A third tube, to carry compressed air, is then introduced through the center of the condenser. This tube passes through a two-hole rubber stopper at the upper end of the condenser. A delivery tube is provided through the second hole of the stopper to conduct the materials raised to a second wide-mouthed bottle, representing a storage bin. The upper inlet of the water jacket is connected to a source of steam supply, which is, in this case, a copper boiler; the lower outlet tube is closed off by means of rubber tubing and a screw clamp as shown.

Steam is introduced into the outermost tube, i.e., the water jacket, of the condenser and passes into the wide-mouthed bottle through the narrow space between the condenser jacket and the inner condenser tube. The paraffin melts gradually and accumulates at the bottom of the bottle. When a sufficient amount has melted, the compressed air is turned on. This may be done by blowing through the central tube or by the use of some other source of air under pressure. The "sulfur"-water-air mixture then rises through the intermediate tube and passes by way of the delivery tube to the storage bin. Pebbles added to the paraffin will not be affected by the steam and will therefore demonstrate the effectiveness of the process in purifying the sulfur and will help to explain the great purity of the substance when mined commercially in this way. The apparatus may be cleaned by continuing the passage of steam for a short time after the paraffin has been raised and the compressed air turned off.

It is desirable to disassemble the apparatus immediately after use, to clear out the passageways (by sending steam through them), and to make a well in the bottle holding the wax by inserting some cylindrical object, such as a large test tube or small bottle, in the molten wax

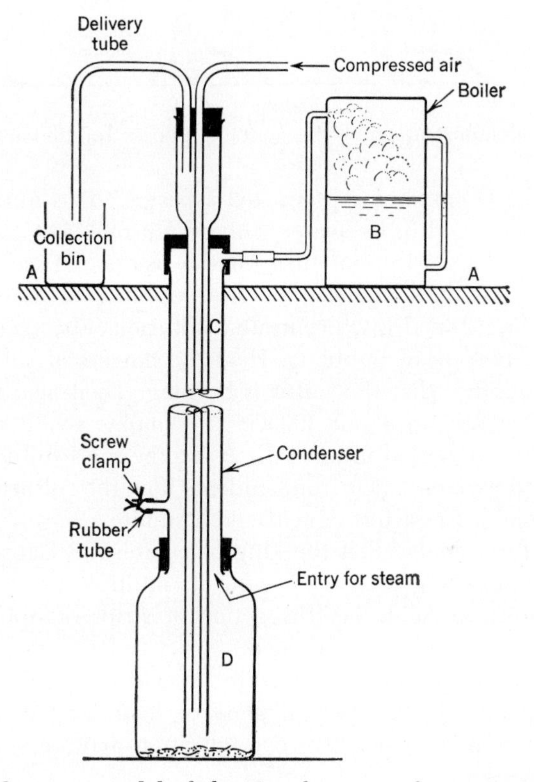

Fig. 14-9. A laboratory model of the Frasch process for mining sulfur. (*Courtesy of Samuel Lebowitz, Charles Evans Hughes High School, New York City.*)

representing the underground deposit. After the wax has hardened, remove the bottle by filling it with hot water.

Making Sulfuric Acid. Sulfuric acid is made by adding water to sulfur trioxide. This latter substance can be effectively produced in a laboratory demonstration of the contact process.

We have found the most successful way to do this to be the method illustrated in Fig. 14-10. The hard glass tube *C* contains a porcelain boat filled with flowers of sulfur. This tube is connected to a second

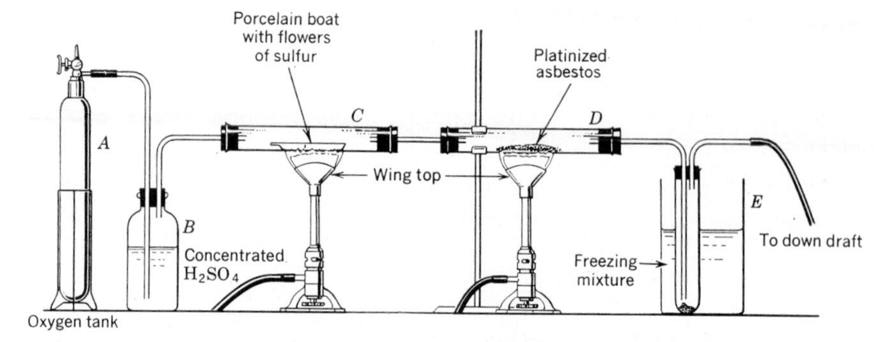

Fig. 14-10. A demonstration of the contact process for making sulfuric acid.

hard glass tube *D* containing platinized asbestos.[2] This in turn leads to a test tube *E*, immersed in ice water with added rock salt, as shown.

To start the demonstration, turn on the oxygen, *A*, so that a gentle stream of the gas, as evidenced by the bubbling at *B*, enters the apparatus. The liquid in *B* is concentrated sulfuric acid to keep the oxygen dry yet show the rate of bubbling. Heat the flowers of sulfur in *C* until a purple glow shows that the sulfur is burning. Then heat the platinized asbestos in *D* gently to about 400°C. The smoky, white sulfur trioxide formed may be condensed in test tube *E*. To the solid sulfur trioxide may be added a little water. Elicit from students how the sulfuric acid formed may be identified. (Test for an acid and a sulfate.)

Why is sulfuric acid called the king of chemicals? Can your students devise some interesting way of showing its multiple uses?

Shipping Sulfuric Acid. Try the action of strips of iron and lead on dilute and concentrated sulfuric acid.

Now your students will see why sulfuric acid of less than 78 per cent concentration must be shipped in glass or lead-lined containers while acids of greater than 78 per cent concentration may be shipped in steel drums or tank cars.

The Displacement of One Chemical Process by Another. Sulfuric acid was originally made by the lead-chamber process, introduced in Birmingham, England, in 1746. Its use marked the beginning of chemical manufacture on a large scale, as the industrial revolution got under way.

In recent years this process has gradually been superseded by the contact process. The size of the reaction chambers required by the older method and the cost of the lead from which they needed to be made were two factors partly responsible for the change. In addition, another

[2] Moisten asbestos fiber in a solution of chloroplatinic acid and ignite it in a flame. The platinum compound is reduced to metallic platinum.

disadvantage of the older process is that only dilute sulfuric acid, often impure and not more than 78 per cent concentrated, can be made. If greater strength acid is required, this dilute acid must be concentrated by evaporation and heat, an expensive procedure. The chamber process can compete with the contact process only if somewhat dilute acid is required, as in the manufacture of phosphate fertilizer or the pickling of steel.

The shifting from one chemical process to another might be discussed from the point of view of economics and of conservation.

Purification of Chemicals by Crystallization. Crystalline chemicals need to be purified before they can be used commercially. This is accomplished by means of crystallization and recrystallization.

Students may take some impure potassium nitrate and purify it in the following manner: Dissolve it in pure water (see the solubility curve, Fig. 13-2) and then evaporate part of the water. As the solution becomes more concentrated, crystals of potassium nitrate of a rather high degree of purity begin to separate from the solution.

By filtering out these crystals and dissolving them again in pure water, students can repeat the process and obtain crystals of a still higher degree of purity. Such crystals are said to be recrystallized.

The "mother liquor" left after a crop of crystals has been removed may be evaporated still more, thus producing second and even third crops of crystals of decreasing purity.

A more difficult type of experiment might be suggested to students interested in a special project. This consists in purifying a mixture of salts by fractional crystallization. To crystallize in this way one must take advantage of the fact that the two substances to be separated must differ markedly in relative solubility in hot and cold water (Fig. 14-11). For example, potassium chlorate, though far less soluble than copper nitrate, is five times more soluble in water at 80°C than at room temper-

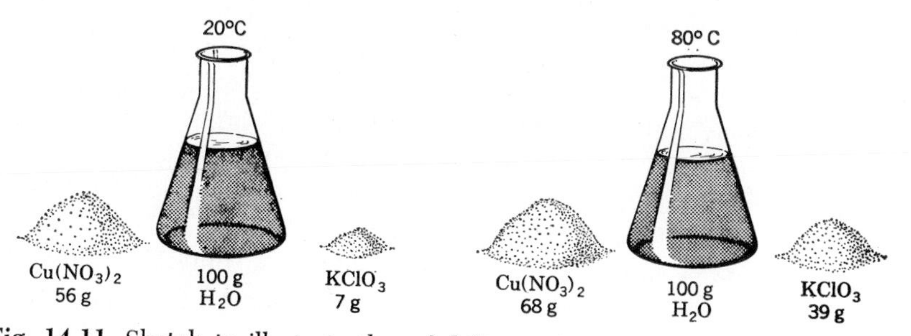

Fig. 14-11. Sketch to illustrate the solubilities of copper nitrate and potassium chlorate in cold and hot water.

ature, whereas the solubility of copper nitrate varies only slightly with temperature.

Add to 50 cubic centimeters of water in a beaker 15 grams each of the two salts, and heat with constant stirring until the mixture is all dissolved. Using a fluted filter paper, filter the solution rapidly. Evaporate the filtrate by boiling until white crystals of potassium chlorate begin to form, then set it aside to cool. Should a light green precipitate appear, it is a basic salt of copper and may be dissolved by adding several cubic centimeters of dilute nitric acid to the solution. As soon as room temperature has been reached, remove the white crystals from the solution by filtering and then wash them with a few cubic centimeters of cold water. When the water has completely drained off, give the crystals two more washings. Should the crystals have a bluish tinge they may be redissolved in a small amount of boiling water and allowed to crystallize once more. They should be spread out on the filter paper and left to dry for several hours. Finally, they may be weighed.

14-14. Nonmetallic Building Materials

Mortar. To make mortar one must mix sand with wet, freshly slaked lime.

To make quicklime, wrap an iron wire around a small chip of marble (about 5 millimeters) and hang it in the hottest part of the flame of a blast lamp or Meker burner (Fig. 14-12). When this is heated as hot as possible for 15 to 20 minutes, calcium oxide or quicklime is produced.

To slake the lime, pour boiling water, a little at a time, on the lump of quicklime in an evaporating dish. Care must be taken not to add too much water, just enough to be taken up readily by the lump. Students may note changes in volume and appearance and evidences of the evolution of heat.

Finally, there should be a smooth, stiff paste. This should prove basic when tested with litmus. The paste may now be mixed with a little sand and water added if required.

Concrete. Ask students to mix 1 tablespoon of portland cement with about 2 tablespoons of clean sand. Enough water should be added to make a stiff paste. Part of this mixture should be rolled into a ball, placed in a wide-mouthed bottle, and corked tightly. The rest should be poured into a small greased cardboard box. Each sample of concrete should be examined after 2 days.

What advantage has concrete over mortar as a building material? What is reinforced concrete? Perhaps your students might make some, using a heavy wire mesh, and compare the relative strengths of the two kinds of concrete. A student might report on prestressed concrete as described in the July, 1958, issue of *Scientific American.*

Glass. "People who live in glass houses" are what we modern home dwellers seem to become as large picture windows and entire sides of glass replace walls that were formerly constructed of wood and other building materials.

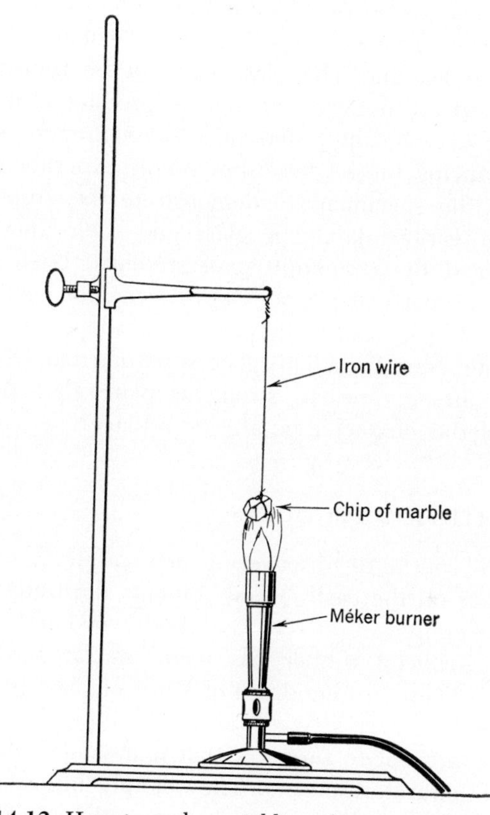

Fig. 14-12. How to make quicklime from a marble chip.

Students may wonder what are the raw materials from which glass is made. Are they abundant?

The simplest way to prepare glass is to use a piece of wire (preferably platinum) with a small loop in it. Heat the wire in a flame, then dip it into some powdered sodium carbonate. Continue to heat it in the flame until a clear bead is formed. Dip this into some powdered silica and heat until the two chemicals fuse. Next, dip the hot bead into some powdered calcium carbonate and heat once more. The product will be a small bead of glass.

If your students want to prepare larger quantities of crude glass they might proceed as follows: Have them mix 1 gram of fine, clean sand, 1 gram of powdered sodium carbonate, and 2 grams of yellow oxide of lead (litharge) thoroughly in a mortar and heat this mixture in an old porcelain crucible. As a scum forms, it should be scraped from the molten mass with a glass rod. When the material has cooled, the glass will form a hard, brittle layer at the bottom of the crucible. If a blue-colored glass is desired, a small crystal of cobalt nitrate should be added before the heating. The glass will not be transparent because the chemicals used are not pure enough to produce clear glass.

Your students may be interested in a Glass Properties Unit Kit.[3] A booklet accompanying the kit describes simple experiments that can be performed with the specimens to demonstrate the properties of glass.

An exhibit of various kinds of glass and their unusual properties might be arranged by a committee of students. Each student might make a report on a particular type. One student, for instance, might tell about the kind of glass called Pyroceram developed at Corning Glass Works in Corning, New York. This glass is harder than steel, lighter than aluminum, and fifteen times as strong as plate glass. What materials might a glass of this character be able to replace?

A FEW SUBSTITUTION PRODUCTS

"Scientists are constantly discovering new products to substitute for those found in or on the earth." Can students illustrate this statement? Here are a few examples. Concrete saves both wood and steel for bridges and buildings. Artificial rubber has made us far less dependent on natural supplies. There are hundreds of kinds of plastics with thousands of different uses.

One thing we are apt to forget is that man-made substitutes are not independent of natural resources. They simply utilize other materials from the storehouse of nature. Even water, though theoretically unlimited in supply, is not unlimited in fact. Thus substitution products need to be considered in the total framework of natural resource use.

14-15. Asbestos and Possible Substitutes

Ask students to test samples of asbestos fiber, glass wool, rock or mineral wool in a flame. Notice that they are all noncombustible.

As our supply of asbestos from Canada diminishes, here are possible substitutes for use as fireproofing and insulating material. Mineral wool, when made from blast-furnace slag, is, in addition, an example of the utilization of a waste product.

[3] Science Service, 1719 W St., N.W., Washington, D.C.

14-16. Plastics

Several plastics can be made in the school laboratory.

Phenol Formaldehyde Plastics. These plastics may be made from phenol, 40 per cent formaldehyde solution (formalin), and sodium hydroxide. If a colored plastic is desired, add a little dye just before adding the lye. The bottom of a small matchbox or a metal lid may be used as a mold. This experiment might best serve as a demonstration.

Place 5 grams of phenol crystals (carbolic acid) in a 50 milliliter beaker and melt them. Add 8 grams of formalin. Heat the mixture until the formalin dissolves in the melted phenol. CAUTION: Phenol is very irritating to skin tissue; exercise care in handling it!

Crush several pellets of sodium hydroxide (do not handle with the fingers) and sift them into the melted mixture. A viscous paste will form. Add more sodium hydroxide if the mixture is too thin. Pour the plastic into the matchbox mold and allow it to harden, a process which may take several days.

Resorcinol Formaldehyde Plastics. Dissolve 3 grams of resorcinol in 5 milliliters of water in a 50-milliliter beaker. Add 3 to 4 milliliters of formalin and heat the beaker on a ring stand until the solution boils. While the boiling continues add a few drops of 15 per cent sodium or potassium hydroxide. The mass will solidify into a brittle, red solid, which will become darker red on further heating.

Have students find out the sources or "raw materials" from which the ingredients of these plastics (phenol, formaldehyde, sodium hydroxide, resorcinol) come. Then they might discuss the values of these substitution products from a natural resources point of view. Figure 14-13 traces the origins of phenol and formaldehyde and the making of a phenolic resin. This and other flow diagrams in animated-cartoon form may be found in the pamphlet, *The ABC's of Modern Plastics*, Union Carbide Plastics Company, Division of Union Carbide Corporation, New York.

Other Plastics. Groups of students might report on "the plastic age," describing some of the plastics made directly from natural sources: nitrocellulose and cellulose acetate from cotton, cheap plastic from lignin, protein plastic from casein, rubber from trees.

Another group might report on synthetic plastics, describing and illustrating the two types, condensation and polymerization plastics. Exhibits would enhance the interest of these reports.

Testing Plastics. Your students might write to plastic manufacturing companies for samples, which could be subjected to various tests:

1. Is the sample flammable when held in a flame? (Use caution!)
2. Can the solid plastic be shaped after being immersed in boiling water?

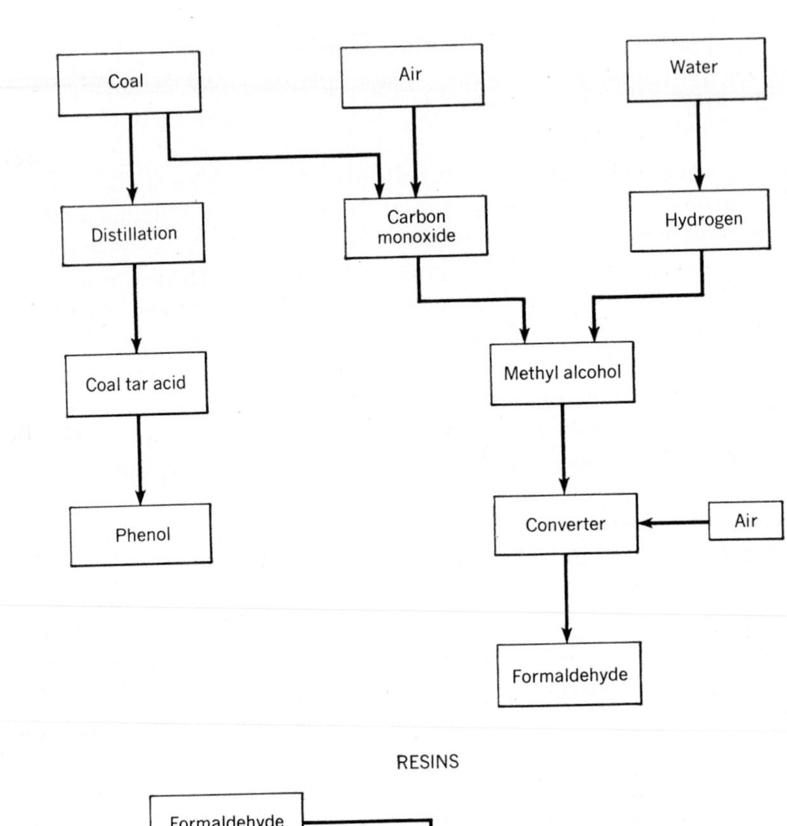

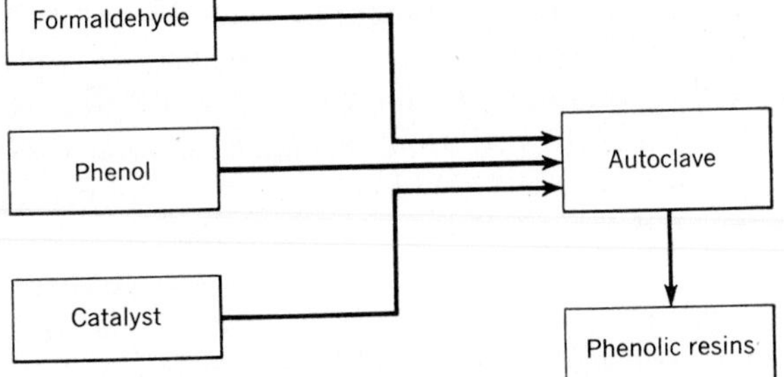

Fig. 14-13. Man-made substances come from basic natural resources. This phenol formaldehyde synthetic comes from what basic resources? Are they abundant?

3. Does the plastic transmit light?

4. Can the plastic transmit light with no reflection from the sides of the plastic tube? (Lucite will do this.)

14-17. Borazon: Harder than a Diamond

Your students might bring in a report of the new substance made of boron and nitrogen, borazon. This substance, as hard as or even harder than diamonds, was produced by Dr. Robert H. Wentorf of the General Electric Laboratory, by duplicating temperature and pressure conditions existing several hundred miles under the earth's surface.

Your students might discuss what are the implications of such a discovery. (Borazon may eventually take the place of industrial diamonds for grinding rocks, as in the bottom of oil wells, for grinding steel castings as in car cylinders, and for grinding expansion spaces in the concrete of modern highways.)

Dr. Wentorf's work is another illustration of the way research in science, designed originally to give man a better understanding of the universe, often finds direct and practical application. It may happen that by this means an industry becomes revolutionized, or the resource outlook for a particular substance becomes drastically changed.

15

Our Energy Sources: Conventional

Were it not for the energy that man has learned and is still learning to harness, civilized existence, as we know it, would disappear. The growing realization of our dependence on energy and the ever-increasing demand for its use, plus the fact of its unequal distribution among the countries of the world, have made it necessary for us to consider the wiser use of our sources of energy.

This chapter is concerned with ways of deriving energy from our conventional sources: moving water, coal, petroleum, natural gas. It deals also with the conversion of this energy into electricity, a form most serviceable to modern man.

Our fossil fuels, constituting as they do some of our most important nonrenewable resources, are gone when used. This chapter explores ways of conserving these dwindling resources by wiser, more efficient use.

ENERGY IN GENERAL

15-1. Basic Considerations

You might want to bring to your class for discussion a paragraph like the following:

The history of man on earth can be told in the unfolding picture of his harnessing of energy. Coming down to our brief moment in history, we find that every man, woman, and child in our country now has the equivalent of eighty-four servants working for him 8 hours of every day.

Modern Man's Energy Requirements. You might want to include in class discussion our present energy needs for heating, transportation, industry, and electrical generation. Your students may be interested in making a "pie" or other type of representation of the percentage of our total energy consumption used in each area, or the share of world energy that we in the United States utilize. This might eventually lead to a discussion of world energy problems. Volume 2, Fuels, *Minerals Yearbook* (1955) (Sec. 19-6*d*) would be an excellent source of information.

For students in the upper high school a good summary of the ways energy may be harnessed and the status of the world's energy resources may be found in a special issue of the *Esso Magazine*, entitled "Energy and Man" (Esso Petroleum Company, Ltd., London). Another stimulating source of information is *The Challange of Man's Future* (Sec. 19-2*i*).

Sources of Energy. You may wish to have your students analyze and explain the statement, "The sun is the ultimate source of all our energy." Let them trace the connection between the sun and our fossil fuels; the sun and wind or water power; the sun and the energy in the atom (Fig. 15-1).

What are the main commercial energy sources used in the world? Can your students find out anything about the relative and changing rate of the use of these conventional sources in our own country?

Kinds of Energy. Illustrate and discuss with your students the kinds of energy available to us—heat, mechanical, chemical, electrical, radiant. This may lead immediately to the problem of changing one kind of energy to another.

Transformations of Energy. There are a number of ways of demonstrating to your students some of the transformations of energy. Have your students draw also on their own experience, as, for example:

1. Let them recall examples of heat produced by running, light by turning on electricity, motion by burning gasoline in an automobile.
2. By means of a storage battery, students may connect in parallel an electric fan, an electric light, a eudiometer for electrolysis of water, a heating pad. They may note into how many other forms of energy the chemical and then electrical energy of the battery is converted.
3. Strike a large "strike anywhere" match and let it burn. Ask students to trace the energy changes.
4. Pass strong sunlight through a magnifying glass. At the focus, enough light is converted to heat so that a piece of paper may be set on fire.
5. You and your students might use the hydrologic cycle (Fig. 11-7*b*) in a study in transformation of energy.

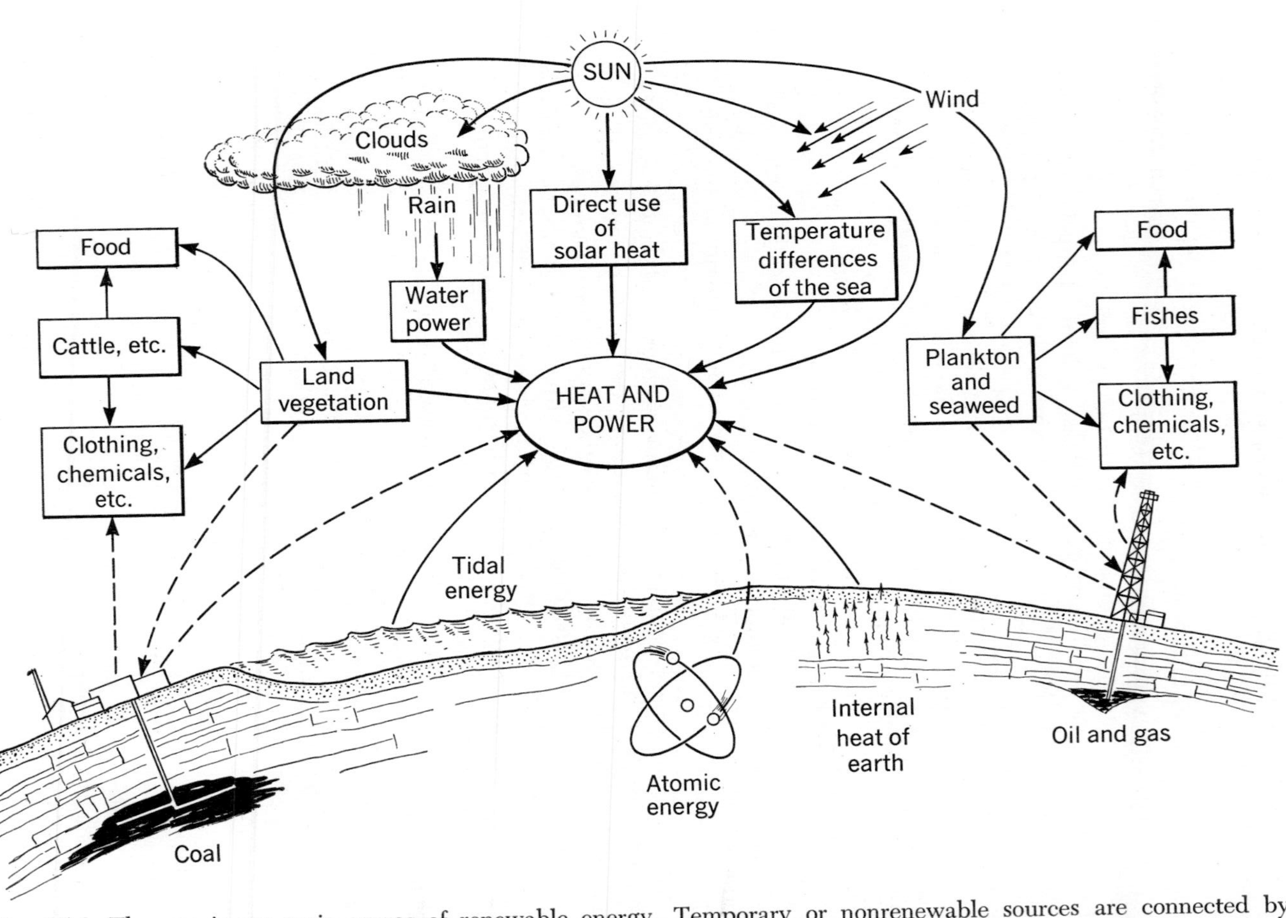

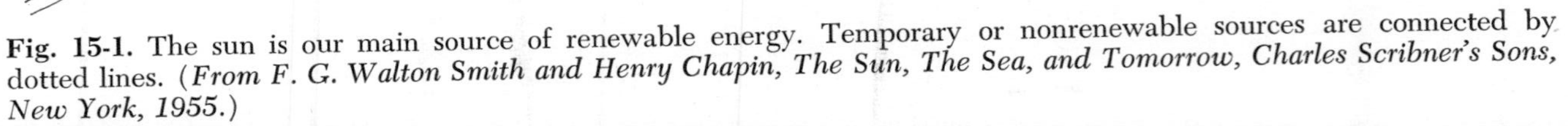

Fig. 15-1. The sun is our main source of renewable energy. Temporary or nonrenewable sources are connected by dotted lines. (*From F. G. Walton Smith and Henry Chapin, The Sun, The Sea, and Tomorrow, Charles Scribner's Sons, New York, 1955.*)

Can Energy Be Created or Destroyed? You may want to discuss with your students the fact that for all "ordinary" physical and chemical relationships energy can be neither created nor destroyed but simply transformed from one kind to another. For the extraordinary world within the atom, however, we now know that matter may be converted into energy. It is believed, too, by the evidence from astronomy, that in parts of the universe energy is changing into matter. Our added knowledge requires an extension of the familiar laws of conservation of matter and conservation of energy to include conservation of matter-energy. For all everyday changes, however, the older conception of the laws seems adequate.

How Energy Is Measured: Force, Work, Power. You may now want to introduce your students to the concepts of force, work, and power and how they are measured. Push a block of wood across the demonstration table. Elicit from students that this is an example of force, the push or pull on an object, causing it to move. Students might give dozens of examples of force at work in their lives any moment of the day.

To help students understand the scientific meaning of work (a force moving an object a certain distance) have two students of different sizes step up on a table. The class might then calculate the work each of these students accomplished in getting on the table (weight times distance).

The class may determine the horsepower of these two students in this way: Let someone time each of them, preferably with a stop watch, while running up a flight of stairs. Knowing the weight of the person W, the vertical height of the flight of stairs H, and the time taken in seconds T, we have the necessary data for the calculation of the individual's horsepower. This is expressed by the formula

$$\text{Horsepower} = \frac{WH}{550T} \qquad (1 \text{ hp} = 550 \text{ ft-lb per sec})$$

Men and beasts, of course, cannot keep up their greatest sprint of horsepower for any but short periods. But engines in our machine age can keep on producing horsepower for the world's work, with one proviso: They need fuel, just as we do. If the fuel supply should run out, the engines would cease to work.

ENERGY FROM WATER

15-2. Water Pressure

Water Has Weight. Students may weigh an empty milk bottle and then weigh it filled with water. Having found the weight of 1 quart of water (about 2 pounds), they may calculate its density, namely, the weight of 1 cubic foot of it. (There are about 31 quarts in a cubic foot.) Water weighs 62.4 pounds per cubic foot.

Water Exerts Pressure. Punch several holes one above the other in the side of a gallon can. When the can is filled with water, students

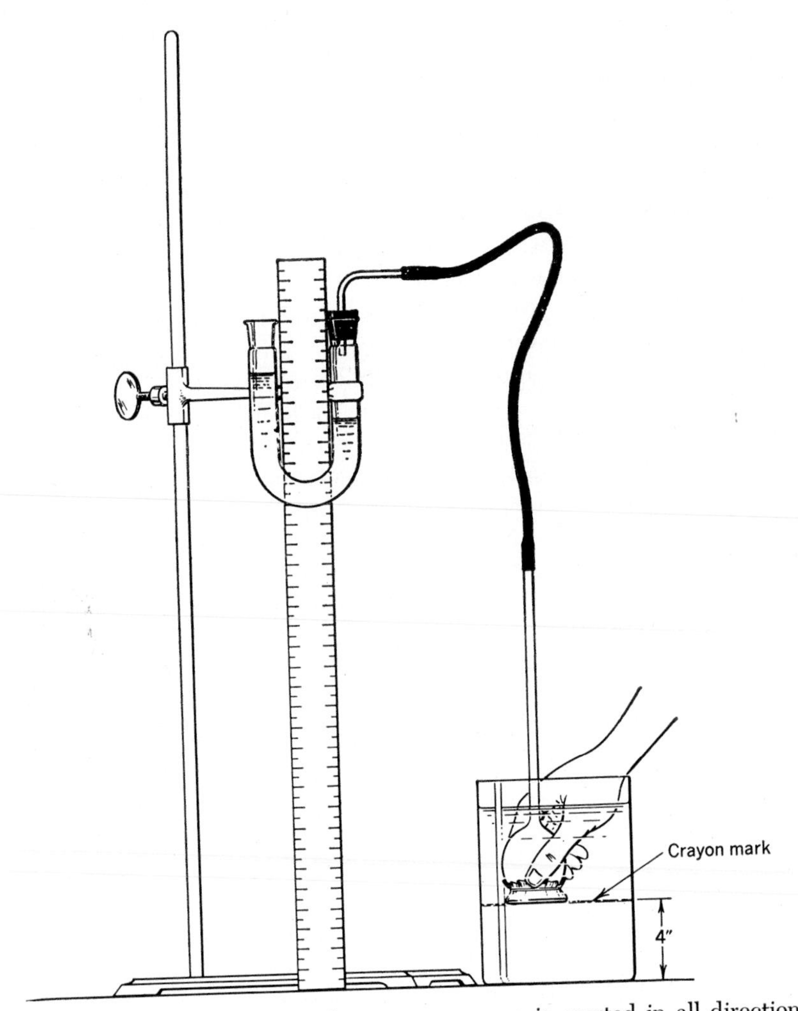

Fig. 15-2. Experiment to show that water pressure is exerted in all directions. The relation of water pressure to depth may also be demonstrated.

may note that it comes out of the bottom hole with the greatest speed and the farthest spurt. (This can also be done with a stout paper bag.)

Tie a sheet of rubber, perhaps from a torn balloon, around the bulb of a short thistle tube. Fill the bend of a U tube with water and attach one of its ends, by means of a rubber connection, to the stem of the thistle tube. Clamp the U tube to a ring stand and place a yardstick directly behind the open end of the U tube (Fig. 15-2).

On the inside of a battery jar or large pail, make a wax crayon mark about 4 inches from the bottom. When the container is filled with water, insert the thistle tube until the rubber-covered end is just opposite the mark. Ask students to notice that the water in the open end of the U tube rises. Elicit from them that this is because of the pressure being exerted on the rubber.

Keeping the thistle tube level with the mark but turning it sidewise and then upward, note that the water level in the U tube remains constant. As the thistle tube is slowly withdrawn from the water, the pressure goes down. Why?

Pressure and Water Levels. Construct a model like Fig. 15-3*a* or 15-3*b* or use a commercial vessel with connecting tubes of different shapes.

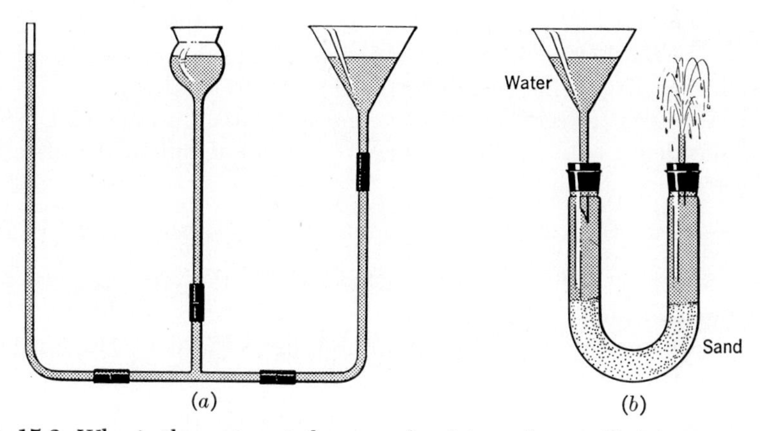

Fig. 15-3. Why is the water at the same level in each vessel? (*a*) Homemade apparatus; (*b*) device that may be used to illustrate the way an artesian well works, the sand being the porous layer and the glass tube the pipe that reaches ground water.

Pour water into one of the receptacles and note that the liquid is at the same level in each. Can your students figure out why this is so?

Students may learn by means of these experiments that water pressure is exerted equally in all directions at a given depth and that the pressure increases only with the depth and is independent of the shape of the vessel or container. What then are the pressures with which engineers need to reckon when constructing a dam to hold water that is to be used for power?

Calculating Water Pressure. Students may calculate the pressure exerted on the bottom of a tank of water 5 feet high and 1 foot square.

$$\text{Volume of water} = 5 \times 1 \times 1 = 5 \text{ cu ft}$$

$$\text{Weight of water} = 5 \times 62.4 = 312 \text{ lb}$$

The pressure (force per unit area) is therefore 312 pounds per cubic foot.

Next, students may calculate the pressure exerted on a tank of water 5 feet high, 4 feet long, and 3 feet wide.

$$\text{Total force} = 5 \times 4 \times 3 \times 62.4 = 3{,}744 \text{ lb}$$

Note that the pressure on 1 square foot is $\frac{3{,}744 \text{ lb}}{12 \text{ sq ft}} = 312$ lb per sq ft, or 5×62.4. In other words, the pressure is calculated by multiplying the height H by the density D.

$$P = HD$$

Comparison of these two problems, one with the other, shows that the pressure on the bottom of the tank is dependent, not on the size of the tank, but simply on the height of the liquid and its density.

Hoover Dam towers 726.4 feet above bedrock (Fig. 15-4). The maximum depth of water is 589 feet. Your students might calculate the water pressure on the bottom.

$$P = HD = 589 \times 62.4 = \text{about } 36{,}800 \text{ lb per sq ft}$$

This is the force on only 1 square foot! Using the crest dimension of the dam, 1,244 feet, and the depth of water, 589 feet, students may go on to calculate the approximate area of the surface of Hoover Dam subject to water pressure.

$$1{,}244 \times 589 = \text{about } 730{,}000 \text{ sq ft}$$

What is the water pressure on the top of the water level? There is, of course, no pressure of water on top.

What is the average water pressure on the face of Hoover Dam?

$$\frac{36{,}800 + 0}{2} = 18{,}400 \text{ lb per sq ft}$$

What is the total force on the face of the dam? (It can be shown that the total force equals the average pressure times the area.)

$$\text{Total force} = 18{,}400 \times 730{,}000 = \text{approximately } 13.4 \text{ billion lb}$$

Quite a force with which to reckon!

Both the pressure and the total force are crucial calculations in the construction of dams. Your students will now see why the bottom is made much thicker than the top, the greater pressure at the lower depth requiring more concrete to prevent the dam from bursting.

The Story of a Dam. A student report on some of the "vital statistics" of one of our large dams might be interesting at this point. *The Story of*

Fig. 15-4. Hoover Dam and power plant at Boulder Canyon, Colorado River. (*U.S. Bureau of Reclamation.*)

the Hoover Dam (U.S. Reclamation Service), for instance, is a useful booklet. Similar pamphlets on other dams can also be secured from the U.S. Reclamation Service.

15-3. Using Water's Energy

For hundreds of years men have used the energy in flowing or falling water to turn wheels for grinding or sawing. In New England one can still see some of the old undershot, overshot, or breast wheels. Today, water-power plants use either the Pelton wheel or the turbine.

Water in Motion: An Energy Source. To understand how falling or flowing water can be used for power, your students might begin with some simple experiments. Ask them to devise ways of showing that water in motion can move obstacles in its path, marbles or pebbles, clay or soil.

Students might plan to use an open trough, such as the metal gutter along the eaves of a house. Sections may be put together by overlapping or with clay. An elbow section would help to show the action of water around bends. The degree of slope or grade can be controlled. Marbles, shot, or soil might be used. The demonstration table in a science room is usually long enough to show the force of the water.

A Model Water Wheel. A student may be interested in building a water wheel as shown in Fig. 15-5. When it is mounted on a shaft, a

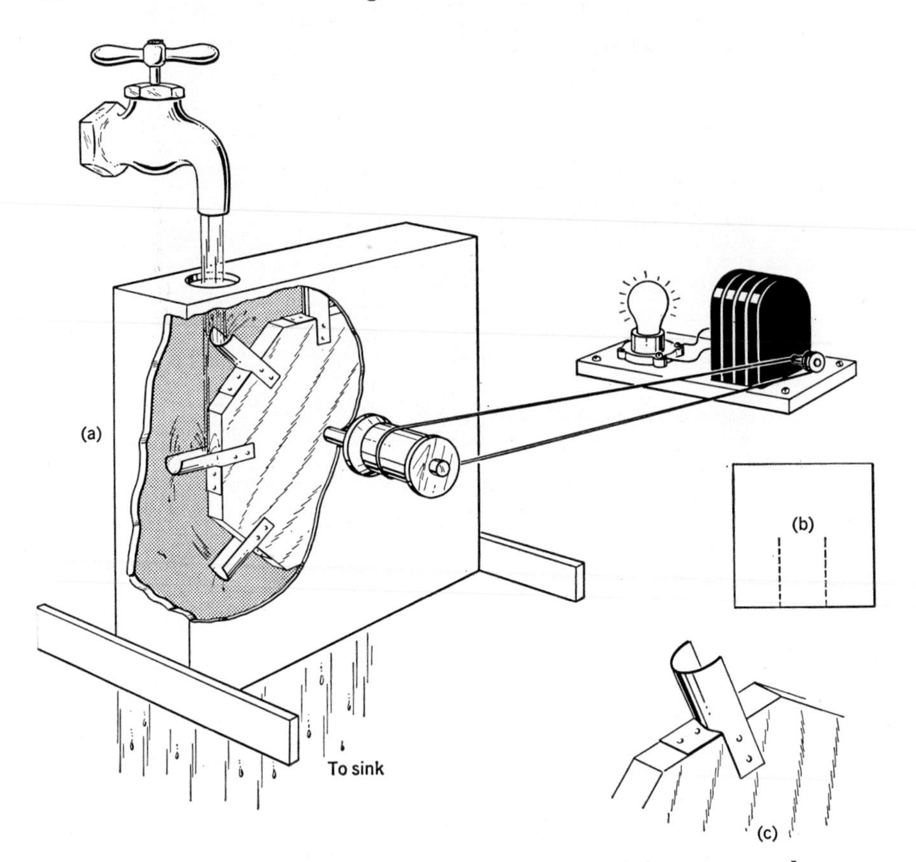

Fig. 15-5. A homemade water wheel. (*a*) Water wheel driving a toy dynamo; (*b*) how to cut tin for cup; (*c*) how to fasten cup to wheel. (*From Morris Meister, Living in a World of Science, Charles Scribner's Sons, New York, 1939.*)

strong spray may be directed against the blades with a hose and nozzle. Have your students find out under what conditions of elevation and supply the Pelton wheel would be particularly useful.

The Turbine. Students might bring to class pictures of modern turbines. How are turbines mounted? How is the water directed against the blades? How is the power transmitted to the electrical generator?

How Efficient Are Modern Water Wheels? The work done upon a water wheel is the product of the weight of water which passes through it multiplied by the head of water (the difference in level between the reservoir and the tail race). The efficiency of modern water wheels of both types is frequently from 80 to 90 per cent.

Ask your students to calculate the efficiency of a 5,000-horsepower turbine at a falls where the head is 136 feet and each turbine can handle 22,500 cubic feet of water per minute. If your students live near a place where water power is utilized they can obtain data themselves from the power company.

$$\text{Work done per minute} = 22{,}500 \times 62.4 \times 136 = 191{,}000{,}000 \text{ ft-lb}$$

In terms of horsepower this is $\frac{191{,}000{,}000}{33{,}000}$, or 5,800 hp input. The output is 5,000 hp. Therefore, the efficiency is $\frac{5{,}000}{5{,}800}$, or about 86 per cent.

From Water to Electricity. Have your students trace the story of the development of water power in our country. They will note that early in our history, since colonial times, falling or flowing water has been used as a source of power. It was not, however, until the commercial use of electricity developed around 1880 that the power of falling water could be used at a distance by electrical transmission from the power site.

If your students are ingenious enough they may be able to light an electric light by means of their homemade water wheel. To accomplish this, they will need to couple the wheel by means of a pulley to a small dynamo, which in turn is wired to a flashlight bulb (Fig. 15-5). They will require a faucet from which water will flow with great pressure. (If the water tank is on top of the building, the pressure will increase the farther down one goes.) To receive the full effect of the water pressure they can fit a one-holed stopper into the faucet and insert into the hole a glass tube, to which is attached a piece of rubber tubing and then another piece of glass tubing, which can steer the flow of the water directly against the wheel paddles.

There are, of course, many things that can go wrong with this experiment. The light bulb may need to be tested with a battery; the dynamo may have to be checked. Perhaps the water pressure is at fault. The best learning experience of all may come through the discovery of "what's wrong."

Water Power and the Future. Are we using all our available water power? It is interesting to note that government studies show that in 1950 less than 20 per cent of the potential hydropower of our country had been developed.

One of the present difficulties is that potential sources are not near our large centers of population. Someday it may be possible and economically feasible to transmit electricity over far greater distances than at present.

Water is a unique source of energy; unlike coal, oil, and gas that are irreplaceable, water is with us always—at any rate, as long as nature functions as it does at present. The greater the use of water as a source of energy, the less we will need to dig into our exhaustible fuel resources. It may, however, come to pass in the foreseeable future that atomic power will dwarf all other sources (see Chapter 16).

15-4. Using the Power of Steam

Fill a Pyrex test tube one-quarter full of water. Cover the outside of a cork stopper with petroleum jelly and insert it into the mouth of the test tube. Holding the test tube with the corked end pointed away from you and everyone else, bring the bottom of the tube into the flame of a bunsen burner. The water boils—and watch out! Steam takes about 1,700 times the space of the water from which it comes. This enormous expansion accounts for the fact that steam can move a piston (as in the steam engine) or turn a wheel (as in the steam turbine).

This experiment might also be tried: Punch holes with a nail and hammer diagonally across from each other on the two broad surfaces of a small pepper can (½ inch from the bottom and close to the corner). Put 2 tablespoons of water in the can and close the lid. Suspend the can from the ring of a ring stand by means of a handle made of thread, which is taped to each side of the can. The can should balance and swing freely. The apparatus is now ready for heating. As soon as the water begins to boil the can will start to whirl. Elicit from students that the force of the steam is responsible for the motion.

Now your students are ready to study Watt's steam engine and how it works. (They may use a physics textbook as reference.) Why was this invention so revolutionary?

A Model Turbine. Students might make a simple steam turbine (Fig. 15-6) and operate it. All steam engines apply the fundamental principle of using the power of moving steam to drive wheels that transfer the power to machines through belts, couplings, gears, or some other method.

Fig. 15-6. Simple model of a velocity steam turbine.

What is needed to produce the steam? Notice that we are right back to our fuel resource problem.

One of your students might report on the gas turbine, which uses the power of the expanding hot gases from liquid fuel combustion directly, instead of burning coal to produce high-pressure steam.

HARNESSING ELECTRICITY

We push a button—a light goes on, or our vacuum cleaner starts to work, or a bell rings, or the elevator takes us upstairs, or—one could go on and on with the things that can happen by that one small motion. How is electricity harnessed to accomplish all these everyday miracles that we take so much for granted?

Your students will need, first of all, to find out by simple experimentation something about static and flowing electricity, then about magnetism and the relationship of magnetism to electricity. (See any general science or physics text or workbook.) This will lead to an understanding of the workings of motors and generators.

15-5. Motors

The Simplest of All Motors. One of the most important uses of the magnetic effect of electricity is in the electric motor. Put the north pole of a bar magnet near the north pole of a compass; the needle is repelled and pushed away. If you follow the needle with the magnet, the needle can be kept spinning around and around, for it is constantly repelled by a rotating magnetic field. In a certain sense, this is a highly oversimplified motor.

A series of electromagnets so connected that the magnetic field rotates is more practical than a moving magnet. An armature consisting of such electromagnets will rotate continuously in a magnetic field.

Making a Toy Motor. Here are directions for making a motor (Fig. 15-7): To make the field magnet use a thick strip of sheet iron. It should

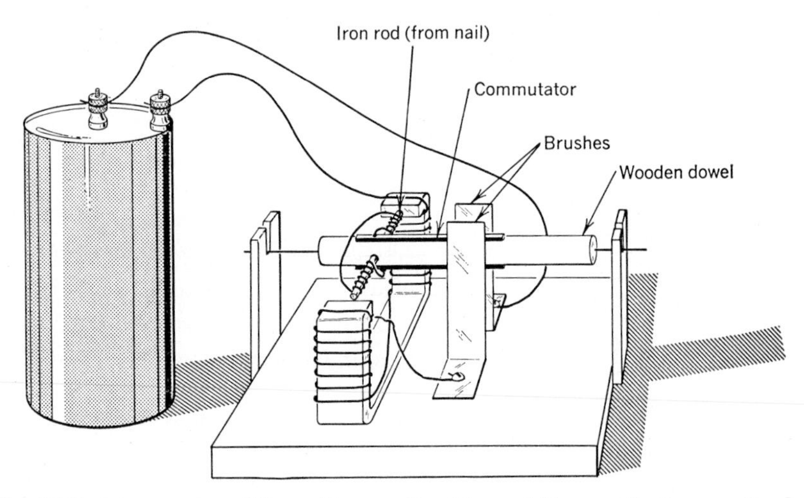

Fig. 15-7. A toy motor. (*From Hyman Ruchlis and Harvey B. Lemon, Exploring Physics, Harcourt, Brace and Company, Inc., New York, 1952.*)

be bent to a U shape and nailed to a piece of wood. Around the iron wind several hundred turns of magnet wire. (It is important that the windings be in opposite directions on each arm of the U.) To make the armature A, cut a nail to serve as a rod and wind about 50 turns of magnet wire on it. Insert the iron rod halfway into a piece of dowel stick. For the commutator, attach two metal strips to the dowel rod with a tape and mount the dowel so that it will rotate freely. When the model is connected as shown it should operate as a motor.

Your students may find other directions in a number of books on electricity. More advanced students will want to go on to study the various types of electric motors and how they have been improved.

Students might count the number of electric motors of one kind or another used in their homes. Have them compare the operation of an electric motor with that of a gasoline engine. They might picture the difficulties of trying to run an electric fan or vacuum cleaner with a gasoline motor.

15-6. Generators

Our Dependence on Electric Power. Can any of your students recall a power failure in their community? They might recount what happened or what may happen as lights go out, electrically controlled oil burners and refrigerators cease to function, radios, TVs, and telephones become silent.

Such a discussion might lead directly to a study of the electric generator or dynamo, the machine responsible for converting energy of motion into electrical energy.

The Principle of the Generator. Connect a coil of insulated copper wire to a galvanometer. Thrust a bar magnet in and out of this coil and ask your students to watch the needle of the galvanometer move as current is induced in the coil. Now, try keeping the magnet stationary and move the coil. What are the results? Repeat the experiment, using in turn a stronger magnet, a coil with more turns of wire, a more rapid motion.

These simple experiments, originally performed by Michael Faraday, are basic to an understanding of the giant generators in our modern powerhouses. You may want to go on to study a-c and d-c generators and transformers whose invention has made it possible to deliver electrical energy several hundred miles from a power station.

Energy for the Generator. A generator is really an electron pump, with the ability to make electrons move through a circuit. Discuss with your students that the source of the electrical energy is the mechanical energy of the rotating armature of the generator. Some outside source of energy —water power from a dam or heat energy from the burning of a fuel— is now commonly used to create this motion. As our fossil fuels dwindle what other sources of energy are we trying to develop?

More Energy for Peak Loads. Here is an interesting problem in connection with the variable loads carried by generators.

Take a small hand generator and ask a student to turn it over rapidly while the circuit is open. Then suddenly short-circuit the generator by connecting the two terminals with a wire or metal bar. A large amount of current now flows in the wire but the generator becomes harder to turn. Your students can perhaps figure out that what happens is this: When the circuit is completed, electrical energy is produced as the coil rotates in the magnetic field. The energy for this electricity is supplied by the extra work that must be done to keep turning the coil. Your students will now be ready to study this phenomenon in more detail and to reach the generalization expressed in Lenz's law: When an electric current is induced in a conductor cutting through a magnetic field, the direction of the induced current is such as to give rise to a new magnetic field that opposes the original motion.

Electric companies must be mindful of Lenz's law. As consumers use more electricity the generators tend to slow down, just as did the hand generator in the experiment. To keep generators at a uniform speed at those times of day when demand is high, it becomes necessary to burn more coal and apply greater steam pressure. To get energy, we must supply it.

A Recent Development: The Fuel Cell. Here is material for a student report: A new type of electric generator known as the "fuel cell" promises to have fairly immediate application in rail traction and may provide the means of converting energy into electric power without using a turbine and generator. The fuel cell, developed in Great Britain by F. T. Bacon and his associates at Cambridge University, is found to be more efficient than a steam turbine generator. The cost of hydrogen, the pri-

Fig. 15-8. Four generator units on "full load" operation at the Hungry Horse Project power plant, Montana. (*U.S. Bureau of Reclamation.*)

mary fuel required, makes its application in most instances economically impractical at present. The cell uses hydrogen, oxygen, an aqueous potassium hydroxide electrolyte, and sintered nickel electrodes. It produces electricity as a result of the reaction between hydrogen and oxygen under pressure.

Scientists have suggested the combination of photoelectric equipment to produce hydrogen by means of solar energy with a fuel cell of the Bacon type as a feasible future central-station power source.

15-7. Public versus Private Power

"From whom do we consumers buy our electricity?" This question will lead to a gathering of data.

Many industrial plants generate their own electric current, using steam, diesel, or hydropower. Current is manufactured and sold by large electrical power companies, 85 per cent of the power produced in the United States being sold by private companies, the rest by government, either municipal or Federal (Fig. 15-8). An important by-product of the flood control program of the Tennessee Valley Authority is abundant, inexpensive electricity, with benefits to large numbers of rural families in the region. Development of other such projects is a burning issue in certain regions, an issue made bitter by politics. Whether the government should be in the power business is a question your students will eventually face as voters. Might a discussion of the issues be fruitful in your class?

ENERGY FROM FOSSIL FUELS

15.8. Coal

Coal, of course, is one of our basic fuels. Today more tons of coal are mined than any other mineral in the United States. The coal produced in this country each year has a greater dollar value than any other single mineral except petroleum.

A student might report on how much of our coal is wasted at present. (In a modern steam power plant the supply of coal represents two-thirds of that which started from the mine, one-third being lost in mining and transportation. Much of the fuel is also wasted as it burns in the fires of boilers, and often less than 4 per cent of it is converted to useful work.)

Although we have already mined our best and most easily accessible reserves of coal, our supply is thought to be adequate for many years to come. We must consider, however, that coal is a nonrenewable resource, for we mine what took nature millions of years to create. What we are really doing as we dig it out of the earth is drawing on our capital stock of the "fixed" sunshine of bygone ages.

You might discuss with your students that research will bring to light new and more efficient ways of utilizing and conserving our coal, all the way from the mine to the multitude of places where it is used. As our resources of petroleum shrink, we may perhaps come to depend more and more on these "black stones" which have locked within them invaluable stores of energy. For an excellent booklet on coal, its origin, nature, uses, mining, and preparation, write for *Facts About Coal* (U.S. Bureau of Mines).

A Field Trip to the Coal Mines. If you can establish contact with a coal-mining community; if your students can go down into the underground city which is a coal mine; if they can talk with miners, union officials, mineowners, then your class may bring back to school a wealth of material to be explored in the classroom.

In science, for instance, models of mining and processing might be constructed, a study might be made of the miner's lamp, samples of coal from the region and from the school's coal bin might be analyzed, comparative fuel values might be studied.

In one school, which offered a field trip to the anthracite region of Pennsylvania as part of the senior-year experience, community ties with the school became so strong that groups of students and teachers were not regarded as "outsiders" but as neighbors who exchanged visits and became friends. Students came back to the classroom, not only with new human relationships established, but also with some insight into the problems which geography, geology, and economics impose on people. They learned how a community, too long a one-industry region, was attempting to pull itself up by the bootstraps. Here is the material of science and social studies come alive!

If a visit to a coal mine is out of the question, perhaps you might wish your students to have the vicarious experience. You may obtain a film called *Modern Coal Mining* (Goodyear Tire and Rubber Company, Modern Talking Picture Service, Akron, Ohio). Another interesting film is *Powering America's Progress: A Modern Story of Bituminous Coal* (U.S. Bureau of Mines).

The Davy Safety Lamp. Turn on the gas in the bunsen burner. Place a square of fine-mesh wire gauze on a tripod above the chimney of the burner and ignite the gas above the gauze. The flame will burn above but not below the wire gauze. The conductivity of the metal prevents the temperature below the gauze from reaching the kindling point of the gas. If you have a Davy safety lamp, your students may examine it and point out the purpose of the gauze.

A homemade safety lamp may be fashioned in this way: Roll a 4-inch square of copper gauze into a cylinder. Fold a circular piece of gauze, a little larger than the diameter of the cylinder, over one end of it to make

Fig. 15-9. Safety inspector making a test for flammable gas in a second mining gangway. (*Bureau of Mines, U.S. Department of the Interior.*)

a lid. Fit a cork of suitable size tightly into the base of the cylinder and affix a small candle to the cork by means of a protruding nail forced through it. A loop of wire attached to the top of the cylinder may serve as a handle.

Into a large-mouthed bottle or cylinder pass illuminating gas from a gas jet. Light the candle and cover the cylinder with the gauze lid. Now lower the cylinder into the bottle of gas. Nothing will happen, or there may be a small flash inside the cylinder as the candle goes out. If a naked flame is cautiously brought to the mouth of the bottle, the gas will burn explosively.

You might want to discuss with your students how the safety lamp's invention and use mark our growing awareness of the need to protect workers in the dangerous trades (Fig. 15-9).

Gravimetric Analysis of Coal. When coal is heated, the substances that first escape are *moisture,* followed by *volatile matter.* On further heating, the *fixed carbon* is burned off in contact with air, until only the *ash* remains.

"Fuel ratio," by which coals are classified, means the proportion of fixed carbon to volatile matter. For anthracite coal this is a much higher number (over 10) than for bituminous coal (between 3 and 6).

Here are details of the steps to be taken in the analysis of a coal sample.

1. Pulverize the coal in a mortar and grind it to a powder.

2. Weigh out (to centigrams) about 2 grams of the powdered coal in a covered crucible.

3. Heat the uncovered crucible in a drying oven for about an hour and weigh the crucible, contents, and cover again after cooling. The loss of weight represents the *moisture* content of the coal.

4. Heat the covered crucible until smoke no longer comes off. This time, the loss of weight represents *volatile matter.*

5. Heat intensely the uncovered crucible, inclined in a clay triangle on a ring stand, until all the carbon is burned off. Also burn the carbon from the cover.

6. The loss of weight represents the *fixed carbon.* The weight of the residue is the weight of the *ash.*

Coke and By-products of Soft Coal. Students may arrange the apparatus for the destructive distillation of cannel coal as in Fig. 15-10. *A* is a used Pyrex test tube with coarsely ground cannel (soft) coal. *B* is empty. *C* contains a piece of filter paper wet with lead acetate solution at the bottom; strips of moistened red and blue litmus paper are held by a rubber stopper at the top. *D* is filled with water. The test tube *A* is heated until four test tubes of gas have been collected and discarded. A fifth is collected and tested with a lighted splint. The illuminating power of the flame may be noted. What is the gas called? (coal gas.)

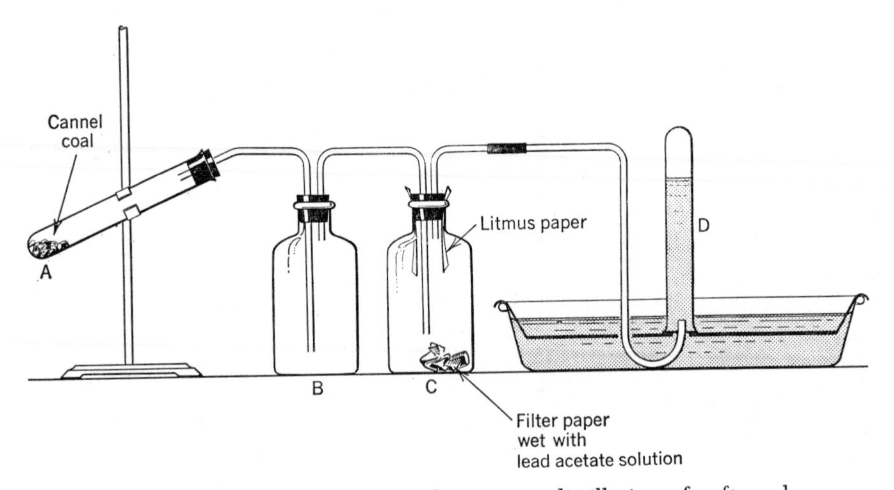

Fig. 15-10. A device to show destructive distillation of soft coal.

The residue in *A* may be examined. What is it? (coke.) What is it used for? Students may note the color and odor of the liquid in *B*. What is it? (coal tar.) What are its uses? What is the significance of the test in *C*? Has the gas any commercial value?

Coal Tar: From Waste to Resource. You may want to examine this bit of history with your students: Prior to World War I about 75 per cent of the coke in our country was wastefully produced in beehive ovens. All the volatile products either burned or escaped into the air from the top of the oven. Millions of dollars worth of coal tar, coal gas, and ammonia (an impurity in the coal gas) were thus completely wasted.

During the war there was an increasing demand for these important by-products and a realization that we were unnecessarily wasting valuable natural resources. This led to the construction of by-product ovens. Now, instead of producing only coke (needed for making pig iron as a fuel and a reducing agent), we get coal gas (a valuable gaseous fuel), coal tar (with its myriad derivatives), and ammonia (which can be converted to fertilizer).

From the point of view of resource use it is interesting to note that coal tar was a source of trouble to the early gas makers. They did not know what to do with it, since there was not yet a demand for road tar. They therefore got rid of it by allowing it to flow into nearby streams.

It was through chemistry that the problem was solved. One of your students might report on Perkins's discovery that dye could be produced from coal tar, and how this led to the production of the fantastic number of coal-tar derivatives available today.

Students may note the transformation of coal tar from a waste product to one of our truly valuable resources.

Fertilizer from Coke Ovens. The soluble portions of coal gas, passing through water, are dissolved. The chief product of this kind is ammonia, which in solution becomes ammonium hydroxide. How can this be made into fertilizer? Some student may suggest neutralization (Sec. 7-8) and this is what is actually done. The solution is run through sulfuric acid until ammonium sulfate crystals form. These are washed and whirled dry and are sold as commercial fertilizer, supplying both nitrogen and sulfur as plant nutrients.

The Coal Situation. Your students' study of coal might terminate in a summary of the situation. Although coal is by far the largest store of fossil organic substance, its utilization lags. Scientific and technological advances suggest that it may be used in the future not as a fuel but as a chemical raw material. On the other hand, as fossil fuels dwindle and if atomic energy remains too expensive, coal may be needed increasingly as a fuel.

15-9. Petroleum

Fuel requirements for our modern motors consist of a cheap liquid that will vaporize readily and burn violently when mixed with air. Petroleum, from which we obtain the motor fuel, gasoline, and fuel oil for diesel engines and furnaces, is at present one of our most important "energy" resources. It is also the one that is dwindling most rapidly.

To start this unit, you might want to demonstrate the principle upon which the operation of the internal-combustion engine depends, for this engine is one of the chief users of petroleum.

The Principle of the Internal-combustion Engine. Repeat or recall the experiment on making a "safe" explosion (Sec. 10-7). This simple demonstration may be used to illustrate the explosion taking place in an internal-combustion engine—the can, representing the cylinder; the match, the spark plug; the illuminating gas, vaporized gasoline; the explosive mixture, the mixing of gasoline and air in the carburetor; the lid, the piston.

Now your students may go on to the study of the detailed workings of various types of internal-combustion engines, their advantages and disadvantages. (Refer them to a physics textbook.)

How do we obtain the fuel to keep all these modern engines going? Such a question might be the next problem for your class. Perhaps, at this point, you might want to show a movie such as *The Evolution of the Oil Industry* or *Petroleum and Its Uses* (U.S. Bureau of Mines).

Prospecting for Petroleum. The physical principles involved in detecting oil by the seismic method are quite within the scope of science classes. The reflection of sound is the crowning concept.

If you are near a place where echoes are possible, try some experiments. You will discover that you must be at least 20 to 25 yards distant from the reflecting surface if the echo is to be distinct from the original sound. The greater the distance, the longer the time before the reflected wave reaches the ear. It is possible to measure the distance between yourself and a cliff or other reflecting surface by the time it takes the echo to return to you.

Now your students are ready "to get a bang" out of understanding the principles of the seismic method of prospecting. As the sound of a dynamite explosion passes down through the earth it is reflected from the hard rock dome which covers the oil deposit. The reflection is timed and the position of the dome under the earth is estimated.

A modification of this method, making use of stereophonic tape recordings of the underground echoes from test explosions, has produced even clearer information about subsurface rock formations. This method played an important part in the discovery of new oil fields in France.

Mining Petroleum. The story of the mining of petroleum can be told in a variety of ways. There are many free pamphlets, filmstrips, and films on all phases of the industry, available from such companies as Standard Oil Company and Shell Oil Company.

Thanks to modern technology, great savings in oil-drilling operations are now effected. In the early days only about 25 per cent of the oil was recovered from a reservoir. Now it is possible, particularly in the abundant fields, to recover more than 80 per cent of the available oil.

Improved methods enable oil companies to drill for oil at a lower depth than could previously be reached. The "life" of oil wells can be increased by forcing the natural gas back into the wells. If the oil is withdrawn slowly rather than rapidly, oil yields may be increased. These are a few of the conservation measures that may be applied at the source.

Great advances have also been made in the storage of oil, by preventing its evaporation and deterioration in tanks and pipelines. New protective systems have minimized fire losses.

Distillation of Crude Petroleum. Several students might help you in setting up this demonstration experiment: Arrange the apparatus as shown in Fig. 15-11. If you do not have or cannot make by glass blowing

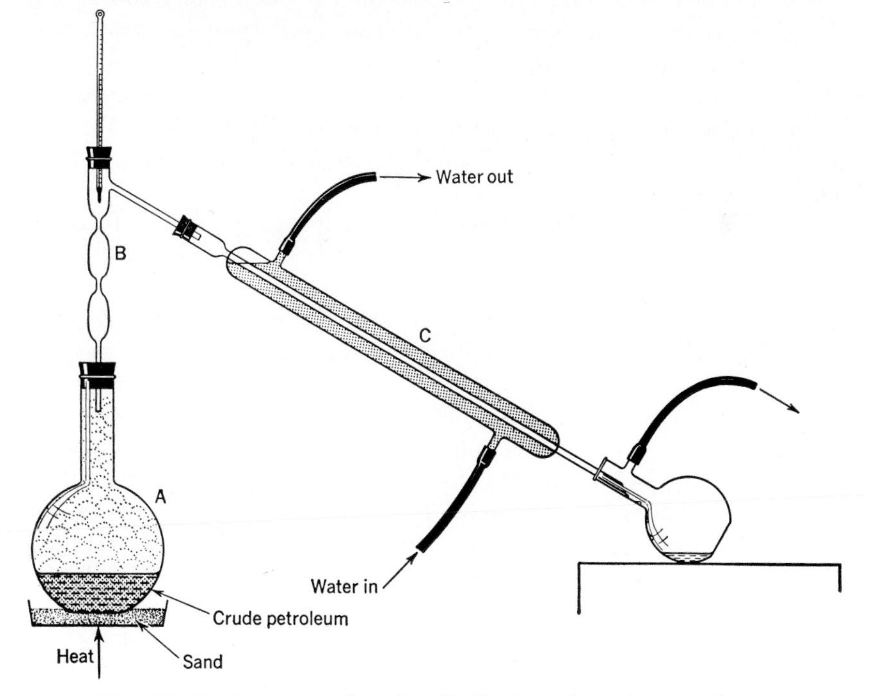

Fig. 15-11. Apparatus for the distillation of crude petroleum.

a fractionating column, you may still obtain reasonably good results, although an efficient fractionating column will demonstrate more clearly the industrial operations involved in petroleum distillation.

Place 100 milliliters of petroleum in flask *A* and then connect the fractionating column *B* and the Liebig condenser *C*. Use a 150-milliliter side-arm flask *D* to collect the volatile distillate. Connect a long piece of rubber tubing, reaching almost to the floor, to the arm of *D* to remove vapors far from the flame. (A hot plate would be safer to use.)

When about 15 milliliters of distillate have been collected, the liquid may be tested for unsaturated hydrocarbons. This is done by adding a little dilute potassium permanganate solution to a portion of the liquid. If unsaturated hydrocarbons are present, the solution should be decolorized. To test the volatility of the distillate, moisten a wad of cotton with a few drops of the liquid and see whether it will ignite in a burner flame.

More and Better Gasoline. Students might report on methods that have succeeded in improving the yield of gasoline—cracking (both thermal and catalytic), polymerization, alkylation, the blending of casing-head gas with other gasolines.

Other students might deal with the synthesis of gasoline from carbon monoxide (from coal) and hydrogen by the Fischer-Tropsch process, and the manufacture of gasoline from oil shales and from tar sands. Even though these methods cannot at present compete with gasoline from oil wells because of high costs, is it important that they be developed?

The American Petroleum Institute, 50 West 50th St., New York, has many interesting free booklets, among them *The Conservation of Petroleum.*

Some Tests for Gasoline. *Volatility.* Set a watch glass on a beaker of boiling water on an electric heater and place on the glass 10 drops of gasoline. (Be sure to keep the gasoline away from all flames, for it is highly flammable.) Notice how long it takes for the gasoline to vaporize completely. The experiment might be repeated with 10 drops of kerosene or other fuel oil.

Vaporizing Temperature. An ordinary side-arm distilling flask (Fig. 15-11), with the fractionating column omitted, may be used for this experiment. The thermometer should have a range of −10 to 360°C. Into the flask put 100 milliliters of gasoline and a few glass beads to prevent bumping. A hot plate is superior to an open flame for greater safety. After the condenser is connected and the heat applied, collect the distillate in a 100-milliliter graduate.

These data should then be recorded: The temperature at which the first drop of distillate appears (known as the "initial boiling point"); the volume of the distillate collected at 20° intervals; the volume of the residue left in the distilling flask.

It might be interesting for students to plot a graph of the percentage of distillate against the temperature range. They might also make a table recording the volume of collected distillate from the initial boiling point to 100°C. The higher the value, the more efficient the liquid as a low-volatile gasoline.

Other kinds and grades of gasoline may be tested in this fashion and the results compared.

Combustion. This is an experiment best done as a demonstration. Put *one* drop of gasoline into a warmed wide-mouthed bottle. Cork the bottle and shake it well. After removing the cork, *cautiously* bring a lighted splint near the mouth of the bottle. If the result is negative, the test may be repeated by adding one drop of gasoline at a time until the vapor burns explosively.

The experiment might be tried again with other grades and kinds of gasoline.

Specific Gravity of Liquid Fuels. Students may test the specific gravity of various grades of gasoline as well as fuel oils. The lighter oils flow freely and burn more readily, but the heavier oils yield more Btu per gallon.

Pycnometer Method. Weigh a dry, empty bottle with a stopper inserted. Next, fill the bottle with the liquid to be tested, stopper it, and reweigh it. A final weighing is made when the bottle is filled with water. From these three weighings your students can compute the specific gravity of the liquid, namely, its weight divided by the weight of an equal volume of water.

Hydrometer Method. Float a hydrometer in a tall jar nearly filled with the liquid to be tested. To obtain the specific gravity directly, read on the hydrometer scale the position of the surface of the liquid.[1]

Varied Uses of Liquid Fuels. After your students become acquainted with the lighter and heavier fractions of petroleum's distillation, you may want to discuss the uses to which these fractions are put. This will involve the use of gasoline for automobiles, fuel oil for diesel engines and oil burners. The pros and cons of using fuel oil, as against coal or gas, for space heating might also be discussed. What are the promising fuels of the future?

Other Uses of Petroleum. Perhaps some of your students might be interested in setting up an exhibit of petroleum products. Aside from fuels and lubricants, these would include alcohols, detergents, insecticides, plastics, resins, textiles, and synthetic rubber. Under what conditions might these uses become as important as petroleum's use as a fuel?

[1] For an experiment describing how absolute specific gravity readings may be converted to the American Petroleum Institute scale, see How Can Fuel Oils Be Tested? in *Test It Yourself* (Sec. 19-2*w*).

Petroleum and Conservation. As a reading lesson to be followed by discussion, you might use this excerpt from *Resources for Freedom* (Sec. 19-2*f*).

> Petroleum is the great enigma of future energy supplies. For years it has been predicted that the nation's crude oil supply would be exhausted within one or two decades, yet discoveries and output have

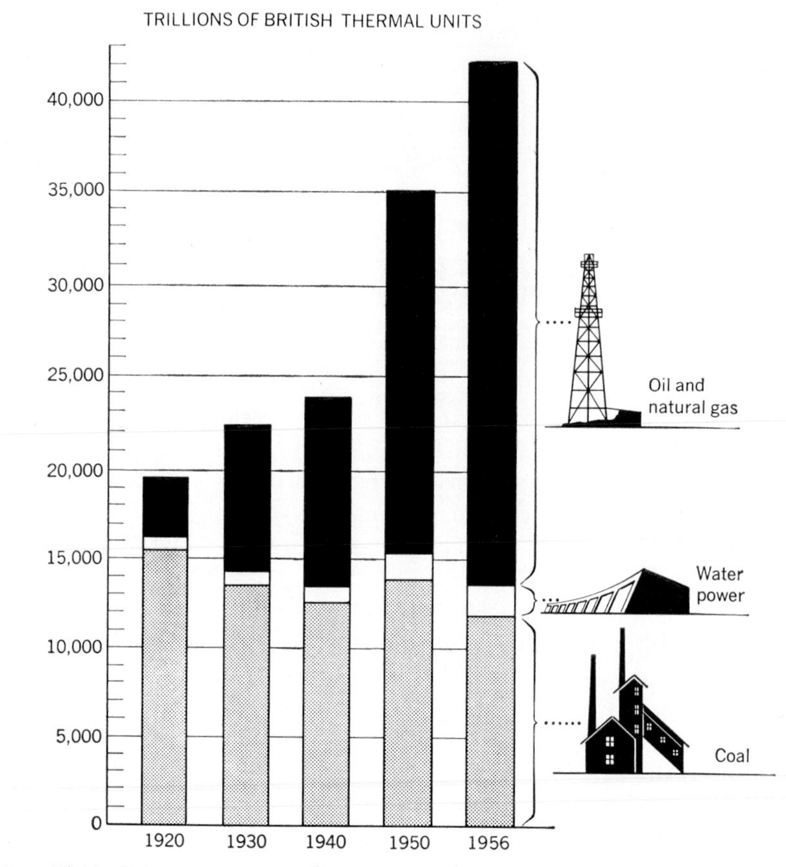

Fig. 15-12. Primary sources of energy in the U.S.A. (*From Teacher's Handbook, Petroleum School Series, American Petroleum Institute, New York.*) SOURCE: U.S. Bureau of Mines.

> continued to rise.[2] Between 1950 and 1955, however, a new warning signal has appeared; United States demand for oil has begun to outstrip domestic production, and for the first time the nation has become a heavy net importer.
>
> Faced with an approximate doubling of oil demand by 1975, the United States may find it economic to turn increasingly to several new

[2] See Fig. 15-12.

and expansible sources of liquid fuel—imports of crude and "synthetic oil" from domestic shales and coal.

There is, in any event, need for action on the side of oil *use*, so that all available supplies can be made to go further. There are many points at which the Nation could reduce consumption and physical waste of liquid fuels with little or no inconvenience. The oil and automobile industries in particular could assume the obligation of leading the Nation toward a more efficient use of its liquid fuel supplies; consumers themselves can contribute strongly if they are kept properly informed of conservation measures.

Ask your class what such "conservation measures" might be.

The Auto Engine of the Future? A strong contender for the automobile engine of the future is the free-piston engine. One of your students might report on this engine, which is now ready to compete with diesel power. The use of this engine is particularly interesting from the conservation point of view, since the machine can probably burn crude oil or shale oil. Of what advantage would this be?

The Auto Fuel of the Future? Students might begin to project their thoughts to the years ahead. Perhaps an electrochemical device or some other form of storage unit for electricity may power automobiles in the foreseeable future.

As our production of oil approaches its peak—estimated for no later than 1965—while our demand continues to soar, scientists are beginning to look for other methods of propelling our cars besides the burning of gasoline or fuel oil. The storage of electricity by some means may be one of the answers. It will be interesting to watch developments.

15-10. Natural Gas

Here is a little background material: Natural gas was not considered a great natural resource until the mid-1930s. Twenty years later the number of families using it had doubled, and today industries and municipalities are increasingly turning to natural gas as a fuel.

The tasks of extraction, processing, and distribution take unusual forms in the case of this particular fuel. It is usually found and drilled for in association with petroleum, actually coming out of the same hole. About half is now used locally and the rest is transported by an ever-growing network of interstate pipelines to utility companies hundreds of miles away.

In speaking of "Conservation at the Field," the authors of *Resources for Freedom* (Sec. 19-2*f*) make this statement:

Great strides have recently been made in reducing the percentage of "flaring" and other losses of gas. . . . The natural gas still flared represents a tremendous waste of fuel which would have great value

in future years, and this is properly a matter of serious concern to the State governments involved.

What chemically is natural gas? What is flaring? What advantages and disadvantages are there to the use of natural gas as a fuel? These are questions which your students might raise and try to answer.

The problem, too, of controlling production of natural gas by state and Federal laws is an up-to-the-minute issue for class thinking and discussion.

Properties of Natural Gas. If your community uses natural gas as a fuel, then your students are familiar with its properties, particularly the way it burns in their gas stoves or bunsen burners.

Making It in the Laboratory. Students can make natural gas, or methane, in the following way: Mix 5 grams of fused sodium acetate, $NaC_2H_3O_2$, with 3 grams of soda lime, $NaOH + CaO$. Heat this mixture in a Pyrex test tube generator. Collect the gas by water displacement. (The calcium oxide of the soda lime is to keep the mixture porous and infusible. It does not in any way enter into the reaction.) Burn the methane. Observe the color and luminosity of the flame.

SOME FUEL CONSERVATION MEASURES

15-11. Utilizing Fuels Completely

More Complete Combustion. Measure out exactly 50 milliliters of water in each of two beakers of the same size and kind, and read the temperature of the water. Set one beaker on an asbestos mat supported by a ring and ring stand. Heat the water for about 3 minutes with a luminous flame of a bunsen burner (representing incomplete combustion). Turn off the flame and ask a student to record the temperature of the water.

Repeat with the water in the other beaker, using a nonluminous flame (representing complete combustion). Ask students to compare results.

Now your class is ready to discuss the fuel saving that could be effected by complete fuel combustion. What other advantage does complete combustion have (Sec. 12-5)?

Do we have complete combustion in our automobile engines? What would be the advantages if this were possible? What are the pros and cons of smaller cars for the future?

Do we have complete combustion in our space-heating furnaces? In our industrial furnaces? (Smoke is an indication of incomplete combustion.) How would more complete combustion help?

15-12. Better Insulation of Homes

Elicit from students that saving of fuel, and incidentally lowering of fuel bills, could be brought about by preventing the leakage of heat from our homes and other buildings.

Is Motionless Air a Good or a Poor Insulator? Attach a few matchsticks, by means of wax drippings from a candle, to a long metal bar or thick wire which is held horizontal by clamping each end to a ring stand. Sawing a similar bar in two and leaving an air space of about $\frac{1}{8}$ inch between the two pieces, attach matchsticks to both sections and clamp horizontally. Heat the end of each metal bar with a bunsen burner and note what happens to the matchsticks in each case. Ask your students to explain.

Your class will recall that air in motion is able to transfer heat but motionless or "dead air" prevents its transfer. Use is made of this principle in home insulation.

Insulating Materials. Students may place wads of paper, rock wool or glass wool, cotton, asbestos fibers, and cork on a hot plate or radiator and see how well or how poorly heat is conducted through these materials. They may compare the results with the heat conduction of a block of metal when placed on the radiator.

Students may reason that the porous or fibrous materials used in the experiment are good heat insulators because they trap air and keep it motionless.

Keeping Heat Inside. Your students will now understand why the walls and roofs of their homes can be insulated by using rock wool or other lightweight material full of dead air spaces. Aside from keeping heat inside during the winter, will insulation have any effect on comfort in summer?

Storm windows or the more modern glass "sandwich," with air between the two panes, helps to insulate the home. Your students may also suggest other ways such as weatherstripping, storm doors, closed vestibules. Mirrorlike sheets of aluminum, placed in the walls and roof, may be slanted in such a way as to reflect heat rays back into the home.

Has the color of the paint on the outside of a house any effect on heat insulation?

15-13. Less Fuel for Radiant Heating

Perhaps some of your students have radiant heating in their homes. They might describe it to the class. Better still, a field trip might be arranged to an unfinished home at the time concrete is being poured over the pipes. Does radiant heating save fuel? (Because a room can actually be kept cooler and still be comfortable, there can indeed be considerable fuel saving.) Is radiant heating satisfactory in other ways? What about using sunlight directly for space heating (Sec. 16-2)?

15-14. Bringing Outside Heat Indoors: The Heat Pump

There is a relatively new method of heating that is based on the reverse principle of refrigeration. Students may recall or may want to repeat the experiment on the cooling effect of evaporation (Fig. 10-7). Perhaps they have already discussed the fact that refrigerators make use of this principle by withdrawing heat from objects to vaporize a liquid like ammonia or freon. Could this principle be applied to the cooling of a house in summer?

If the refrigeration process is reversed, use might be made of the heat evolved when the gaseous refrigerant is condensed. Could this heat be utilized to warm the house in winter?

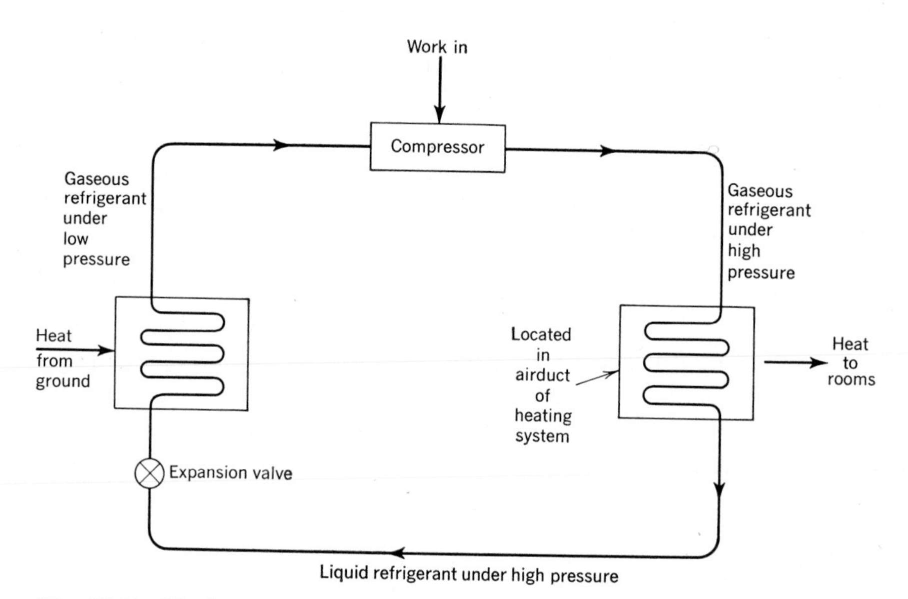

Fig. 15-13. The heat pump, a refrigerator in reverse. In winter, heat from the ground warms the liquid and vaporizes it. In the condenser the refrigerant gives up its heat of condensation and warms the house. A simple valve reverses the direction of the refrigerant in summertime, so that heat is removed from the house and delivered to the ground.

The heat pump (Fig. 15-13) accomplishes these two purposes. A student might reproduce the diagram on the blackboard or throw it on the screen and explain the operation of the pump as the refrigerant takes heat from the ground in winter (or the house in summer) and delivers it at a higher temperature to the place where it is needed (the house in winter or the ground in summer).

The heat pump, while requiring power to run the compressor, utilizes the heat stored in the ground and thus saves fuel. In places where there are no great seasonal extremes of temperature, the heat pump may have a good future. Students might report on the operation of these pumps already installed in some areas of the United States, such as California,

Oregon, and Florida. What about their cost as compared to other methods of heating?

15-15. Our Fossil Fuel Situation

One of your students might report on the present fuel situation. He might first want to look up an article, The Fuel Situation, from the October, 1956, issue of *Scientific American* to see how much the situation has changed since that time. The author is Eugene Ayres, retired manager of research for the Gulf Oil Corporation. In reviewing the situation of all the fossil fuels and their possible sources, Ayres concludes, "All signs indicate we are within sight of the end of the fossil fuel era on our planet."

From the viewpoint of conservation, this means that our technology must move rapidly forward in developing other sources of energy. At the same time we shall need to utilize every means of research and invention to use our remaining resources of fossil fuels with maximum efficiency and economy.

16
Our Energy Sources: Future

The energy sources of the future now being developed by scientists are selectively explored in this chapter. Here may be found experiments and other techniques dealing with the utilization of direct solar energy, the possibilities of sea-water power, and the harnessing and use of atomic energy. Consideration is given to the relationship of these new energy sources to our conventional sources and how this applies to conservation.

SOLAR ENERGY

You might want to start by recalling with your class that the sun is the ultimate source of all our energy, whether we use hydroelectric power or fossil fuels.

Students who are artistically inclined might enjoy illustrating pictorially the various transformations of energy, starting with the sun. Why are scientists turning increasingly to direct sunlight as an energy source?

16-1. How Do We Obtain Energy Directly from the Sun?

Radiant Energy. Have students expose the backs of their hands to direct outdoor sunlight for several minutes, or if this is difficult, have them hold their hands 4 or 5 inches from a glowing 100-watt lamp. How can students explain the warming of their hands? This will lead to a discussion of radiant energy and its absorption by objects.

How Radiant Energy Travels. This is an interesting way to demonstrate the straight-line propagation of radiant energy. Prepare two squares of tin foil. Coat the left-hand surface of *A* with paraffin and blacken the right-hand surface. Cut an *X*-shaped aperture in *B* (Fig. 16-1). Place the squares about 4 inches apart and place an intense source of radiation, a carbon arc or a 400-watt lamp, at *C*. Students may note how the paraffin on *A* melts in the shape of the aperture.

Selective Absorption of Radiant Energy. Select two pieces of the same kind of material, one white, the other black. Students may place both pieces of cloth in the direct rays of the sun or a 100-watt bulb and put a thermometer under each. They may check the temperature of each at the start of the experiment and at the end of each minute up to five. They will notice that the thermometer under the black cloth records a greater increase of temperature, because the black cloth absorbs radiant energy more readily and is better able to convert it into heat.

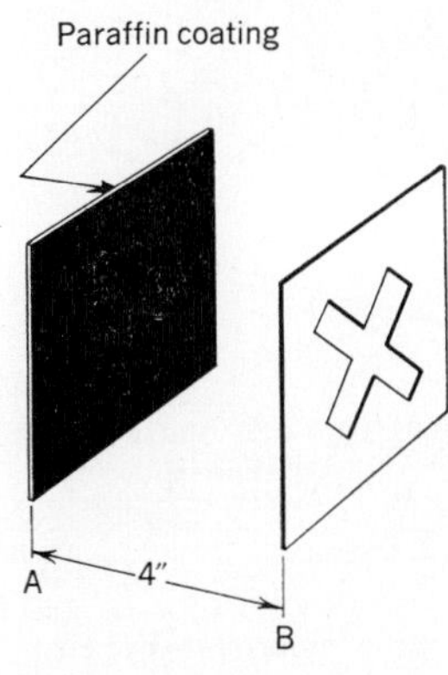

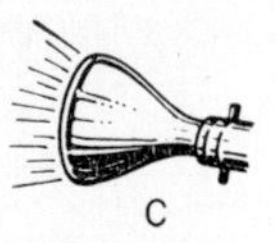

Fig. 16-1. Radiant heat melts the paraffin in the shape of an *X*. How does the energy travel?

If you live in a region where it snows, your students may try the same experiment, selecting a clean spot where the snow is even and undisturbed. After the sun shines on the two cloths for a day or two, under which cloth will the snow have melted the most?

The Greenhouse Effect. Hold a piece of plate glass between a student's hand and a source of radiant energy. Does most of the energy seem to come through as heat?

Repeat the experiment using a bunsen burner instead of the sun. Your students will notice that very little heat from the burner penetrates the glass.

From these experiments your students may learn that window glass allows most of the radiant energy of the sun to go through, while almost completely shutting out the heat radiation of warm objects. To put it another way, the radiant energy of the sun can come through but cannot be radiated out by a glass window. This is the principle of an antique invention, the greenhouse (Fig. 16-2*a*).

Into two terrariums students may place about an inch of soil, into which are inserted thermometers. One is covered with a piece of window glass and both terrariums are placed in direct sunlight for a few hours. Temperature readings are taken once more. Why is one reading so much higher than the other?

Here is another experiment students might try. Take a box not more than several inches deep and fit it with a glass lid. Fit a piece of blackened metal over its bottom. Place a thermometer (reading up to 300°F) in it and put the box in direct sunlight. Notice how very hot it becomes

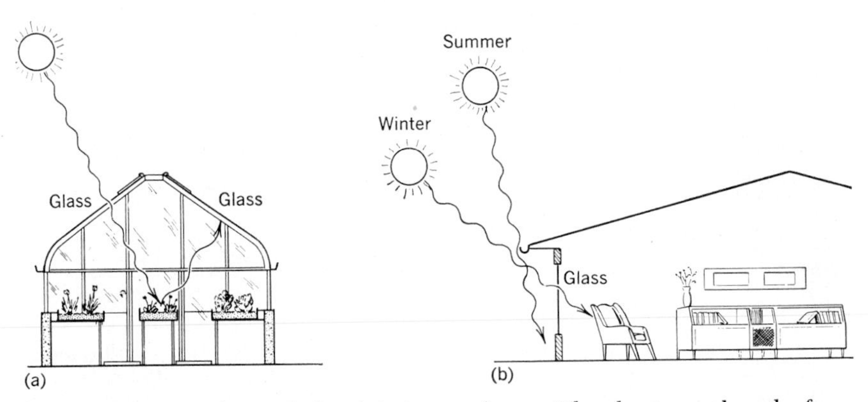

Fig. 16-2. Heating by sunlight. (*a*) A greenhouse. The short wavelengths from the sun penetrate the glass. The longer heat waves are trapped inside; (*b*) a home. Sunlight warms this room in winter. The wide eaves shut out the sun's rays in summer.

inside. A simple device for capturing sunlight, isn't it? But nobody yet knows how to make the black box cheaply enough.

16-2. Solar Space Heating

Elicit from students that humanity's primary need for energy is quite simply to keep warm; therefore it is not surprising to find that so large a proportion of our present energy consumption goes into space heating. Better use of the sun to do this job would seem sensible, since space heating does not call for high temperatures.

Which Rooms Are the Warmest? Ask your students which of the rooms in their homes are warmest, those facing south or the others. This may suggest to them that we might utilize the sun, the original source of our energy, to warm the house directly. Large glass windows on the southern side of a house would let in the heating rays of the sun (Fig. 16-2*b*).

Storing Solar Energy for Heating Homes. Students will be aware that heating homes by the sun's rays has certain disadvantages, especially when the sun is not shining! Can the sun's rays be stored?

Trapping the Sun's Rays to Heat Water Tanks. The glass-topped box with its bottom of blackened metal (Sec. 16-1) finds application in solar-heated houses. By having a roof window of two or three layers of glass permanently curtained by a sheet of copper painted black, the sun's rays are effectively absorbed. This heat energy is then transmitted to and warms the water in specially designed tanks.

Utilizing Heat of Solidification. Another method of storing solar energy makes use of the principle that heat must be added to change a solid to a liquid at the same temperature, and that this latent heat is given up to the surroundings when the liquid solidifies (Sec. 11-13).

Fill a test tube approximately half full of powdered Glauber's salt (hydrated sodium sulfate), insert a thermometer, and heat the tube in a beaker of water until the salt has completely melted.

Then carefully remove the test tube from the water and clamp it in such a way that the thermometer is easily read. Temperature readings should be made every 30 seconds as the liquid cools. As soon as crystals begin to form, temperature observations should be made every minute until the solid has cooled to room temperature. (Students may plot a time and temperature curve on a graph.) They will note that while the liquid is solidifying the temperature remains nearly constant. Elicit from students that this is due to the evolution of heat, known as heat of solidification.

In a solar-heated house designed by Dr. Maria Telkes in Massachusetts, Glauber's salt is heated and melted in the sun while at the same time the sun warms the rooms of the house. When the sun goes down and the house begins to cool off, the salt starts to solidify once more and gives up some of its heat of solidification to the air in the house. The melted Glauber's salt will, however, keep up its temperature of 90°F until it has completely solidified. It has a high latent heat so that the process is a very slow one. This enables the house to remain at an even temperature of about 70°F. Sunlight has been the only energy source.

What about Solar Energy and Heat of Hydration? Heat some crystals of copper sulfate (about 10 grams) in a porcelain dish, holding a funnel over the dish. Note the moisture condensed on the funnel. Continue to heat until the crystals change to a whitish crumbly powder. After it has cooled to room temperature, place this powder in a test tube and insert a thermometer. Add 10 cubic centimeters of water at room temperature. Be careful! The temperature will mount very rapidly and the color will turn blue as the anhydrous copper sulfate hydrates.

Here's a bit of research. Can your students devise a way of using solar energy to release the heat energy of hydration? What might be the disadvantages of this system over the use of heat of solidification?

Solar Energy Can Cool Buildings Too. Have one of your students report on modern methods of refrigeration and the use, in some instances, of a gas flame instead of an electric pump. Students may think it odd that a flame produces a cooling effect. Actually the heat of the flame circulates the fluid and generates the high pressure needed to liquefy the gas (Sec. 12-4). Could solar energy accomplish the same purpose? Refrigeration engineers are busily at work with just such plans in mind. Soon we may have solar devices that will cool our buildings in summer, warm them in winter, and store excess heat for a rainy day.

16-3. Other Solar Energy Devices

Solar Energy into Steam. Students may take a curved mirror and concentrate the sun's rays on water in a shallow dish. They will notice how the temperature of the water rises. How high will the temperature go? It is possible, by means of a large curved mirror, to concentrate the sun's rays on a water boiler and thus to make steam. Although quite efficient, the mirror is at present too expensive to be applied to steam making on a large scale.

You might ask students to place a metal plate, blackened on one side and shiny on the other, over a shallow dish of water, with the blackened side toward the sun so that the sun's rays are allowed to fall on it. Students may note the rise in the temperature of the water at various intervals.

It was reported in January, 1956, that an Israeli scientist, Dr. Harry Tabor, succeeded in making water boil by using the sun's rays in somewhat the manner described above.

A Solar Cooker. Here is an ingenious experiment for one of your students to rig up if you live in a hot, sunny country: Cover an umbrella frame with metal foil. Then turn its inside toward the sun, and place a grid holding a teakettle on the handle. Will the water boil? A device like this was invented by George O. G. Lof, an engineer of Denver, Colorado; it is used as a backyard solar cooker for grilling frankfurters as well as boiling water.

A Solar Cooker for India. Here is a news item that might be brought to class: It is reported from Bombay that a portable solar cooker, simple to operate and requiring no maintenance or repairing costs, has been developed by The National Laboratory of India. The cooker is designed to serve a family of three or four persons and gives the same cooking service as a 400-watt electric oven. Allowing for wet and foggy days, such a solar cooker can be used 280 to 290 days of the year in an area like Bombay, and 310 days in dry areas like the Punjab.

Your class might want to discuss what an invention like this could mean to the peoples and the economy of countries like India.

A Solar Still. An enterprising student might want to try building a solar still of the kind devised by Dr. Maria Telkes (Fig. 16-3*a*). Mount the frame facing the sun and pour briny sea water into the top, drenching the black towel or pad. As the sun's rays heat the pad, the sea water evaporates; a stream of fresh water, warm but salt-free, should trickle out of the lower spigot.

A device of this kind was put into every pilot's emergency equipment during World War II. It saved many airmen forced down into the sea.

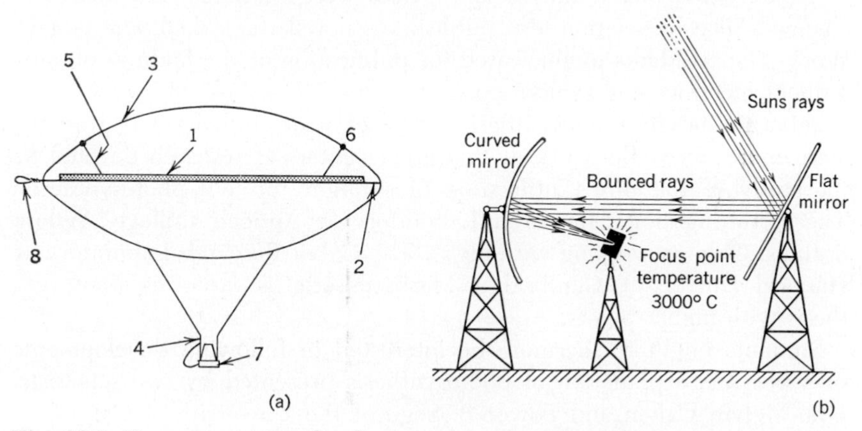

Fig. 16-3. Two promising solar devices. (*a*) The solar still showing (1) black porous pad, (2) pad support, (3) transparent envelope, (4) water-collecting chamber, (5) pad suspension, (6) attaching reinforcement, (7) plug, and (8) towing loop; (*b*) the solar furnace and how it works.

Have your students find out what are the present possibilities of desalting the sea by solar energy on a large scale.[1] Is it still too costly? What might an economically feasible method do toward solving some of our problems of water shortage?

A Solar Furnace. Have your students study the device pictured in Fig. 16-3*b* and explain how it works.

The Solar Battery. Ask a student to report on the solar battery, the "silicon wafer" that can convert useful amounts of the sun's energy directly into electricity. This was described in *Scientific American,* December, 1955, as well as in other scientific publications.

Special Solar Energy Problems. Your students may now want to take a backward glance at the problems of solar energy. They are by this time

[1] Cecil B. Ellis, *Fresh Water from the Ocean,* The Ronald Press Company, New York, 1954 David S. Jenkins, Fresh Water from Salt, *Scientific American,* March, 1957.

aware that the "diluteness" of sunshine and its intermittence create difficulties not encountered by the use of conventional fuels. Perhaps your students could try to make a comparison of present costs. How much does it cost, for instance, to produce and maintain for a given time a certain temperature by means of a bunsen burner? By means of a solar device?

16-4. Keeping Abreast

Applied Solar Energy. There has been formed an Association for Applied Solar Energy, which in 1955 sponsored the first World Symposium at Phoenix, Arizona.[2] Many solar devices were exhibited and ideas exchanged. The association also publishes a newsletter called *The Sun at Work.* Your students might watch for publication of the findings of subsequent meetings and symposiums.

Solar Research: Photosynthesis. Some of your students may want to learn more about the work of two great centers of research devoted to the study of the direct utilization of sunlight through photosynthesis. The Kettering Solar Research Laboratory at Antioch College, Yellow Springs, Ohio, is working with algae. The Cabot Research Laboratory at Harvard University, Cambridge, Massachusetts, is exploring photosynthesis with higher plants.

Students might furthermore be interested in following developments of a possible explanation of photosynthesis presented by two scientists, Drs. Melvin Calvin and Power B. Sogo of the University of California, in *Science,* March 15, 1957. They present evidence that plants have a mechanism similar to the photobattery and suggest that the chloroplasts of plant cells capture sunlight just as a photobattery does and turn it into a kind of electrical current merging with the chemical reactions taking place in photosynthesis. Has this theory received any further confirmation? Are scientists advancing other theories? If so, what are they?

16-5. Sun Power and the Future

Here are some considerations for class discussion: Viewed in the light of the world's power needs, the present sun-powered gadgets may possibly foretell the day when the boundless energy of the sun will be harnessed to run the world's factories, to light and heat our houses, to distill drinking water from the sea, to power space vehicles (Fig. 16-4), to cook our meals, and to do all the other jobs now being performed by coal, oil, gas, and wood—all of which are exhaustible.

It has been estimated in *Energy Sources: The Wealth of the World*

[2] *Proceedings of the World Symposium on Applied Solar Energy* and *Proceedings of the 1959 Advisory Council Conference,* Association for Applied Solar Energy, Phoenix, Ariz.

(Sec. 19-7*a*) that the total sunlight falling on the earth for about three days equals all the energy in the world's reserves of coal, oil, and wood, plus all atomic fuels. So far, man has been able to trap only a small fraction of this potential power.

Silicon wafers, glass-covered troughs, concave reflecting mirrors, sun-

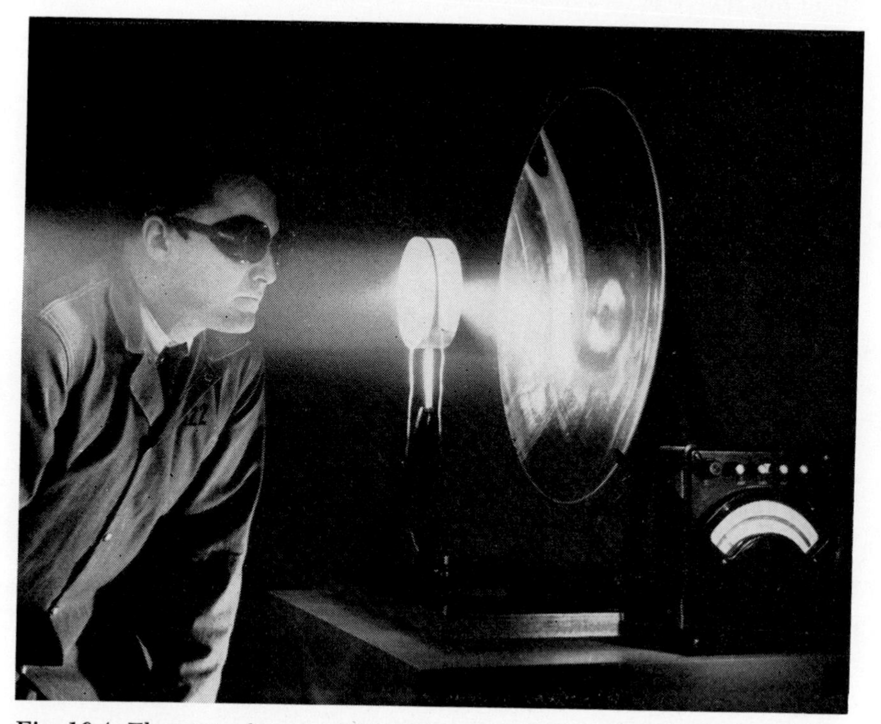

Fig. 16-4. Electricity from sunlight. The sun's rays, gathered by the large concave mirror at the right, are focused on a special assembly of thermoelectric materials that convert the intense heat directly into electricity. Westinghouse Research scientists are using the apparatus to study the feasibility of such a system for supplying the electric power requirements of space vehicles. (*Science Talent Institute photo.*)

heated air blown through chemicals to absorb and store the heat, solar cookers and stoves—these are no longer dreams but are present actualities. Someday they will be inexpensive enough and sufficiently perfected to be more common.

As our other energy sources dwindle we shall still have the energy of the sun and the energy of the atom to fall back on. It is interesting to note that in the United States we have already spent many billions of dollars for atomic devices. A fraction of that sum spent on the development of solar devices might well revolutionize the future for us.

You may at the same time want to raise these questions with your class. Dare we rely too heavily on technology's ability to solve all our problems? Is it not true that when cost of production rises too high, our standard of living suffers? Until we have assurance of new and plentiful energy resources, which can be produced at sufficiently low cost, what ought our policy be in regard to our present energy fuels?

POSSIBILITIES OF POWER FROM OCEAN AND AIR

16-6. Tides

To harness successfully and economically the power of sea tides, with their predictable periods, would supply us with tremendous power.

If your students live near the seashore, they might try to construct a miniature dam provided with gates that would catch and hold the flood tide. Then, at ebb, the water could be released to turn a toy water wheel. A student might report on the present status of tide power plants in the world.

16-7. Temperature Differences

Another student might tell the story of the development of sea-water turbines operating on the temperature differences in the levels of the water of tropical seas.

An excellent source of information for both of these projects is *The Sun, the Sea and Tomorrow* (Sec. 19-7*i*).

16-8. Winds

In the classroom, the air driven by an electric fan may simulate the wind. Your students might hold pinwheels or a toy windmill in its path. What is the history of the windmill? What is the chief difficulty about using the wind as a source of power? What is the chief advantage? Might power from air currents hold any future possibilities?

ATOMIC ENERGY

Your students know that they live in the shadow of the atom bomb. They cannot help being aware also that the "friendly atom" has put new and remarkable tools into the hands of man.

"Atoms for what?" is the great unanswered question for students as well as for everybody else. To help answer this life and death question, the first requisite is a knowledge of what atomic energy is and what it can do.

There is a wealth of material on atomic energy in textbooks and other books, in pamphlets, in resource units, and in all kinds of visual aids

(Sec. 19-7). You might find helpful the text unit, *Atomic Energy, Double-edged Sword of Science,* by R. Will Burnett (Charles E. Merrill Books, Columbus, Ohio). To clarify and illuminate your own background, *Explaining the Atom,* by the late Selig Hecht (The Viking Press, Inc., New York, 1947), is outstanding. This is a book to be shared with those students who are ready for it.

There are so many ways of developing with your class the story of atomic energy that we are limiting ourselves to a few suggestions, with a number of experiments and other techniques you might find useful as your plans unfold. A more detailed section on atomic power and reactors has been included for your guidance.

16-9. Beginning the Unit

You might want to start with the fine film *A Is for Atom* available for loan from General Electric Company, Schenectady, N.Y. You might want also to take a backward glance at the concept of the "atom" from Greek times down to Dalton, discussing with your students how Dalton's atomic theory helped to explain many phenomena of the physical world.

Now you might want to move forward to the story of man's penetration of the atom—his discovery that the atom is anything but indestructible.

16-10. Some Experiments and Procedures

Becquerel's Experiment. Your students may repeat this famous experiment in the following manner:

Place a piece of radioactive uranium ore (pitchblende or carnotite) on top of a piece of metal, perhaps a coin or a key, which is resting on a sheet of photographic paper wrapped in opaque black paper. Leave it for several days. When the photographic paper is developed it will be darkened except where the metal object was placed. The rays emanating from the uranium affected the paper in the same way as sunlight.

This experiment may be varied by using a luminous-dial clock with a coin or piece of metal taped over one or two numbers. The clock with an X-ray film over its face should be left in a totally dark place for 3 or 4 days for satisfactory exposure.

Observing Atomic Breakdown. Using a strong magnifying glass or microscope, students may examine a luminous watch or clock dial. Soon they will observe tiny "sparklers" emitted from the minute amount of radioactive material mixed with the paint. (The discovery of radium by the Curies in 1898 was made possible by the previous discovery of Becquerel, who actually suggested the investigation of uranium ores to the Curies.)

Cosmic-ray Tracks. If some of your students are interested in examining cosmic-ray tracks, special film for this purpose may be obtained from scientific laboratories. Such film can be exposed for a period of time, developed, and the tracks examined with a microscope. These films may yield important information. The scientific laboratory that supplies the film can also give information to guide you as to what kinds of tracks furnish important data.

Nuclear particles, no matter what their origin, are fascinating to study and can become the central objects of an engrossing hobby (see also Making a Cloud Chamber—Sec. 16-12).

The Electron. Turn on an electric light. Ask your students what actually is taking place.

If you have a Crooke's tube, send a current through it. As the electrons strike an object (a zinc sulfide screen) in their path, they produce a green glow. The stream can be deflected from its path by a magnet, something that does not occur with ordinary light.

The Attack on the Atom. The story of the attack on the atom, the discovery of the nucleus and the particles it contains, might be told by student reporters using charts and diagrams or might be enacted by "living models" (Sec. 16-11). As the story unfolds, certain insights may be strengthened by emphasis. The international character of science is, for instance, well illustrated in the story of atomic energy. The free exchange of information and ideas enabled scientists to share in a common search and to hasten the process of discovery.

Something else that may happen is the flash of insight that teachers and students share as they begin to comprehend the beauty, simplicity, and order found within the infinitely small atom, as well as the infinitely vast heavens. "What about us; how do we fit in?" does not need to be spoken to be pondered.

Can Man Transmute Elements? This was a question asked by scientists when they discovered that radium undergoes natural disintegration and transmutation.

A student might report on Lord Rutherford's first artificial transmutation and the search for better "bullets" than radium particles. This will lead to a discussion of atom-smashing machines.

Atom Smashers. Interested students might bring reports to class describing briefly the Van de Graaff electrostatic generator with its enormous spheres, the cyclotron, and the more recent betatron, synchrotron, and bevatron. By means of these machines, atomic bullets at unheard-of speeds become very effective atom smashers. Your most adventurous students might want to make a working model of the Van de Graaff generator (Sec. 16-12).

Others of your students might bring to class a report on "Hilac" (heavy ion linear accelerator) designed especially to accelerate the nuclei, or ions, of very heavy atoms. This accelerator may permit the synthesis of elements heavier than mendelevium[2a] (101) and opens up a new field of study of elements 84 to 90. It is also being used to study the effects on living cells of very heavy particles. Current science periodicals will carry the story as it unfolds, or students may contact the Atomic Energy Commission in Washington.

A Chain Reaction. Set up some ninepins on your demonstration table and try to make a "strike" with a ball. This is a simple example of a "chain reaction."

Or students might prepare the following demonstration: Set up a fence of wire netting on a table. Using about three dozen mousetraps and twice as many corks, set the mousetraps, placing them close together, with two corks on each trigger. Toss a single cork into the enclosure. How many mousetraps are necessary for the reaction to maintain itself? Now you are ready for a discussion of how a chain reaction can be set in motion by nuclear bombardment.

Here is a technique sent us by Fern Kent of Meany Junior High School, Seattle, Washington, that is much cheaper than using mousetraps and corks and also easier to do: Make two bases of "toy" clay of about 6 to 8 inches wide. Insert matches into the clay, using those with a head to represent atoms which will undergo fission and headless matches to represent those which will not (Fig. 16-5*a* and 16-5*b*). By using two bases it is easy to illustrate a mass that will support a chain reaction and one that will not.

The students can soon set up the match heads and duds in such a way as to show the two reactions. One burning match is then used to represent the particle that sets off the fission.

To help students see the difficulty in hitting the nucleus of the atom, marbles might be used to represent the nucleus. Place them in the middle of the floor. Blindfold someone who is a good marble player and have him try his luck at hitting the nucleus from the side of the room. If he desires to use an alpha particle, use a ping-pong ball. From the students will soon come the suggestion that many atomic bullets are used, so you might permit them to try.

Critical Mass. A group of students might set up the demonstration shown in Fig. 16-5*c* for the class. Light one match and demonstrate that a chain reaction will not occur. Bring the two masses closer together until a chain reaction is supported. Students will need to experiment with the placement of the matches in the clay as well as the distance between the flasks. If flasks are not available, tin cans might be substituted and placed one above the other rather than horizontally.

[2a] Nobelium (102) has now been synthesized.

Separating Uranium 235 for Atomic Fission. Separating fissionable uranium 235 from uranium 238 can be done in various ways; the gaseous diffusion method, although still expensive, is the most important.

Separation of Substances by Means of a Barrier. The simplest way of illustrating this is to separate sand and gravel by means of a sieve. Have

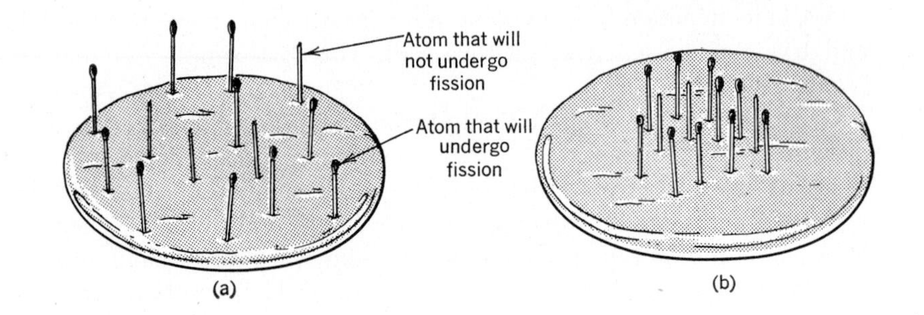

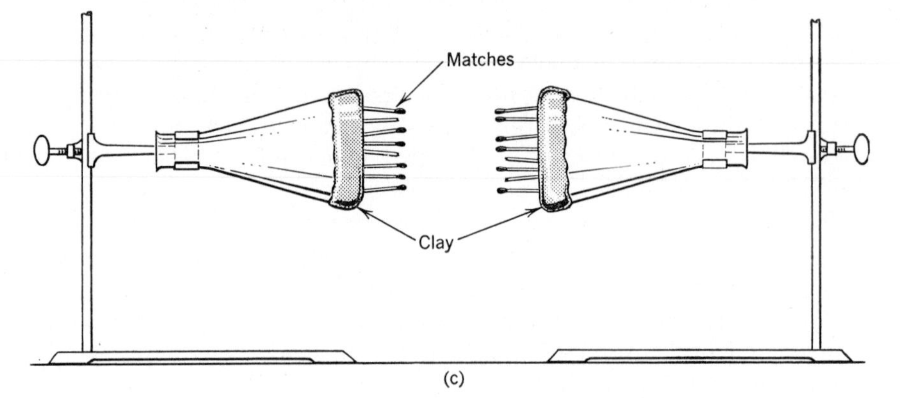

Fig. 16-5. Using matches to demonstrate a chain reaction. (*a*) This arrangement will not support a chain reaction; (*b*) this arrangement will; (*c*) this arrangement may be used to illustrate critical mass. One match is lit and the ring stands are brought closer and closer together.

students note that the problem of isotope separation is similar in principle, for we are dealing with atoms of different sizes.

Gaseous Diffusion through a Barrier. To illustrate the separation of uranium 235 from uranium 238 by gaseous diffusion through a barrier, try this experiment:

Set up a porous cup with a stopper and glass tube in a jar, as shown in Fig. 16-6. Allow hydrogen or illuminating gas to fill the jar. Bubbles may be observed rising from the end of the glass tube dipping into the water. Elicit from students that the gas is going through the porous walls of the cup and forcing air out at the bottom. Now shut the gas off and remove the jar. The slowly rising water in the tube indicates that the gas inside the cup is going out.

Relation Between the Density of a Gas and Its Rate of Diffusion. Place concentrated hydrochloric acid in one crucible and concentrated ammonium hydroxide in another at either end of a meter-long large-diameter glass tube. Insert stoppers and allow the diffusion of the gases to occur until a white ring of smoke, NH_4Cl, is observed forming inside the tube. Quickly measure the distance from each end of the tube to the ring of smoke. Determine the relationship between density (or molecular weight) and the rate of diffusion. It will be seen that the smaller the density of the gas, the greater the velocity of its diffusion.

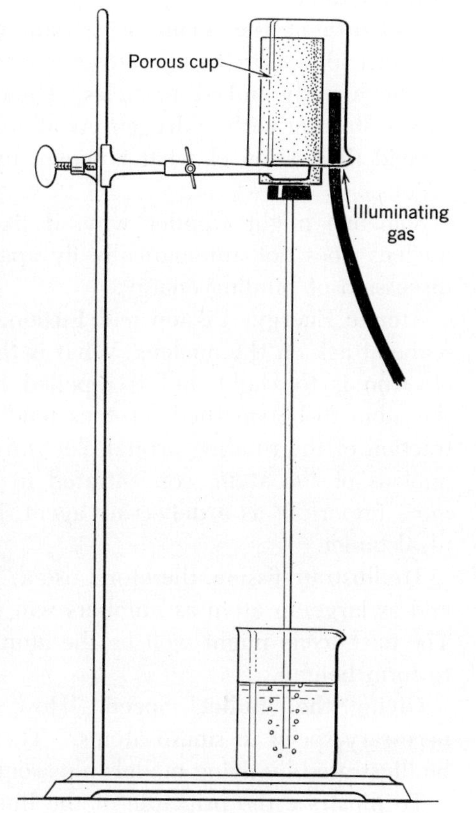

Fig. 16-6. Demonstration of gaseous diffusion through a porous cup.

Uranium 235 Is Still Costly. A single gaseous diffusion plant costs about a billion dollars. Only the United States, Great Britain, and Russia have such plants. That is why uranium 235 cost in 1955 about \$25 a gram ($1/28$ ounce).

Your students might be interested in figuring out how many pounds of uranium 235 were involved in President Eisenhower's billion-dollar release of this atomic fuel in February, 1956. They will need to divide the price of a pound (\$25 × 28 × 16) into a billion dollars, which comes out roughly to 89,000 pounds.

In discussing uranium with your class you might want to show the film *The Petrified River* (U.S. Bureau of Mines).

16-11. Living Models: A Teaching Device

One of the most ingenious teaching devices we have come across is the use of boys and girls themselves as "models" for atom building and atom smashing.[3] With boys as protons, girls as electrons, and boy-girl units linked arm-in-arm as neutrons, many concepts can be easily dramatized in this manner.

Structure of the Atom. First, students might act out the repulsion between like particles, the attraction between unlike, and the neutrality of the already linked particles. Then students might begin to build atoms, starting with hydrogen. As atoms are designed, students will have a vivid illustration of what is meant by atomic number, atomic weight, isotopes.

Someone might wonder why, if like charges repel each other, the nucleus does not automatically fly apart. This will lead directly into a discussion of binding energy.

Atomic Energy: Fission and Fusion. Now for the big dramatic scene —the attack on the nucleus. What is the best "bullet" for this task? The electron is too light and is repelled by the outer orbital electrons of the atom to be smashed. Protons tend to be deflected somewhat by attraction of the rotating orbital electrons, although the positively charged nucleus of the atom, concentrated in a much smaller volume, is even more important as a deflecting agent. Neutrons, being neutral, make an ideal bullet.

To illustrate fission, therefore, use a "living model" neutron for a bullet and as large an atom as numbers will permit, to represent uranium 235. The next scene might well be the atomic fusion of two hydrogen atoms to form helium.

Giving the "Bullet" Speed. "How does the atomic bullet get the necessary speed to smash atoms?" The answer to this question can also be illustrated by living models plus some classroom "props."

To illustrate the principle of the linear accelerator, benches or chairs may be used as drift tubes (Fig. 16-7). You will need to explain the idea of alternating current. When the current reverses, the boys and girls at the ends of the drift tubes shift places. When you clap your hands, students quickly make this change. Start an "electron" slowly down the accelerator. It is attracted toward the drift tube by opposite charges but "can't make up its mind" so goes to the center of the tube and coasts. While it is going through a drift tube the current alternates twice, so, as the bullet emerges, it is attracted toward the next tube. When it gets to the center of the gap between tubes it is also "kicked from behind" by the repulsion of similar electric charges and drifts through to the next tube, only faster this time, etc.

Students will now be ready for a discussion of the cyclotron, which, unlike the linear accelerator, forces the bullet into a circular path.

[3] Dr. Don Stotler, Supervisor of Science Education, Public Schools, Portland, Ore.

Dr. Stotler has even used his living models to illustrate the Wilson cloud chamber and the Geiger counter.

Some teachers will find these dramatizations highly useful teaching devices; others will decide that for their particular classes this method would not be effective. We have heard of several other teaching devices which might appeal to you. One teacher uses gumdrops of various colors to represent the different atomic particles, with toothpicks to

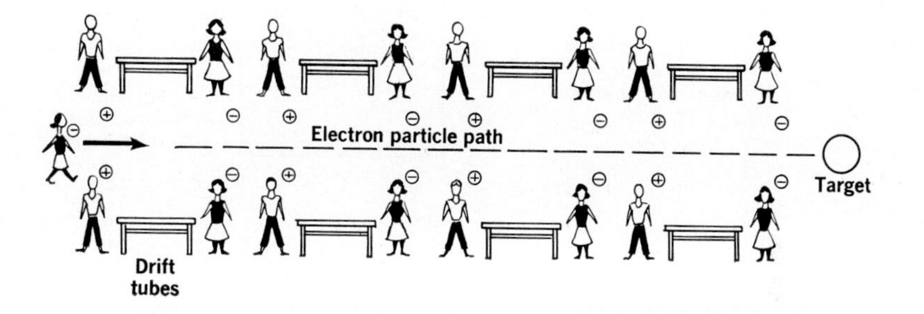

After "current" has alternated

Fig. 16-7. Dramatizing the principle of a linear accelerator with positive charges (boys), negative charges (girls), and drift tubes (benches). An electron (girl) starts through the accelerator. Note what happens when the current alternates.

hold them in place. At other times she uses "pigtail" Christmas-tree lights of different colors with appropriate wiring and switches. These ideas may suggest something to you that will help you to develop your own way of teaching these concepts.

16-12. Atomic Energy Instruments

Making a Cloud Chamber. The cloud chamber invented by the Englishman, C. T. R. Wilson, in 1912 gives scientists a way of detecting the paths of radioactive particles.

To witness cosmic-ray and other nuclear tracks, your students might make their own cloud chambers. There are directions in a number of books and magazine articles. Two types were described in The Amateur Scientist section of *Scientific American,* September, 1952, and April, 1956.

One simple model, suggested by Dr. Vincent Schaefer, is shown in Fig. 16-8. The dimensions are not critical but suggest approximate sizes.

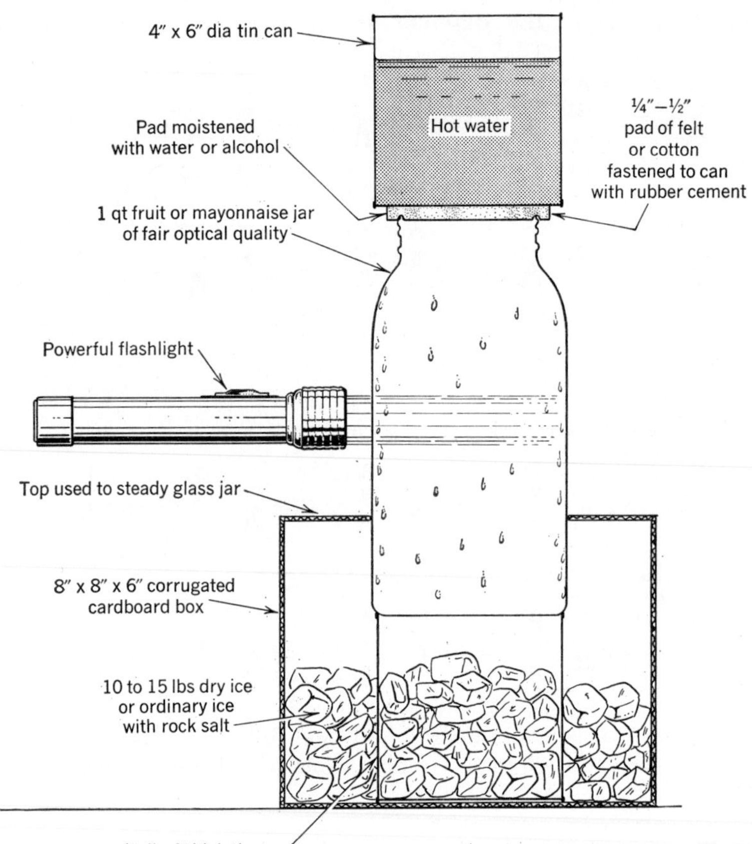

Fig. 16-8. Assembly of a continuous cloud chamber.

A number of helpful suggestions for the use of a cloud chamber may be obtained from Research Information Services, General Electric Research Laboratory, P.O. Box 1088, Schenectady, N.Y.

Making a Geiger Counter. The principle of a Geiger counter is this: Voltage, but not quite enough to establish conduction in the gas, is supplied to the detector tube. The gas in the tube is ionized when particles such as cosmic rays hit the tube. The increased conductivity of the gas causes a momentary current to flow. This may be heard as a click in an earphone.

A homemade Geiger counter, similar to the one in Fig. 16-9, makes it possible for high school students to experiment with cosmic rays and radioactive materials. The circuit can be constructed on a bread board,

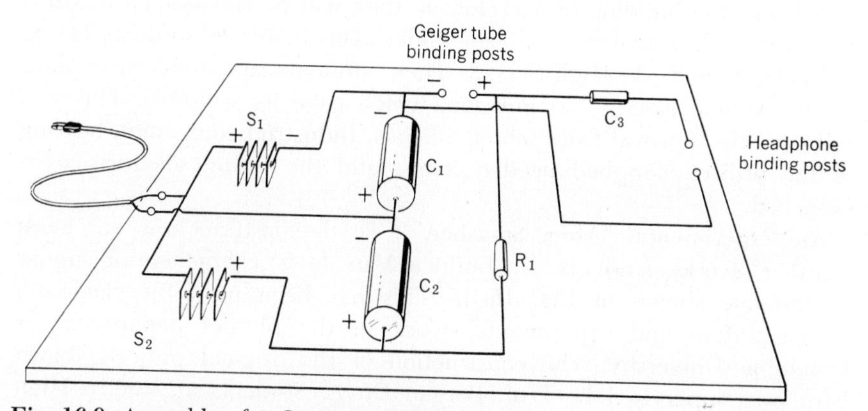

Fig. 16-9. Assembly of a Geiger counter.
S_1 and S_2—100-ma selenium rectifiers
C_1 and C_2—16-mf 200-volt (working voltage) electrolytic condensers
C_3—0.002-mf bypass condenser
R_1—1.5 megohm, ¼-watt resistor
(From Classroom Experiments for "Planet Earth," National Academy of Sciences, Washington, D.C.)

with standard radio parts, for a cost of under $20, including the tube and earphones.

A regular 110-volt a-c power outlet may be used. (A momentary peak close to 175 volts is reached during each cycle.) The circuit is so constructed that the voltage is doubled in order to operate a *low* voltage (300-volt) Geiger tube.[4]

To detect cosmic rays, the Geiger tube should be wrapped with lead foil to a thickness of 1/16 inch. This protects the tube from normal radiation while permitting radiation from cosmic rays to penetrate. To detect beta and gamma rays, the tube should be left uncovered. To detect gamma rays alone, the tube should be covered with aluminum foil.

When all connections are made as in the diagram, the circuit may be plugged into a 110-volt a-c power source. CAUTION: *No connections should be touched while the counter is thus plugged in.*

[4] One supplier of these tubes is Electronic Products, Inc., 111 East Third St., Mount Vernon, N.Y.

Directions describing the construction of a battery-operated Geiger counter, which is portable and very sensitive, may be obtained in the pamphlet *Classroom Experiments for "Planet Earth,"* National Academy of Sciences, Washington, D.C.

A Student Cyclotron. If your young "nuclear physicists" should want to attempt the building of a cyclotron, they will be encouraged to know that just such a project has been undertaken by seven students at the Mineola, New York, High School. These students submitted their plans to the Atomic Energy Commission, which gave its approval. This was followed by approval from school officials. Industrial companies, hearing of the project, supplied needed items, and the young scientists were launched.

An Experimental "Atom Smasher."[5] To demonstrate how an "atom smasher" works, students can build a Van de Graaff generator similar to the one shown in Fig. 16-10. This has been used for classroom demonstration and experimental work in the physics department at Columbia University. The construction of the original project, shown here, was supervised by Prof. Bergen Davis. Students at Suffern High School, Suffern, New York, built one.

Figure 16-10*a* shows the general arrangement; *A* represents a Micarta tube 36 inches long, secured to a base and fitted with a brass cover *B*. This tube need not be Micarta; it can be an ordinary mailing tube of equivalent diameter treated with paraffin or shellac. *C* represents the support for the apparatus, which may be bakelite, hard rubber, or even wood. In the original construction *D* is an aluminum pulley, but for simplification this pulley may be a brass tube plugged with a block of wood and fitted with a metal shaft. A piece of wire is then soldered to the inside of the brass tube and the shaft. The pulley inside the globe, also indicated by the letter *D*, is made in exactly the same manner. *E* is a simple support that permits adjustment for the height of the upper pulley and, therefore, regulates tension on the belt. *F* is a split brass rod to which is attached a horizontal strip of lead into which three needles have been forced. These needles must be of exactly the same length. A tapped hole and a screw permit regulation here. *G* is a half-section of brass tube, also fitted with needles. *H* is a brass rod, adjustable laterally and wound with Christmas-tree tinsel. *J* is a section of flattened brass tubing and *K* is a piece of lead, hammered over and fitted with needles, as illustrated. The belt used in the apparatus is a strip of ordinary adding-machine paper. One must be careful in overlapping and gluing this to make sure that the needles *K* will not dig in or catch on the joint.

The driving system for this equipment (Fig. 16-10*b*) is a 1/5 horse-

[5] *Science Observer,* 1938.

power motor which runs at 3,200 rpm. In the construction described here a 200-ohm relay is connected into the motor circuit so that three speeds are made possible. This is acomplished by the switching mechanism. Because the circuit may not be suitable to every motor, it is recommended that a tapped resistor be used instead. The purpose of the resistor is merely to bring the paper belt up to full speed without

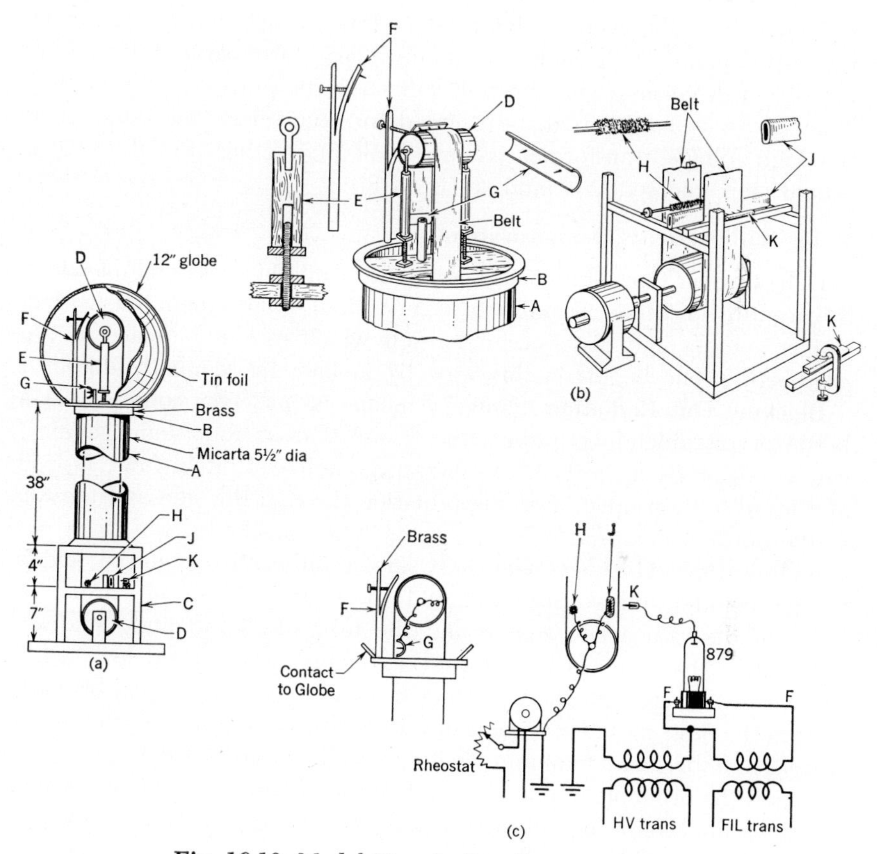

Fig. 16-10. Model Van de Graaff atom smasher.

danger of tearing it, which would happen if full torque of the motor were applied instantly.

In operation, the electrical charge is sprayed on the belt by transformers connected to an 879 tube or RCA 2 × 2A, as illustrated in the circuit diagram (Fig. 16-10*c*). It is recommended that switches be placed in the primary side of the filament transformer and in the primary of the high-voltage transformer. When the apparatus is to be set into operation, it is important that the paper belt be brought up to its maximum speed first. The circuit to the filament of the tube is then closed, after which the high-voltage (2,650 volts) circuit is completed. The operator will see the charge being sprayed upon the belt from pins *K*. These charges are picked up at the top by *F* and conveyed to the globe. It is not unusual to get sparks 12 inches long from this equipment.

Although it would be advisable to have an all-metal globe at the top (which might even be larger than the 12 inches here specified), the experimenter will find that an ordinary cardboard globe, either metallized or covered with tin foil, will serve the purpose quite as well. When the mechanism is to be stopped for adjustment, make sure that the high-voltage transformer is turned off first; otherwise, if the belt should stop, the sparks would set it on fire.

16-13. Radioactivity Demonstrations

Detecting an Ore. Students might build a pile of rocks, one of which is carnotite or other uranium ore. A student might then test with a Geiger counter and discover for himself which rock is radioactive. (In prospecting, one begins in this way, by looking for gamma radiation.)

Blocking Out Radiation. Show by means of a Geiger counter that a bottle of pitchblende is radioactive. Show that its radiation (gamma) can be cut off by a sheet of lead. Wrap the bottle of pitchblende in lead and leave the top open. Test the radiation through the side and the top of the bottle.

Radioisotope Thickness Gauge. Using a radioactive material and a Geiger counter, place one, two, and then three pieces of cardboard between the radioactive source and the tube of the counter. Students will notice that the cardboard prevents some of the particles (beta) thrown off the material from getting through. The more layers of cardboard, the less radiation penetrates it. (This may also be tried with various numbers of aluminum sheets instead of cardboard.)

This is the principle of one kind of radioisotope thickness gauge, which measures and controls many different types of sheet materials—metals, paper, plastics, rubber, textiles.

In discussing the gauge it might be pointed out that one of its great advantages is that no mechanical contact with the material is necessary, and measurements can be made continuously without stopping production.

Do Plants and Animals Absorb Radioactivity from Water? [6] Waste water from the atomic reactors at Hanford, Washington, is discharged into the Columbia River. The Atomic Energy Commission periodically

[6] West Coast Science Teachers Summer Conference 1954, in *The Science Teacher*, February, 1955.

samples and examines fish and plants from the river for signs of radioactivity.

After placing goldfish or other aquatic life in water made radioactive with phosphorus, $Na_3P^{32}O_4$, students may dissect an organism and locate areas of radioactivity with a Geiger counter or by exposure to X-ray film. Phosphorus 32 is available for high school laboratory experiments in 10-microcurie lots from the Atomic Energy Commission.

This exercise lends itself to a cooperative teamwork approach, using techniques from biology, physics, and chemistry. Another similar experiment involves the use of radioactive iodine. A rat fed on a glucose and water diet for several days is given a diet containing radioactive iodine. By using a Geiger counter, and also by preparing a radioautograph, the group can see in what part of the rat's body the tagged iodine is concentrated and try to determine why.

Studying Genetic Changes Induced by Radioactivity. The Atomic Energy Commission recently gave the green light to a project proposed by two junior high school students and their teacher.[7] The project consists of feeding radioactive materials to guppies to determine any genetic changes in the fish.

Other Experiments. Many other demonstration experiments may be found in *Laboratory Experiments with Radioisotopes for High School Science Demonstrations* and the more recent *Teaching with Radioisotopes* published by the Atomic Energy Commission.

16-14. Harnessing Atomic Energy for Power

Elicit from your students that one of the greatest contributions of the atom to the welfare of man will be the creation of useful and eventually, it is hoped, inexpensive power.

Discuss with your class the fact that atomic reactions give off heat as well as radiation. This means that atomic power is a compact and concentrated source of heat. One pound of uranium has the energy equivalent of about how many pounds of coal? (about 3 million). In other words, fissionable material can supply an amount of energy far in excess of that which can be supplied by an equivalent weight of fossil fuel.

Reactors: Atomic Ovens. Your students are probably already aware that the energy of the atom is harnessed by means of reactors, which may be likened to furnaces, in which the chain reaction or continual splitting of atoms required to produce atomic energy takes place. The chief fuel for this furnace is uranium 235, the supply of which is by no means limitless.

[7] Leon Kurtz, P.S. 7, New York City.

Depending on the type of power reactor used, the energy is removed in the form of hot air, steam, hot water, or other heated fluid. So far, scientists have not found an economical way of producing electricity directly from atomic energy. At present, therefore, heat from the atomic reactor is generally used to make steam to drive the turbine to turn a generator to produce electricity. This is the traditional way, except that atomic heat is substituted for the usual fuels. Atomic engineers are challenged by the problem of producing this atomic heat at reasonable cost.

Kinds of Reactors. Reactors can be classified in several ways, but perhaps the most significant classification from the students' point of view is this:

1. The kind of reactor that is a burner-upper of fuel, making no new fuel as it operates. Examples are the "swimming pool" reactor and the submarine reactor.

2. The kind of reactor that makes some fissionable material, but less than it burns. This reactor is called a converter. The most notable example is the one that produces plutonium at Hanford, on the Columbia River in Washington.

3. The kind of reactor that makes more atomic fuel than it burns. This is called a breeder. Reactors of this type are under construction both in our country and in Great Britain and perhaps also in the Soviet Union.

A free basic guide describing and illustrating the various kinds of nuclear reactors is available from the Minneapolis Honeywell Regulator Company, Wayne and Windrim Aves., Philadelphia 44, Pennsylvania.

The Breeder: Is It Perpetual Motion? To make more fuel than is burned in a breeder—isn't this an example of the impossible? Have scientists succeeded in the invention of a perpetual-motion machine? It might seem so, but have your students examine what happens more closely.

Let us take the case of a breeder with plutonium as the fuel (Fig. 16-11). The number of neutrons emitted per fission of plutonium 239 is about three. The number of neutrons that are spent per fission can be added as follows:

1 neutron to keep up the chain reaction and cause the next fission
1 neutron to transmute a fertile uranium 238 atom to replace the fissionable plutonium 239 atom just burned
X neutrons which go to parasitic, structural, and leakage losses
$2 + X$ = total neutrons spent per fission

Thus the net number of neutrons per fission of plutonium 239 is about $3 - 2 - X$, or $1 - X$, neutrons per fission available to transmute additional uranium 238 to plutonium 239. This "extra" plutonium 239 represents a salable product that could be used to provide the initial charge for new stationary power plants, to refuel atom-powered airplanes and naval ships, or to arm nuclear weapons. It could thus be used for peacetime or wartime purposes.

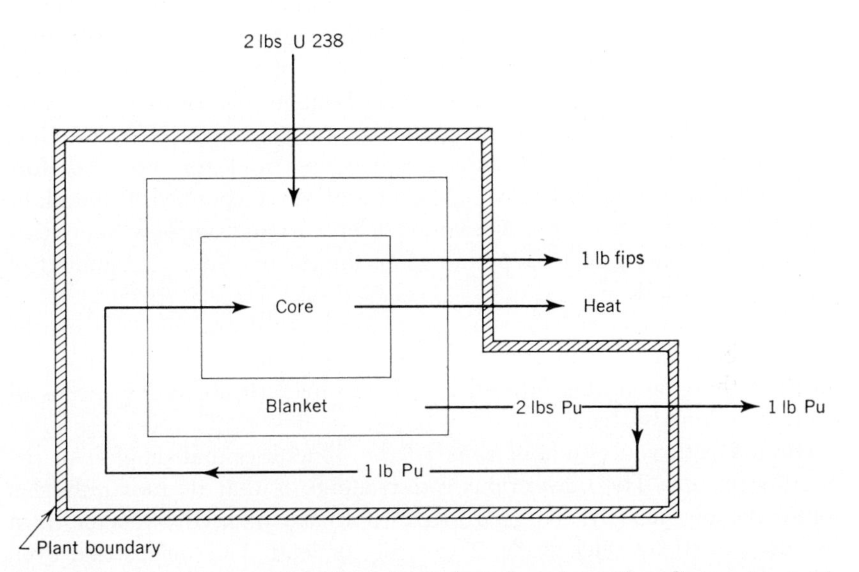

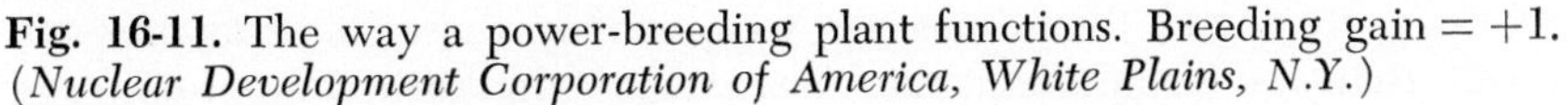

Fig. 16-11. The way a power-breeding plant functions. Breeding gain = +1. (*Nuclear Development Corporation of America, White Plains, N.Y.*)

Looking again at the $1 - X$ factor, it can be seen that if X is greater than unity, then breeding is not possible and part of the uranium 238 must be left behind unburned. To keep X as near to zero or as small as possible is an engineering problem that carries with it some of the most difficult and subtle technical feats that can be imagined.

Here then is the "balance sheet" of a breeder reactor that has theoretically reduced the X losses to zero.

Input	*Output*	*Result*
2 lb U238	1 lb Pu 1 lb fips (fission products) Heat	2 lb U238 used 1 lb Pu produced Breeding gain, 1 (This would happen only if there were *no* losses.)

Thus it can be seen that 2 pounds of material go into the reaction and 2 pounds of material come out, so that the law of conservation of mass-energy has not been violated.

Resources for the Atomic Reactor. If the nuclear reactor becomes the basic "furnace" of the future as a source of energy and power, what are the basic raw materials that will be needed to feed it?

For the atomic "furnace," your students will discover that purified natural uranium and pure carbon in the form of graphite, as moderator, are needed. Other substances, such as "heavy water," can be substituted for the carbon. Liquid sodium is being used in some reactors as a coolant.

Uranium is not a rare element. It is about as plentiful in the earth as copper and more abundant than zinc or lead. However, uranium ores are less concentrated than those of copper and zinc and therefore more difficult to purify. Every continent and every country on the globe contains some uranium ore. Ask your students to find out how many tons of coal are equivalent to 1 pound of ordinary uranium; to 1 pound of pure uranium 235.

When the nuclear reactor operates it produces heat. This heat can be used to boil water, run steam turbines, generate electricity. It might even be that the heat produced could be piped to homes by means of central heating systems.

Discuss with your students some of the difficulties and dangers of the nuclear reactor. The one serious disadvantage is that its radiations can injure persons nearby. To guard against this danger, the reactor must be surrounded by thick walls of concrete or lead. This means that even small reactors and their housings weigh many tons. But students will recall that the "Nautilus," the "Sea Wolf," and other atom-powered submarines have already put to sea.

Atomic powerhouses are even now being fashioned and some are actually in operation. Students might report on Great Britain's atom-powered electric plant, Calder Hall.

Radioactive Wastes. The problem of what to do with "hot" radioactive wastes, the "useless" ashes of burned-out uranium, is a difficult one. These wastes are not easy to throw away, for although in time they become less radioactive, the unpurified fractions may be "hot" for millennia.

A small, purified fraction of these waste products of atomic piles can be used in advanced research in the sciences. It is thought that their rays, similar to X rays, may become useful in the sterilization and preservation of foods. Researchers are investigating other possibilities. But when all is said and done, there will remain an increasing amount of waste that will have to be disposed of as atomic power plants multiply.

Students might refer to publications of the U.S. Bureau of Standards[8]

[8] *Maximum Permissible Amounts of Radioisotopes in the Human Body and Maximum Permissible Concentrations in Air and Water,* Handbook 52, Mar. 20, 1953.

on allowable levels of radioactivity for bodies of water. They might calculate the amount of radioactive waste that could be safely disposed of in a nearby water mass. Ask students to recall the experiment with the goldfish (Sec. 16-13) and to predict the outcome of excessive radioactive waste disposal on aquatic life.

"Why not dump it all in the ocean?" a student may ask. The oceans, of course, are enormous and form a vast reservoir for our waste products. In the past, it has seemed inconceivable that man could produce enough waste to cause any measurable change in the open ocean. But the quantity of atomic power that may be developed within our lifetime would produce, according to oceanographer Bostwick H. Ketchum, enough radioactive waste products within a year to make a detectable change in the ocean. Successive accumulations, year after year, would have an unpredictable influence on the whole life cycle in the sea. He concludes, "The magnitude and importance of atomic energy develop-

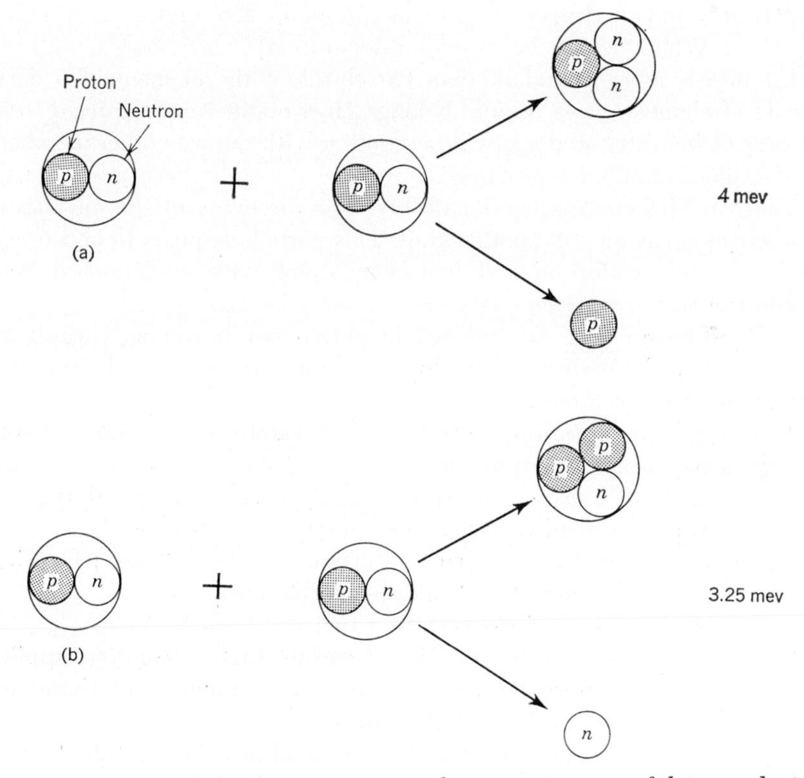

Fig. 16-12. Two of the fusion reactions that may prove useful in producing power. (*a*) Two deuterons forming a tritium nucleus plus a proton; (*b*) two deuterons forming a helium 3 and a neutron.

ments merely emphasize the necessity for thinking of the future as we plan for today."

This problem of the disposal of atomic wastes is a serious conservation concern and needs to be approached in the same way that we attempt to deal with other pollution problems. Can we afford to let any part of our environment become *not quite lethal*?

A Future Possibility: Deuterium and Lithium as Fuels. Our energy sources of the future may possibly reside in two of the lightest elements, deuterium and lithium. Fusion of one or the other of these elements is presumably involved in the hydrogen-bomb reaction, and this same fusion reaction (Fig. 16-12) may someday, in the foreseeable future, be quite generally harnessed for peaceful power.

The abundance of deuterium is virtually inexhaustible. Have your students look up the percentage of deuterium in ocean water. How could deuterium be extracted from the sea? Have students refer back to isotope separation (Sec. 16-10). Compare the atomic weights of deuterium and hydrogen (2:1); of uranium 238 and uranium 235 (1.01:1). Which would be an easier separation?

Lithium is more abundant than two-thirds of the elements. To what family of elements does lithium belong? How might it be extracted from its ore? (Chemistry students will be familiar with the way other members of the alkali family are produced.)

The Mu Meson: Another Possibility. The discovery of the mu meson has set scientists on still another trail. This particle appears to encourage the fusion of deuterium and hydrogen atoms with evolution of heat (as in the fusion reaction).

Cost of Power. We are anxious to obtain our power as cheaply as possible. This depends on a number of factors, some of which your students will think of themselves.

1. The source of power (wood, coal, natural gas, gasoline, atomic energy, wind, water, solar energy)
2. The cost of transporting power (transportation of fossil fuels is far more expensive than that of atomic energy, for instance)
3. The type of engine used (steam, turbine, gasoline, diesel, jet, turbojet, other newly invented or yet undesigned engines)
4. The energy liberated per pound of fuel

Cost of power, dwindling supplies of certain fuels, emerging supplies of others, money spent on research and development—all these are factors in the energy picture of the future.

When Future Sources Become Present Realities. Your students may discuss what changes might take place if we were no longer dependent on fossil fuels. What difference would it make to us? To other nations? What use might be made of the remaining fossil fuels? How might

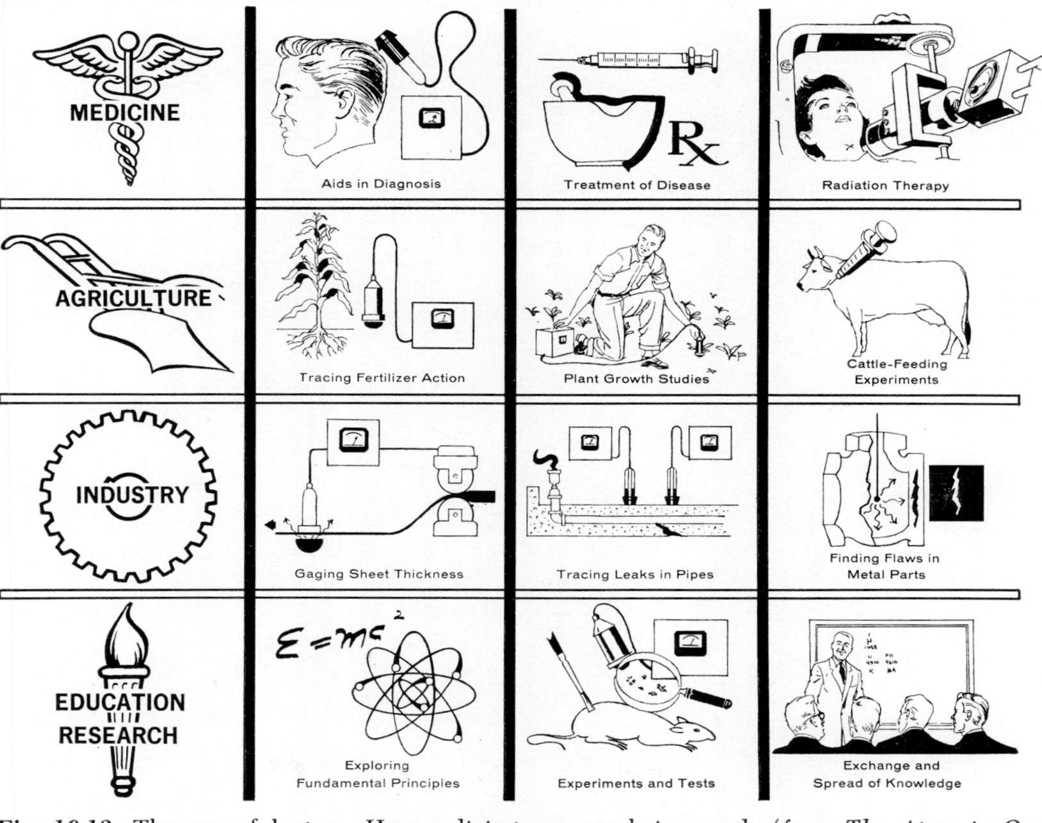

Fig. 16-13. The peaceful atom. How radioisotopes are being used. (*from The Atom in Our Hands, Union Carbide Corporation, New York, 1955.*)

such use affect other natural resources? What has this to do with conservation?

But What about Today? When musing of the future with your students you will no doubt want them to take a good hard look at today. Our "fuels of the future" are, among other things, still exceedingly expensive. It is hard to predict when their cost can be reduced enough to be competitive. Has this any bearing on the conservation of our present fuel sources?

16-15. Student Survey of Atoms for Peace

Have various class committees survey the literature on atomic power plants; radioisotopes in medicine; radioactive products in industrial research, in agriculture (Fig. 16-13).

This information might first be organized as a panel discussion and presented to the class. The class might then want to plan a student assembly program on the general topic of the peaceful atom. Various members of the class might make the presentations; others might prepare charts, diagrams, and pictures to illustrate the talks.

An excellent pictorial story of the use of radioisotopes in medicine, agriculture, industry, education, and research may be found in *The Atom in Our Hands* (Sec. 19-7*j*).

An Atomic Energy Club. A science teacher in a small suburban high school[9] met the challenge of the age of the atom by helping students to organize an atomic energy club.[10] There were no qualifications as to membership. Those who wished to make models got busy on cyclotrons and reactors. Even a working model of a Van de Graaff atom smasher was successfully completed (Sec. 16-12). Art students made all kinds of charts; writers and reporters were kept busy with articles; technicians and stagehands assisted with assembly programs and plays.

Each year the club activities culminated in a special program such as The History of Atomic Energy, The Tools of the Atomic Scientist, The Peaceful Atom (a play) and The Hiroshima Story.

[9] Gerrit C. Zwait, Suffern High School, Suffern, N.Y.

[10] See *Citizenship for an Atomic Age*, a special issue of *School Life*, vol. 35, September, 1953.

PART 4

Conservation as a Study of Future Resources

17

Our Future Resource Discoverers and Developers

This chapter deals with potential scientists and technologists—those students who will be responsible for the discovery and development of our presently unknown resources, the new and to-be-developed ones.

We address ourselves first to these questions: What in general are the characteristics of a scientist-to-be? Once having been identified, how are schools meeting the challenge of their scientifically gifted students?

Included in these pages are a number of suggested ways, both in the classroom and out, of encouraging future scientists. Teachers will also find suggestions for further development of their own professional resources. We conclude with a brief discussion of a conservation program for our future resource discoverers and developers.

FINDING AND ENCOURAGING FUTURE SCIENTISTS

17-1. The Gifted Student as a Future Scientist

Who among the boys and girls now in the nation's classrooms have the ability to become scientists of tomorrow? Many science teachers may feel they could pick potential scientists from among their students with reasonable accuracy. "Hunches," based on classroom experience and observation of the subsequent careers of students, supply a significant piece of evidence. Research of a more formal nature has been going on apace and the results are supplying additional and more accurate tools for identification of the gifted. A summary of over 200 research studies may be found in the Super and Bachrach survey, *Scientific Careers: Vocational Development Theory* (Sec. 19-8*i*).

The picture that emerges of the man or woman of science is that of a person who in scholarship and intelligence is equal or superior to the average college student. His mathematical talent is well above average. He usually possesses good spacial visualization, high mechanical comprehension, superior manipulative ability and dexterity. He displays inner-directedness (often attended by a weakness in social relationships), scientific judgment, flexibility, originality, skill in formulating problems and in designing and carrying out investigations and reporting them.

What is most significant as far as the schools are concerned is that his talents in science and mathematics are displayed early in life, crystallizing somewhere between ten and fourteen (upper elementary and junior high school years). The age at which these interests result in career choice appears to range from fourteen to twenty (high school and early college years).

It has also become evident, through analysis of research studies, that there are two all-important factors which have a direct influence on career choice. The first is the encouragement given by deeply respected *key figures* (such as fathers and teachers). The second resides in academic opportunities, including qualified teachers, and a chance to engage in projects of a research nature with genuine experiences in discovery.

17-2. How Schools Are Meeting the Challenge of the Gifted

Emerging Curricular Patterns in Science Education. Each community, depending on its philosophy and traditions, depending, too, on the preparation of its staff, the nature and destination of its student body, the convictions of its administrative and guidance workers, is gradually coming to grips with the problem of its gifted students. Throughout the country, curricular practices seem to be taking these directions:

The Advanced Course. This course, sometimes called the honor course, may be identified as biology, physics, or chemistry but goes beyond the high school curriculum (as evidenced in texts and syllabuses) into what is recognizably college work. Most of these courses are the established courses *plus more work,* the advanced course meaning *more advanced work.*

The Special Course. This course is organized for special work. Students who take the course have generally taken the established curriculum or are taking this course concurrently with the established curriculum. Such a course is advanced science, in which students work on their own "original" projects in the laboratory much as do scientists (embryo, perhaps). Students either are carefully selected for such courses or select themselves because of their own expressed vocational interest. This type of course is usually found in large high schools where the population permits wider diversification of courses.

The Special Group. In many schools there are no special courses, but special groups. This approach is especially well suited for small schools. These groups meet when possible and when a teacher is available before, during, or after school. They are usually organized as clubs; they may be, and in several instances are, organized as classes. They number in registration anywhere from one student to several hundred. These groups, usually identified as hobby, seminar, scholars, or vocational, are chiefly concerned with learning more about science.

The Advanced School. Even before the Advanced School Study of the Ford Foundation was instituted, a number of schools had developed what they called honor schools or advanced schools within the organization of the high school per se. These advanced schools selected youngsters on the basis of high IQ and general high achievement in major courses (English, social studies, mathematics, science, and sometimes language), and aimed the course work at a higher level than that expected of the general school population. Under certain conditions students were able to attain advanced standing in particular courses when admitted to college.

The Special School. In large cities, particularly New York City, specialized high schools such as the Bronx High School of Science, Stuyvesant High School, Brooklyn Technical High School select students with high IQ and special abilities for advanced work and added enrichment.

The Independent School. Of course there are the private secondary schools, a number of which have high standards of selection. Many of these give advanced work in science and mathematics. Independent schools have a special opportunity for trail blazing, with their smaller classes, more highly selected student body, and greater opportunity for individual project work.

The Individual at School. Whether or not the procedures used involve groups or classes of students, the attempt is still to meet special needs. But many schools are too small to organize special groups. In such schools, we have observed efforts being made for even *one* gifted student. Individual tutoring in certain course work (whether standard or advanced), the practice of apprenticing the student to an interested industrial or university scientist (if not during the regular session, then during the summer session), and if nothing else, suggested readings and conferences—these are some of the practices used. In many cases they are unusually effective because the gifted student so often reacts catalytically to the interest shown and the guidance offered.

School-College Cooperation for the Gifted. Closer cooperation between the school and college is helping to bridge that ofttimes wasteful gap. Already there are various plans designed to accelerate gifted students. Thus, some colleges and universities offer "early admissions" while others are admitting qualified students from selected schools with "advanced standing." Then there are institutions of higher learning that work closely with a particular school or school system, thereby smoothing the transition for both students and teachers.

17-3. One Experimental Plan

Identification and Selection of Students. Here is an example taken from one city public school system, that of Portland, Oregon,[1] to show how students are selected for special work in science.

> The general plan of identification has made use of the results of such standardized tests as the American Council on Education (A.C.E.) Psychological Examination for High School Students, the Ohio State Psychological Examination, and the Iowa Tests of Educational Development, as well as I.Q. tests, both group and individual. In addition to the testing program, other information has been used:
>
> 1. Recommendations from teachers.
> 2. Rating sheets upon which teachers indicate their estimates of a pupil's rank—minimum to maximum—in such characteristics as industry, accuracy, initiative, reliability, cooperativeness, leadership, and emotional stability. These are filed in the counselor's office.
> 3. Grades—past and present.
> 4. Counseling data, such as results of personality test and records of participation in activities both in and out of school.
> 5. Interests as revealed by the Kuder Preference Records and by the pupil's own declarations.
> 6. Pupil's occupational choices and career plans.
> 7. Case studies which include anecdotal recording. These may reveal the areas in which students could be expected to excel.
>
> **The Science Program.** Since the initiation of the program in the fall of 1952 three main types of classroom organization have been used in the special classes provided for gifted students. These have been designated as the *seminar,* the *special section,* and the *enrichment class.* The seminar is a small group of five to eighteen students of high ability who are engaged in an elective study which is different from, and generally over and above the prescribed high school course. A special section is also a small group of five to eighteen students of high ability who are engaged in studying within the framework of the regular Portland course, but with the addition of comparative and supplementary materials for purposes of greater depth and breadth and with a more intensive and scholarly approach to all phases of the work. An enrichment class is of normal size, twenty-five to thirty-five members, made up of

[1] *Science Classes for Exceptionally Endowed Students in the High Schools of Portland, Oregon,* Portland Public Schools, Portland, Ore.

students of high ability who follow the regular Portland course which is expanded and enriched and uses more difficult materials than those usually tried in regular classes.

All of these classes enjoy one common advantage: *relative homogeneity of intellectual ability*, which makes possible the use of more difficult materials and more efficient class procedures. Instead of the unilateral teacher-student relationship which may tend to prevail in the heterogeneous classes, intra-student discussions can be frequent and profitable in the special class with the teacher acting as critical participant instead of presiding authority. As attitudes of responsibility develop in the class as a whole, students may often find themselves participating in the teaching process.

The seminar and special section have in common the advantage of small size. This facilitates group inter-action and permits greater participation by all members of the group. The special section and enrichment class have in common the advantage of being a regular part of the curriculum. This makes it easier to schedule students. Many able students who are active in student affairs do not have time to take a seminar as an additional class. The seminar has the advantage, however, since the content is not prescribed, of relieving teacher and pupils from the pressure of covering a certain amount of ground in a prescribed amount of time.

Evaluation of the Program. Since the beginning of the Portland school program, individual high schools and individual teachers have been given as much freedom as possible in developing special types of classes, selecting materials and working out methods of presenting the material. During the first four experimental years there has been continuous evaluation of the various classes, materials and methods by administrators and teachers.

Evidence on which to base such evaluations has been available from a number of sources: student performance in the classroom, student performance on standardized tests, and the evaluations of students, their parents, and teachers as recorded on anonymous questionnaires. These questionnaires were sent to students at the end of each year of the program, to their parents, and to the teachers in the schools participating in the program. In addition, questionnaires were sent to graduates one year after they had participated in the seminars and special classes.

In brief, the aspects of the program singled out for favorable comment by these groups were: improved study habits; greater opportunity for original research and advanced laboratory work; the stimulation of being in a class of students of equally high ability; the opportunity for more individual attention by the teacher; the better preparation for college type work.

Unfavorable comments about the program were few. Among those things singled out for comment were: heavy assignments taking a great deal of time and energy; too much emphasis on programs, concerts, radio and television appearances; some lack of emphasis on fundamentals while spending time on more difficult concepts; some teachers not being well enough prepared.

Most common comment by teachers on their greatest problem in meeting needs of gifted children were:

A. Lack of time.

B. Too many interruptions.

C. Insufficient materials and poor material management.

A noteworthy effect of the special attention given to superior students is that it seems to raise the general level of scholarship among capable students. One high school reported (1952–53) that the freshman-sophomore honor roll increased 100% as a result of interest in attaining seminar status in the junior-senior year via good grades. The program puts the stamp of approval upon scholastic achievement. Students indicate a desire to be in the special classes and work harder to be eligible for them. The feared development of "intellectual snobs" proved to be groundless. In addition, confidence and prestige which capable students have gained, have brought them into more active leadership in student body and class affairs.

More Experiments Needed. Experimentation like that going on in the Portland schools needs to be and indeed is being multiplied throughout the nation. Development and evaluation of these programs will take time, but there is no easy or quick way to find solutions. Answers will evolve as schools not only profit by the research of others but become involved in research of their own.

Another type of research is that now being conducted by the Physical Science Study Committee, under the sponsorship of various foundations, including the National Science Foundation. A course in high school physics with a new approach is being designed and tried out in pilot high schools and revised in the light of its success or lack of success in actual classroom and laboratory situations. The impact of this experimental course will beyond doubt cause a reappraisal of the traditional physics course and methods of teaching it.

The American Institute of Biological Sciences has embarked on an extensive study of course content in the biological sciences. A newsletter detailing the progress of the study may be obtained by writing to Biological Sciences Curriculum Study, University of Colorado, Boulder, Colorado. At present, plans are being made to develop a national study group in chemistry somewhat along the lines of organization of the PSSC and the BSCS.

17-4. Helping Students to Become Scientists

It is interesting to note that in both the Super and Bachrach study and the report of the Portland public schools there is a shift in emphasis from the traditional science course to a more experimental one, which includes some rudimentary research on the part of students.

When we reexamine regular courses in science we find that students are expected to delve into the works of the great scientists, studying mainly the facts, laws, and principles of the past. Textbooks, workbooks, and laboratory manuals are designed for students to read, examine, and possibly *rediscover*, but rarely to *discover* for themselves. To study the past is both useful and important; the past is indeed prologue. One wonders, however, whether it is sufficient.

If we want to encourage future scientists, ought we not to begin early to give students direct experience in the *doing* of science? In essence, one becomes a writer by writing, a painter by painting, and a scientist by "sciencing." The sooner one starts, the better. If gifted students are to become our originators, should they not receive practice in originating?

A science course designed to this end might be one in which the students, having become acquainted with the history of biological science (now called biology), proceed to deal with the science of biology. Here they struggle over new relationships; they try to do something new; they attempt to solve problems, small, perhaps even trifling ones to begin with, but problems beyond the known. The text becomes a base of operations, a place to jump off into the future. Students do "research" and in so doing wet their cerebral feet in science.

"Sciencing" in Classroom and Laboratory. This handbook, *Teaching Science through Conservation,* has been designed to encourage this "questing" approach to science teaching. The authors hope that through its use some doors will be opened to teachers and their students.

Many additional procedures and techniques designed in the same spirit may be found in these volumes: *A Sourcebook for the Biological Sciences* (Sec. 19-3*e*) and *A Book of Methods,* by Paul F. Brandwein, F. G. Watson, and P. E. Blackwood (Harcourt, Brace and Company, Inc., New York, 1958).

Many, many excellent procedures, supplied by teachers from all over the country, may be found in *Handbook for Teaching of Conservation and Resource-Use,* edited by Richard L. Weaver for the National Association of Biology Teachers (The Interstate Printers and Publishers, Inc., Danville, Ill., 1955).

There are some excellent suggestions, including many ideas for projects, in the yearly *Star: Ideas in Science Teaching,* a selection from winning entries in the Science Teacher Achievement Recognition Program of the National Science Teachers Association.

"Would this be an effective or ineffective technique for me and my class?" is the question teachers might ask themselves as they get "teaching tips" from others. In the final analysis each teacher needs and wants to find his own unique way.

In essence, the teacher is the key to successful work with the gifted. A teacher who is demanding but not coercive, firm but not dominating, who is sympathetic and friendly, whom the student will accept as surrogate parent does much to nurture giftedness. Such a teacher need not be an "expert" in the area (as experience is defined); he need be an expert teacher and an expert at being human. He knows that teaching is a personal invention and he is constantly at work improving the invention.

Field Trips. Those who have shared in the experience of a carefully planned, well-run, and thoughtfully followed-up field trip—to the woods, to a farm, around the school grounds, to a mine or factory—do not need to be convinced of the value of the experience to stimulate students to start "sciencing" for themselves.

For those students who are seriously considering science as a possible career, a visit to a research laboratory may be particularly vitalizing. A former student, a parent, or someone else in the community may be helpful in making the necessary contact. It is an impressive experience to see men of science quietly at work; to have them take time to explain in simple terms what their research is about. The students learn how closely interrelated are the findings of workers in the many fields of scientific inquiry, where artificial boundaries of race or nation are discarded in the mutual search for scientific truth and the increasingly successful attempt to liberate people from pain and disease.

Leaving the laboratory, students may be confronted with headlines of horror and death, with the all too vivid paradox of the inventions of science that might have blessed mankind being misused to torture and destroy. Large questions may form themselves in the young people's minds: "Does this have to be? Who or what is responsible? Can we do anything about it?" These are questions to which there are no ready answers, but at least a start is made when the query is put and the search begun.

Students might be interested in finding out what scientists themselves are doing about the social implications of their discoveries. They may look up the report of the special committee set up by the American Association for the Advancement of Science.[2] Students might also keep in touch with the work of the Council for Atomic Age Study of Columbia University, a group organized to make a broad and bold attack on the problems of society and the atom.

Science Clubs and Science Fairs. Many science teachers find time to sponsor a science club in their school. The informal atmosphere of a

[2] *Science*, Dec. 21, 1956.

club, the freedom from the pressure of the curriculum provide special opportunities for teacher and students to adventure along the highways and byways of science. Already there are more than half a million youngsters enrolled in science clubs throughout the nation.

Often club activities culminate in local, regional, and national science fairs. During 1958–1959, for instance, there were 600,000 science fair exhibits by elementary and high school students, leading to the National Science Fair, and 4 million people flocked to see them.

Surveys show that only about half the students who finish high school in the top 20 per cent of their classes go to college. However, more than 76 per cent of National Science Fair exhibitors who are not still in high school have taken advanced education to train for scientific and technical careers, according to a survey by Science Service. It seems that science fairs are indeed helping to find the scientists of tomorrow.

Museum Programs. Some of the museums of our country are making special provision for students interested in science. Here is one from among a number of examples: Every year 200 outstanding science students from county high schools are invited to attend Saturday workshops at the Los Angeles County Museum. A follow-up study shows that 99 per cent of these students attend college and 65 per cent go into some scientific field. Teachers might help to publicize such museum programs or might even help to initiate one.

School Camping. Fortunate the school that has worked out a school camping program, a program that enables teachers and students to study together in the laboratory that existed long before schools. Here is experience at firsthand. Here is a chance to develop a truer concept and fuller appreciation of the things we live by. The program involves the use of the outdoors as an experimental curriculum in which some of the unmet needs of youth can be fulfilled. It is basic learning, by seeing and doing. This outdoor experience takes young people back to the land, where they may find their place in natural interrelationships.

Whether the camping experience of a class is limited to a week end or a week, or whether it extends into the summer season for a lengthier period, it can be meaningful far beyond its time allotment. Camping experiences offer opportunities to contact science at its source. Conservation education, too, becomes not a dry-as-dust series of admonitions but a living experience, with a camp site to plan for, soil to protect, a water supply to ensure, trees to plant, forests to keep safe, wildlife to care for, trails to blaze.

The outdoor educational activities, science and conservation, are only part of the program. Other outcomes of the experience at its best are new recreational interests, improved standards of healthful living, purposeful work experiences, and just ordinary fun and enjoyment.

Above all, the school camp offers opportunities to develop a sense of at-homeness with one's fellows and one's world, sharing outdoor work and play, singing together or being quiet together around a campfire under the stars.

School camping is still in its experimental years and is far from being universal. It is highly developed in some states, Michigan and California, for example, and is still nonexistent in many school systems. Beginnings are hard and slow, but there is a steady growth of the movement. For an excellent survey of camping and outdoor education, consult the May, 1950, issue of the *Journal of Educational Sociology*. You might find helpful the pamphlet *A Study of Conservation Activities in Outdoor Education Programs in California*, by Lola Jean Eriksen (California Department of Natural Resources, Sacramento, 1956). You might also contact the American Association for Health, Physical Education and Recreation, Washington, D.C., for appropriate literature.

Science Camps. There have already been some experiments in the running of science camps or special science programs at regular camps. The tremendous advantages of a summer science program are the laboratory of the out-of-doors and the uninterrupted time so difficult to attain in the crowding pressures of the school year.

Students may bring to such a camp well-planned projects or may develop completely new interests in the new setting. Sometimes a research center or industrial firm will give special guidance to students. Thus, at the science work camp of Fieldston School, New York City, in the summer of 1952, a doctor from a famous cancer research center guided a student project involving the injection of mice with various concentrations of "sarcoma 180" and a study of the subsequent development of cancer. Another future scientist was helped in his research by a firm interested in exploring the possibilities of growing algae for food. In both instances the boys continued their work in the following school year. One boy was permitted to leave classes one afternoon a week in order to work in the research laboratory that was guiding his experiments. Both students were well started on scientific careers before leaving high school.

Science Jobs. Many science students, during the summer between high school graduation and college entrance, find jobs at such places as the National Bureau of Standards and the National Institute of Health in Washington; the U.S. Naval Ordnance Laboratory at White Oak, Maryland; the U.S. Department of Agriculture Research Center at Beltsville, Maryland; the Mayo Clinic at Rochester, Minnesota; the Westinghouse Research Laboratory at Pittsburgh, Pennsylvania; the Roscoe B. Jackson Memorial Laboratory at Bar Harbor, Maine.

A new student conservation program sponsored by the National Parks Association (2000 P St., N.W., Washington, D.C.) is open to high school and college students. It offers young people the opportunity to assist in two national parks by working directly with park staffs in a large variety of projects.

Science Training Programs. Most extensive among opportunities for future scientists are the summer science training programs for secondary school students conducted in over one-hundred institutions with funds provided by the National Science Foundation. In these summer courses, young people still in high school have unequaled chances to extend and enrich their regular schoolwork.

Career Literature. There are literally hundreds of pamphlets and many excellent books on science careers of all sorts. This material makes excellent browsing for students exploring career possibilities.

In one school, an active alumni committee built up a career guidance library that was later administered and kept up-to-date with the help of student curators.

17-5. Improving the Teacher's Own Resources

Professional Groups. By forming a local or regional science teachers organization, teachers may exchange ideas, may keep abreast of recent developments by means of lectures, conferences, and publications. In this manner, they may learn of interesting demonstrations and laboratory experiments not found in textbooks, may glimpse ways of "dissolving the walls of the classroom," thus bringing their students into living contact with the world in which they live.

Some striking material appeared in the April, 1957, issue of *The Science Teacher.* It was headed "On the Target! High School Science Teaching and Today's Related Manpower Shortage. A statement of facts, comments, and action plans and ideas, developed and approved by the Board of Directors of the National Science Teachers Association." Reprints may be obtained from NSTA, 1201 Sixteenth St., N.W., Washington, D.C.

Summer Opportunities. Each year increasing numbers of teachers are using part of their summer holiday for broadening their science experience. The National Science Teachers Foundation, through the Future Scientists of America Foundation, has been instrumental in opening up a number of opportunities for high school science teachers. There are university programs including research assistantships, short-term courses on the new developments in science, vacation workshops, and summer job opportunities offered by industry. The NSTA publishes a list each year in its magazine, *The Science Teacher.*

Opportunities exist also for firsthand experiences in outdoor education. Conservation workshops of brief or extended duration offer enrichment as well as recreation. Societies interested in conservation, universities, school systems, government services—these are some of the organizations offering courses and workshops. Scholarships, too, are available through such organizations as Audubon societies, garden clubs, the National Wildlife Federation, and sportsmen's groups. Further information may be obtained from the Conservation Education Association, c/o Wilson F. Clark, Secretary, Eastern Montana College of Education, Billings, Montana. One might also write for the most recent U.S. Soil Conservation Service pamphlet, *Conservation Workshops Inventory.*

17-6. A Conservation Program for Our Future Resource Discoverers and Developers

Present research reveals unmistakably that there is no shortage of scientific talent in our nation. There is, however, a grave shortage of *developed* talent.

Encouraging More Students to Go to College. Today, fewer than half of those capable of acquiring a college degree enter college, according to the findings of the National Manpower Council in *A Policy for Scientific and Professional Manpower* (Sec. 19-8*p*). In a study made by Charles C. Cole, Jr., *Encouraging Scientific Talent* (Sec. 19-8*n*), it is estimated that the number of high-ability secondary school graduates in the nation now not going to college for financial reasons, but who could presumably be won to a higher education by means of a scholarship program, is between 60,000 and 100,000. It is estimated by Cole that another group of similar size lacks the interest or motivation to go to college. It is with this latter group that teachers may exert an influence.

For those interested in learning more about why we lose so much of our human potential between high school and college, the thought-provoking story is thoroughly documented and discussed in the books mentioned above.

A *National Study of High School Students and Their Plans,* a survey made in the spring of 1955 by the Educational Testing Service and reported in *Encouraging Scientific Talent,* reveals some facts of particular interest to teachers. Today's able high school graduate wants to continue his formal education, realizing that it is essential for the work he wants to do. At the same time he lacks sufficient guidance in high school, particularly about scholarship awards, upon which his college and financial plans may depend.

Encouraging and making it possible for more young people to graduate from college and go on to graduate work would expand the source of the supply from which the nation's scientific and professional persons come and would help to reduce the loss represented by the failure to train many able individuals. But all these potential scientists first pass through the hands of secondary school teachers. What may finally tip the balance in favor of further education is what happens in the classroom day by day. How many persons, we wonder, made up their minds to a life of science partly because their science teacher in high school was such a "great guy"?

Publicizing Awards and Scholarship Opportunities. There are a number of programs supported by professional organizations, industries, business firms, and other agencies that encourage students toward careers in science. In 1954, for instance, the American Society of Metals inaugurated the offering of awards to both students and teachers. This program is administered by the Future Scientists of America Foundation of the NSTA.

Then, too, there are the scholarships provided by Union Carbide Corporation, 30 East 42nd St., New York, for high school and preparatory school graduates who intend to enter business or industry. These scholarships are offered to students with the necessary talents in a variety of fields including business, research, or teaching.

Another important organized effort to recruit young scientists and engineers is now being conducted by the Engineering Manpower Commission of the Engineers Joint Council (29 West 39th St., New York). Circulating material to guidance counselors and secondary school principals has been partly responsible for a marked increase in the enrollment of freshman engineering students. High school science teachers might also want to familiarize themselves with this material.

Many schools already have data in regard to the National Merit Scholarships, four-year college scholarships available to high school seniors. The stipend accompanying each scholarship is based on need and may vary from $100 to $2,200 a year. Further information may be obtained from National Merit Scholarship Corporation, 1580 Sherman Ave., Evanston, Ill.

One of the functions of Science Clubs of America, run by Science Service, is the conducting of the Science Talent Search, sponsored by Westinghouse Educational Foundation. State science fairs, essay contests, the Bausch and Lomb competition (635 St. Paul St., Rochester, N.Y.) are just a few examples of *some fifty programs* throughout the nation.

A "resource file" telling science teachers where they may go for further help in regard to scholarships and other services to themselves and to students may be found in Chapter 18 of *A Book of Methods.*[3]

Encouraging Girls to Enter Science. The encouragement of more girls to enter scientific careers would tap another large reserve of talent. There are, of course, many women who, along with a full and successful family life, could find enrichment and reward in the professional world if they

[3] Paul F. Brandwein, F. G. Watson, and P. E. Blackwood, *A Book of Methods*, Harcourt, Brace and Company, Inc., New York, 1958.

had the background and training. "Time out," and enough of it for the bearing and rearing of children, is by no means an insurmountable obstacle.

Girls might be interested in reading about women in science. Eve Curie's biography of her famed mother, *Madame Curie* (Doubleday & Company, Inc., New York, 1937) or Dr. Alice Hamilton's story of her career in industrial medicine, *Exploring the Dangerous Trades* (Little, Brown & Company, Boston, 1943) are two stirring examples. Biographies of other women may be found in Edna Yost's *American Women of Science* (J. B. Lippincott Company, Philadelphia, 1956). The group includes Annie Jump Cannon, astronomer; Libbie Hyman, zoologist; Katherine Blodgett, physicist; Florence Sabin, anatomist; Margaret Mead, anthropologist. A companion volume by Edna Yost is entitled *Women of Modern Science* (Dodd, Mead, & Company, Inc., New York, 1959).

Other interest-stimulating reference books are *American Scientists*, by C. J. Hylander (The Macmillan Company, New York, 1935) and *American Men of Science*, by J. Cattell (R. R. Bowker Company, New York, 1956).

What about Skilled Manpower? Many students with certain gifts of their own will eventually become skilled workers and technicians. In *A Policy for Skilled Manpower* (Sec. 19-8*p*), it is estimated that in 1954 there were between 8 and 9 million skilled workers and about half a million technicians in the civilian working population of 64 million.

Students who may become the skilled manpower of the future will require special training for their vocations. When and where should this training start? In a regular or a vocational high school? On the job? In a special night school? Or in a combination of several institutions?

A thorough discussion of the wise use of our skilled manpower resources may be found in the publication of the National Manpower Council, *Improving the Work Skills of the Nation* (Columbia University Press, New York, 1955).

And the Others? In the urgent search for science talent there may be danger of neglecting the gifts and contributions of others. What would happen to any society that singled out its scientists, technicians, and skilled manpower only? This country's resources include potential artists, writers, musicians, poets, historians, leaders and workers in government, industry, business, and management. Included, too, are people without special talents but still with unique contributions to make.

It seems evident that in order to develop to the full our country's human potential we shall need to improve and expand our schools, opening opportunities for further education to *all* who seem able to profit from it.

In a democracy, we believe in freedom of choice; we do not believe in regimenting people even to fill pressing needs except in time of national emergency. *To ensure a flow of future scientists, skilled workers, and technicians, we need to give all our young people an opportunity to develop their special gifts to the full.*

We should demand a full social return from our citizens. This in turn implies a full opportunity to each person to develop his special gifts. Soil, water, minerals, and energy sources are important. But it is people who use them and need to use them wisely. And it is to people we must turn for the human use of human beings.

PART 5

Appendix

18

Tools for the Teacher

18-1. Some Solutions and Reagents Referred to in the Text

a. Agar Gel. Culture plates may be purchased at a supply house (Sec. 18-3), or they may be prepared in the laboratory as follows: Boil together and filter into small petri dishes:

Water	500 cc
Agar	7½ grams
Salt	¼ tsp
Sodium carbonate	¼ tsp
Beef bouillon cubes	5 grams

Sterilize the petri dishes on top of a double boiler for 1 hour. After at least 12 hours, sterilize them again.

One dish should be kept covered as a control, to be sure all organisms were killed during sterilization. For the preparation of other culture media, refer to *A Sourcebook for the Biological Sciences* (Sec. 19-3*e*).

b. Algae Culture Medium. Chu no. 10 with modified-iron source (developed by S. P. Chu, 1942).

Table 18-1

Compound	*Grams per liter*
Calcium nitrate	0.040
Potassium monohydrogen phosphate	0.010
Magnesium sulphate (heptahydrate)	0.025
Sodium carbonate (anhydrous)	0.020
Sodium silicate	0.025
Ferric citrate	0.003
Citric acid	0.003

c. Aquarium Cement. For minor repairs this preparation is successful because it sticks to glass, metal, stone, or wood. It also seems to resist the action of sea water in a marine tank.

Mix together the following by weight:

Litharge	10 parts
Plaster of paris	10 parts
Powdered rosin	1 part
Dry white sand	10 parts

Add enough boiled linseed oil to make fairly stiff putty. Apply to the leaks in the tank and allow 4 to 6 days for the putty to harden before you fill the tank.

d. Benedict's Solution. Dissolve 173 grams of sodium citrate and 100 grams of anhydrous sodium carbonate in 800 milliliters of water, with the aid of heat. Filter if necessary and dilute to 850 milliliters. Dissolve 17.3 grams of hydrated copper sulfate in 100 milliliters of water. Pour the latter solution, with constant stirring, into the carbonate-citrate solution and add enough water to make 1 liter.

e. Bromthymol Blue Indicator. Dissolve 1 gram of bromthymol blue in 1,000 cubic centimeters of water to make an 0.1 per cent solution. The color of the solution should be blue; add a drop of ammonium hydroxide to get a deep blue color. This is a stock solution.

When the indicator is to be used, dilute it with equal quantities of water, i.e., for 25 centimeters of stock solution, add 25 centimeters of water. Test the strength of the solution in this way. Blow into a small amount of the solution with a straw; within 30 seconds the blue color should change to yellow. If it takes longer to decolorize the blue solution, add a bit more water, for it is too strong.

f. Buffer Solution. Add the following salts to 1 liter of distilled water:

Sodium dihydrogen phosphate, NaH_2PO_4	28.81 grams
Disodium hydrogen phosphate, Na_2HPO_4	125.00 grams

g. Chlorine Water. Put ½ gram of potassium chlorate in a small test tube; add 1 cubic centimeter of concentrated hydrochloric acid and dilute with sufficient water to stop the reaction. The greenish-yellow solution formed is chlorine water.

h. Cobalt Chloride Paper. Saturate pieces of filter paper in a solution of cobalt chloride. This water solution is red and the paper is red when wet but becomes blue upon drying. Store these dry strips in a closed container. Should they turn pink in storage, heat them in a dry test tube over a bunsen flame or place large quantities in an oven.

i. Cornmeal-agar Medium. Dissolve 15 grams of agar in 750 cubic centimeters of water and heat. Add 100 grams of cornmeal, stirring constantly. When this reaches a boil, add 135 grams of corn syrup or molasses. Boil the mixture *slowly* for 5 minutes. Then pour the medium into sterilized vials or bottles and insert a strip of paper toweling in each, while the medium is still soft. This provides additional space for egg laying and pupation. Plug the bottles with cotton or cover with caps. This quantity should make about twenty-five culture bottles. You may want to sterilize these bottles for 20 minutes at 15 pounds pressure.

j. Daphnia Culture (Modified Knop's solution). Mix 1 gram each of potassium nitrate, magnesium sulfate, and potassium monohydrogen phosphate with 1 liter of distilled water and pour into several battery jars. Then add 3 grams of calcium nitrate. This will precipitate calcium phosphate.

For immediate use add 5 liters of distilled water to 1 liter of stock solution. Inoculate the culture medium with nonfilamentous algae; allow to stand in light until the water becomes greenish. About once a week add a bit of yeast and a small amount of hard-boiled egg yolk made into a paste.

k. Fehling's Solution. Fehling's solution is made in two solutions: Solution *A* contains 7 grams of crystalline copper sulfate in 100 cubic centimeters of distilled water. It may be necessary to warm the solution to dissolve the crystals. Solution *B* contains 11 grams of sodium hydroxide and 36 grams of Rochelle salt in 100 cubic centimeters of solution. Just before using, mix 2 cubic centimeters of each solution, *A* and *B*, in a 6-inch test tube. Shake until the mixture is clear.

l. Formalin. Formalin is an almost 40 per cent solution of the gas formaldehyde dissolved in water. This makes a stock solution.

Usually a 10 per cent solution is the most useful as a preservative or fixative for small forms and also for killing seeds. Prepare this dilution by adding 10 centimeters of formalin to 90 cubic centimeters of water. (To kill seeds, immerse them in the solution for several hours.)

When a 4 per cent solution of formalin is called for, add 4 volumes of commercial formalin to 96 volumes of water. (This is really a 1.6 per cent solution of formaldehyde.)

m. Indophenol. This is the indicator that is bleached when vitamin C is added to the solution. Prepare the solution by adding 1 gram of indophenol to 1,000 cubic centimeters of water to make an 0.1 per cent solution.

You should dilute the fruit juices before performing the demonstration in class. It should take some 15 to 20 drops of the diluted juice to bleach 10 cubic centimeters of the indophenol in a test tube.

When this is added to a substance containing starch a bluish-black precipitate is formed.

This may also be diluted by adding fourteen times its volume of water when used as a stain for wet mounts.

The original solution may be diluted 1 part to 10 parts of water for very delicate work.

Table 18-2. Indicators

Name of indicator	pH range	Color change	
		Acid	Alkaline
Alizarin red (1 per cent aqueous)	4.0– 5.0	Yellow	Purple
Bromcresol purple	5.2– 6.8	Yellow	Purple
Bromthymol blue	6.0– 7.6	Yellow	Blue
Litmus paper	4.5– 8.3	Blue to red	Red to blue
Methyl orange (may be used in presence of CO_2 or H_2S)	3.1– 4.4	Pink	Yellow
Phenol red	6.8– 8.4	Yellow	Red
Phenolphthalein (0.1 per cent in 50 per cent alcohol)	8.3–10.0	Colorless	Red

n. Limewater. Add an excess of calcium hydroxide or calcium oxide to distilled water. Cork the bottle, shake it well, and let it stand for 24 hours. Pour off the supernatant fluid and stopper the bottle to exclude air.

Limewater should remain colorless; when carbon dioxide is added, a milky precipitate of calcium carbonate forms.

o. Lugol's Solution (Iodine Solution). Used for starch test or as a stain. Dissolve 10 grams of potassium iodide in 100 cubic centimeters of distilled water. Then add 5 grams of iodine crystals.

p. Methylene Blue Stain. Prepare the stain in this way. Add 1.48 grams of the dye to 100 cubic centimeters of a 95 per cent ethyl alcohol. This is a stock solution. For use in staining nitrogen-fixing bacteria or other cells such as epithelial tissue, use a diluted stain. Add 90 cubic centimeters of distilled water to every 10 cubic centimeters of the stock solution of the stain.

First, a smear might be made of nitrogen-fixing bacteria. Then this smear is brushed twice over a bunsen flame. This process fixes or causes the bacteria to adhere to the slide preparatory to staining. After the stain has been applied for some 3 minutes, wash it off by dipping the slide into a tumbler of water. Blot the slide dry and inspect it under the microscope. If the stain is too dark, dip the slide into more water, blot dry, and inspect it again under a microscope.

q. Nitrogen Dioxide Detection[1] (Sampling and analytical method, sometimes called the Saltzman method).

1. Reagents. Dissolve 0.1 gram of N-(1-Naphthyl)-ethylenediamine dihydrochloride reagent in 100 milliliters of water. This makes an 0.1 per cent stock solution.

To make an absorbing reagent, dissolve 5 grams of sulfanilic acid in almost a liter of water containing 140 milliliters of glacial acetic acid; then add 20 milliliters of the 0.1 per cent stock solution and dilute to 1 liter.

2. Sampling and Determination. Draw 25 milliliters of the flue gas into 50-milliliter syringes containing 25 milliliters of the absorbing reagent. After collection of the sample, a direct reddish-violet color appears. Color development is complete within 15 minutes at ordinary temperatures. Read in a colorimeter at 540 millimicrons, using unexposed reagent as a reference. Then compare the readings to a previously calibrated standard curve.

r. Nutrient Solution for Nutriculture

Table 18-3

Salt	*Grams per liter*
Potassium nitrate	0.550
Potassium sulfate	0.500
Calcium sulfate	0.760
Magnesium sulfate	0.520
Monocalcium phosphate	0.310
Ammonium sulfate	0.140

For other formulas and for a micronutrient supplement of trace elements, write for *Nutriculture* (Purdue University Agricultural Experiment Station pamphlet S.C. 328, Lafayette, Ind.).

s. Phenolphthalein Solution. Dissolve 1 gram of phenolphthalein powder in 100 cubic centimeters of isopropyl or ethyl alcohol. (A little water may then be added but not enough to precipitate the powder.)

t. Physiological or Isotonic Salt Solutions

1. For frog tissue and for mounting termite's flagellates: Dissolve 7 grams of sodium chloride in 1,000 cubic centimeters of distilled water to make an 0.7 per cent solution.

2. For bird embryos or mammalian tissue: Dissolve 9 grams of sodium chloride in 1,000 cubic centimeters of distilled water to make an 0.9 per cent solution.

u. Potassium Pyrogallate Solution. In demonstrations you may want

[1] Developed by Morris B. Jacobs of the Air Pollution Control Department of New York City.

to plan to use this solution to remove oxygen from the air and thereby test whether seedlings grow in such vitiated air.

Prepare the solution by adding 1 part by weight of pyrogallic acid and 5 parts of potassium hydroxide to 30 parts of water.

v. Preservative for Green Plants. This solution to some extent prevents the usual bleaching of green specimens. Mix together the following substances:

Table 18-4

50 per cent alcohol	90.0 cc
Formalin	5.0 cc
Glacial acetic acid	2.5 cc
Glycerin	2.5 cc
Cupric chloride	10.0 grams
Uranium nitrate	1.5 grams

w. Ringer's Solution (for frog tissue). While isotonic (physiological) salt solution serves a general use in the laboratory, there are times when a more exact solution is needed. To prepare Ringer's solution, dissolve the salts in 1,000 cubic centimeters of distilled water:

Table 18-5

Potassium chloride	0.14 grams
Calcium chloride	0.12 grams
Sodium bicarbonate	0.20 grams
Sodium chloride	6.50 grams

Store in a well-stoppered bottle to prevent contamination.

18-2. Some Conversion Factors

Weight

1 gram = 0.03527 ounce
1 kilogram = 2.205 pounds
1 ounce = 28.35 grams
1 pound = 0.4536 kilograms

Length

1 centimeter = 0.3937 inch
1 meter = 3.281 feet
1 inch = 2.54 centimeters
1 foot = 0.3048 meter

Volume

1 gallon = 3.785 liters = 231 cubic inches
1 cubic centimeter = 0.0610 cubic inch

Temperature

Fahrenheit to centigrade

$C = 5/9F - 32$

Centigrade to Fahrenheit

$F = 9/5C + 32$

18-3. Some Supply Houses for Biology, Chemistry, and Physics Supplies and Apparatus[2]

Ainsworth & Sons, Inc., 2151 Lawrence St., Denver 5, Colo.
Allied Chemical & Dye Corp., 40 Rector St., New York 6, N.Y.
Aloe Scientific, Division of A. S. Aloe Co., 5655 Kingsbury St., St. Louis 12, Mo.
American Hospital Supply Corp., 40-05—168 St., Flushing, N.Y., or 2020 Ridge Ave., Evanston, Ill.
American Type Culture Collection (bacteria), 2029 M St., N.W., Washington 6, D.C.
Bausch & Lomb Optical Co., 635 St. Paul St., Rochester, N.Y.
Biddle & Company, 1316 Arch St., Philadelphia 7, Pa.
Biological Research Products Co., 243 W. Root St., Chicago, Ill.
California Biological Service, 1612 W. Glenoaks Blvd., Glendale, Calif.
California Botanical Materials Co., 861 E. Columbia Ave., Pomona, Calif.
Cambosco Scientific Co., 37 Antwerp St., Brighton 35, Mass.
Carolina Biological Supply Co., Elon College, N.C.
Central Scientific Co., 1700 N. Irving Park Rd., Chicago 13, Ill.
Charles Pfizer & Co., 11 Bartlett St., Brooklyn, N.Y.
Chicago Apparatus Co., 1735 N. Ashland Ave., Chicago 22, Ill.
Clay-Adams Co., 141 E. 25th St., New York 10, N.Y.
Corning Glass Works, Corning, N.Y.
Denoyer-Geppert Co., 5235 N. Ravenswood Ave., Chicago 40, Ill.
Difco Laboratories, Inc., Detroit 1, Mich.
Dow Chemical Co., Midland, Mich.
Eastman Kodak Co., 343 State St., Rochester 4, N.Y.
Eimer & Amend, Greenwich and Morton Sts., New York 14, N.Y.
Erb & Gray Co., 854 S. Figueroa St., Los Angeles 14, Calif.
Fisher Scientific Supply Co., 139 Fisher Bldg., Pittsburgh 19, Pa.
General Biochemicals, Inc., 677 Laboratory Park, Chagrin Falls, Ohio
General Biological Supply House, Inc. (Turtox), 8200 S. Hoyne Ave., Chicago 20, Ill.
Gradwohl Laboratories, 3514 Lucas Ave., St. Louis 3, Mo.
Graf-Apsco Co., 5868 N. Broadway, Chicago 40, Ill.

[2] Addresses were correct at date of publication but may now need checking.

Harshaw Scientific Division, Harshaw Chemical Co., 1945 E. 97th St., Cleveland 6, Ohio
Kelly-Koett Manufacturing Co., 24 E. 6th St., Covington, Ky.
Kimble Glass, P.O. Box 1035, Toledo 1, Ohio
Lederle Laboratories, Division of American Cyanamid Co., Midtown Rd., Pearl River, N.Y.
Leitz, Inc., 468 Fourth Ave., New York 16, N.Y.
Marine Biological Laboratory, Woods Hole, Mass.
Merck & Co., Rahway, N.J.
Monsanto Chemical Co., 1700 S. 2nd St., St. Louis 4, Mo.
Nalge Co., Inc. (plastic ware), Rochester 2, N.Y.
New York Scientific Supply Co, 28 W. 30th St., New York, N.Y.
Nutritional Biochemicals Corp., 21010 Miles Ave., Cleveland 2, Ohio
Nystrom & Co., 3333 N. Elston Ave., Chicago 18, Ill.
Oregon Biological Supply Co., 1806 S.E. Holgate Blvd., Portland, Ore.
Pacific Laboratory Apparatus Co., 3555 Whittier Blvd., Los Angeles 23, Calif.
Polaroid Corp., Cambridge 39, Mass.
Product Design Co. (conservation kits), 2796 Middlefield Rd., Redwood City, Calif.
Research Specialties Co., 2005 Hopkins St., Berkeley 7, Calif.
Sheldon Equipment Co., 149 Thomas St., Muskegon, Mich.
Sprague-Dawley, Inc. (laboratory rats), P.O. Box 2071, Madison 5, Wis.
Standard Scientific Corp., 34 W. 4th St., New York, N.Y.
Testa Manufacturing Co., 418 S. Pecan St., Los Angeles 33, Calif.
United Scientific Co., 204 Milk St., Boston 9, Mass.
Ward's Natural Science Establishment, 3000 Ridge Rd. E., Rochester 9, N.Y.
Welch Manufacturing Co., 1515 N. Sedgwick St., Chicago 10, Ill.
Western Laboratories, 826 Q St., Lincoln, Neb.
Windsor Biology Gardens, Moore's Creek Rd., Bloomington, Ind.

18-4. Some Suggested Laboratory Procedures

If students are to be given the opportunity for firsthand laboratory experience, they must be prepared for it. Students will need to become acquainted with their apparatus, to learn its proper use and care. They will have to handle chemicals—solid, liquid, and gas. Students should be aware of dangers, alert to safety precautions, and know what to do in case of accident. Young people will soon realize that good technical procedures are a prelude not only to safety but to effective work as well.

Before students are allowed to work in the laboratory teachers may prepare them by means of a few (never too many at a time) simple and clear demonstrations. Here are some of the topics with which students should become familiar at appropriate moments:

1. Use and care of apparatus to be handled. (This might include the bunsen burner, ironware, glassware, porcelain, etc.)

2. Glass working, involving such techniques as fire polishing and bending. Students can then make their own glass connections as needed.

3. Handling reagents safely and efficiently, while observing the precautions necessary to maintain their purity.

4. Techniques of weighing on appropriate balances.

5. Special techniques like filtering, evaporating, and reading a graduate.

6. Waste disposal, both solid and liquid, with emphasis on care of the sink.

7. Safety precautions, not only when using chemicals but when heating apparatus. One of the few rules to be inflexibly administered might be that no one starts heating a "setup" (or adds the final chemical) until the instructor has approved the apparatus.

8. Immediate reporting to the teacher of any injury, even the most minor one.

9. Good manners in the laboratory: replacing chemicals in proper order so that the next student can find them; cleaning up carefully so that others may work in good conditions; maintaining enough quiet so that thoughtful work is possible for everyone.

What to Do in an Emergency. Despite precautions, an accident may sometimes happen in the laboratory. The following are suggestions for treatment of minor injuries and for first aid in case of more serious injuries. (In some schools all injuries, even the minor ones, are immediately handled by the nurse.)

Burns. Apply a nonsensitizing antibiotic ointment over the burned area. Cover lightly with sterile gauze.

Cuts. Apply an aqueous Zephiran solution or similar antiseptic.

Something in the Eye. Wash copiously with water.

1. Acid in the eye. After washing with water, wash with 5 per cent sodium bicarbonate or limewater.

2. Alkali in the eye. After washing with water, wash with 5 per cent boric acid.

Something on the Clothes. Pour on water quickly and abundantly.

1. Acid on the clothes. Silk and wool: Neutralize with 5 per cent sodium bicarbonate and rinse. Cotton and linen: Hold stain over open bottle of ammonia water and rinse.

2. Alkali on the clothes. Neutralize with 5 per cent acetic acid and rinse.

Poisons. Since many chemicals are poisonous, the best plan is to keep them all out of the mouth unless directed to taste them. In case of poisoning call a physician at once.

Preventing and Extinguishing Fires. Most organic liquids, gasoline, kerosene, ether, alcohols, etc., are highly flammable and should not be heated over the open flame or boiled near a flame. Sand and soda are more effective than water for putting out oil fires. If a flammable liquid is burning in a dish, the flame may be smothered by putting a glass plate, an asbestos board, or even a wet rag over it to shut out the air.

Be sure that you and your students know how to use the fire extinguisher. If a student's clothes catch fire, he should not run and wave his arms. Prior instructions should make clear that it is best for him to fold his arms over his face and lie face downward on the floor so that a blanket may be thrown over him and the fire smothered.

First Aid Equipment for a Laboratory

- Wool blanket (for smothering fire)
- Chemical fire extinguisher
- First aid kit containing the following:
  - Nonsensitizing antibiotic ointment for burns
  - Aqueous Zephiran solution (or similar antiseptic) for cuts
  - Sterile gauze
  - Band-aids
  - Adhesive tape
  - Scissors
  - Tongue depressors
  - Limewater for acid in eye
  - Boric acid for alkali in eye
  - Eye cup
- Laboratory emergency chart

You may want to hang a wall chart near your first aid kit. Such a chart may be obtained from Fisher Scientific Co., 717 Forbes St., Pittsburgh, or to Eimer & Amend, Greenwich and Morton Sts., New York.

18-5. A Few Added Field Trip Suggestions

A good field trip, like a good classroom lesson, requires thoughtful preparation as well as enthusiasm. Here is an outline which may suggest the kind of planning experienced leaders have found helpful:

Initiating the Trip

- Motivation and purpose
- Making arrangements
- Previsit by teacher

Obtaining Permissions
- Principal or superintendent
- Landowner
- Director of museum, industry, etc.
- Parents

Note to Parents
- Purpose of trip
- Place
- Time of leaving and return
- Cost, if any
- Equipment needed
- Kind of transportation

Planning with Assistant Leaders

Guides, managers, mother or student helpers should be briefed as to age and interest level of the group and the goals of the teacher

Safety
- First aid kit checked
- Rules understood by students
- Forethought given to danger points

Transportation
- All arrangements, including insurance, double-checked

Lunch
- Plans for the kind of lunch (individual or group)
- Plans for lunch groups
  - Carrying committees
  - Preparing committees
  - Cleanup squad

Alternate Program for Rainy Day

Follow-up
- Reports, discussion, conclusions
- Planning new activities as outcome of trip

First Aid Kit for Field Trips
- Assorted Band-aids
- Roll of 2-inch bandage
- Adhesive tape
- Antiseptic
- Scissors
- Naphtha soap for poison ivy, sumac

Equipment for Field Trip
- Notebooks and pencils
- Nature trip equipment
  - Containers (preferably plastic) for specimens
  - Pulp paper magazines for carrying leaves and flowers

Trowels, vascula, knives, insect nets or sieves
Field guides, nature keys, field glasses, if available
Photographic equipment for those who are interested
Made ready in advance: terrariums, aquariums, pressing cases to receive specimens

In addition, these suggestions might be useful:

For soil studies:	Topographic and land-use maps, compasses, sighting levels, soil test kits, soil thermometers
For water studies:	Dip nets, white basins, screw-top jars, thermometers
For forestry:	Diameter tape, increment borer, Biltmore stick
For ecology:	Thermometer or thermograph, light meter, altimeter

You will find in Sec. 5-2 some general suggestions for conducting field trips and in Sec. 9-3 descriptions of sample field trips to the woods. For more detailed guidance, write for *Field Trips: A Handbook for Leaders* (Michigan Department of Conservation, Education Division, Lansing, Mich.).

18-6. The Use of Recordings

If your school has access to a tape-recording machine, you will find this a flexible and useful teaching device. What pictures are to the eye, recordings are to the ear. A half-hour program, student-planned and -produced, can be completely recorded on one tape and used and reused as needed.

Recordings (either tape or disk) have been found particularly useful in three general ways:

1. As an introduction to some unit of study, providing background material and motivation.
2. In the midst of the unit, to illustrate facts, concepts, and skills.
3. For summation, to round out the concepts and to offer enrichment.

Bibliography

19-1. Introduction

Sections 1 through 9 of this bibliography were prepared for us by Mrs. Ethel Shutts, the first librarian of the Instructional Materials Library at Mankato State Teachers College, Minnesota.

In the bibliography, Mrs. Shutts has suggested some useful and up-to-date publications in each area of conservation, without overwhelming the teacher with an enormous number of titles. It is a highly selective listing, and there are literally hundreds of excellent titles that could not be included.

The approximate grade level is indicated in parentheses. Teachers should bear in mind that much valuable material may be found for their students in grade levels above and below their own.

The compiler has most generously offered to assist teachers who do not find what they need in this listing. Write to Mrs. Ethel Shutts, 2626 N.E. Lincoln St., Minneapolis, Minn.

Mr. John Gibbs of The Conservation Foundation prepared the listing of films and filmstrips (Secs. 19-10 and 19-11).

SOME SELECTED REFERENCES RELATING TO RESOURCE USE

19-2. General Reference

Junior High (and Older)

a. The Community of Living Things (grades 7–12), Creative Educational Society, Inc., Mankato, Minn., 1956, in cooperation with the National Audubon Society. An outstanding series well worth the cost as a valuable addition to a school library. For each volume an outstanding authority has chosen approximately 100 pictures for their accuracy and beauty to illustrate the text. Vol. 1. *Field and Meadow,* E. S. Ress; Vol. 2. *Fresh and Salt Water,* B. B. Cadbury; Vol. 3. *City Park and Home Gardens,*

R. S. Lemmon; Vol. 4. *Forest and Woodland,* S. Collins; Vol. 5. *The Desert,* A. Klots and E. Klots.

b. *Cornell Rural School Leaflets,* New York State College of Agriculture, Cornell University Press, Ithaca, N.Y. (four issues per year). A series full of practical teaching suggestions, simple and imaginative. Some leaflets deal with conservation. In this book we have referred extensively to vol. 45, no. 1, *Conservation: A Handbook for Teachers.* Write for list and price of back issues.

c. Eliot, Charles N., *Conservation of American Resources* (grades 7–10), Turner E. Smith & Company, Atlanta, Ga., 1951, 430 pp. A broad treatment of renewables and nonrenewables. Includes units on landscape, nature's masterpieces, and human resources. Interesting style for junior high young people, with suggested activities and excellent photographs.

d. National Audubon Society, *Nature Program* (grades 7–12; teacher), Doubleday & Company, Inc., New York, usually 50 to 65 pages in length, published monthly. May be obtained on a yearly subscription basis with attractive containers for booklets. This series of beautiful booklets with colored photographs covers a variety of subjects such as "Desert Life," "Life on the Forest Floor," "Best-loved Songbirds." Write publisher for list of titles.

e. Parker, Bertha, and others, *Basic Science Education Series* (grades 1–9), Row, Peterson & Company, Evanston, Ill. A series of several dozen colorful, illustrated booklets, many of which relate to conservation. Each booklet is graded.

f. The President's Materials Policy Commission (Paley Report), *Resources for Freedom* (grades 9–12; teacher), 1952. Vol. I. Foundations for Growth and Security; Summary of Vol. I; Vol. II. The Outlook for Key Commodities; Vol. III. The Outlook for Energy Resources; Vol. IV. The Promise of Technology; Vol. V. Selected Reports to the Commission.

g. Stead, William H., *Economic Problems of Natural Resource Use* (grades 7–12; teacher), Joint Council on Economic Education, New York, 1957, 64 pp. Incorporates a study guide "Thinking and Talking It Over" by George L. Fersch. Well-adapted for unit study, with many meaningful graphs and charts.

Teachers and Senior High

h. Allen, Shirley W., *Conserving Natural Resources: Principles and Practices in a Democracy* (teacher), McGraw-Hill Book Company, Inc., New York, 1955, 347 pp. A college textbook. A distinguishing feature is the treatment of the policies of natural resource management in a democratic form of government. Besides the renewables, this book includes a chapter on minerals and one on "human powers."

i. Brown, Harrison, *The Challenge of Man's Future* (grades 11–12; teacher), The Viking Press, Inc., New York, 1954, 290 pp. A thought-provoking inquiry into the condition of man during the years that lie ahead, written by a well-known geochemist from California Institute of Technology.

j. Brown, Harrison, James Bonner, and John Weir, *The Next Hundred Years* (grades 11–12; teacher), The Viking Press, Inc., New York, 1957, 193 pp. This book, written by three scientists from California Institute of Technology, is an inside report based on discussions between leaders of science and industry in America. The questions raised relate to the life or death of our society.

k. Callison, Charles H. (ed.), *America's Natural Resources* (grades 9–12; teacher), The Ronald Press Company, New York, 1957, 211 pp. Each chapter is written by an authority in the field. The chapters are prefaced by an ecological approach to conservation and the relationship of human populations to renewable resources, then forcefully climaxed by a suggested "natural resources policy." With its depth of thought and its realistic approach to solutions, this book is invaluable as a reference work for teachers.

l. Carskadon, T. R., and G. Soule, *U.S.A. in New Dimensions: The Measure and Promise of America's Resources* (grades 9–12; teacher), The Macmillan Company, New York, 1958, 124 pp. This book, based on Dewhurst's survey (Sec. 19-2*n*), shows in simple language and graphic illustration some of the highlights of that survey. It is distributed with the compliments of the Calvin K. Kazanjian Foundation, Inc., Westport, Conn.

m. Ciriacy-Wantrup, S. V., *Resource Conservation: Economics and Policies* (teacher), University of California Press, Berkeley, Calif., 1952, 395 pp. This book focuses on general problems of resource interrelations from a new approach to conservation and relates present economic forces to the success of our democratic society.

n. Dewhurst, J. Frederic, and others, *America's Needs and Resources: A New Survey* (grades 11–12; teacher), The Twentieth Century Fund, New York, 1955, 1148 pp. Highly detailed, technical information on the position of American economic resources, production, and consumption. Among the subjects discussed are consumption requirements (food, clothing, housing, recreation, education, welfare), natural resources, needs vs. resources. Charts, tables, and graphs are used freely.

o. Hatt, Paul K. (ed.), *World Population and Future Resources* (grades 11–12; teacher), American Book Company, New York, 1952, 262 pp. Discusses population, food, material resources, energy resources (including atomic and solar energy). Each chapter is written by a person distinguished in his field.

p. Higbee, Edward, *The American Oasis* (grades 11–12; teacher), Alfred A. Knopf, Inc., New York, 1957, 262 pp. A detailed region-by-region survey of the principal farming areas of the United States. The book deals not with land alone but also with people. Of interest to general readers as well as to the farmer and conservationist.

q. Hogner, Dorothy Childs, *Conservation in America* (grades 9–12), J. B. Lippincott Company, Philadelphia, 1958, 233 pp. Since so much of what the author writes is firsthand knowledge, the material is alive and colorful.

Gives a panorama of American conservation from the distant past into the future age.

r. Ordway, Samuel H., Jr., *Prosperity beyond Tomorrow* (grades 11–12; teacher), The Ronald Press Company, New York, 1955, 208 pp., with a foreword by Paul B. Sears. A readable discussion of the relationship of human, social, and cultural objectives and industrial expansion to the supply of natural resources. Points up the leisure resulting from a prosperity based on abundance and develops an "ethic for the age of leisure."

s. Osborn, Fairfield, *The Limits of the Earth* (grade 12; teacher), Little, Brown & Company, Boston, 1953, 238 pp. An outstanding book about natural resources in all parts of the world and their relation to population and the present world situation. Contains useful information about many countries and makes the reader truly aware of the "limits of the earth."

t. Parson, Ruben L., *Conserving American Resources* (grade 12; teacher), Prentice-Hall, Inc., Englewood Cliffs, N.J., 1956, 550 pp. A broad survey, by categories, of America's resource heritage, with ideas for improving its usefulness through intelligent conservation. Besides the usual items, this book contains discussions of the wealth of the sea and of minerals, teaching aids, and a detailed bibliography.

u. Strauss, Michael W., *Why Not Survive?* (grades 11–12; teacher), Simon and Schuster, Inc., New York, 1955, 272 pp. A rather complete coverage of renewable and nonrenewable resources, including newer subjects such as solar energy. Offers a philosophy that, with recognition of the need for conservation before bankruptcy arrives, America can continue its leadership toward rising levels of living.

v. Thomas, William L. (ed.), *Man's Role in Changing the Face of the Earth* (grades 11–12; teacher), University of Chicago Press, Chicago, 1956, 1231 pp. Contains fifty-four chapters by fifty invited experts on such subjects as the influence of fire, deforestation, soil erosion, tillage, irrigation, mining, urbanization on the land; gives accounts of floods, earthquakes; discusses ports and channels, etc. A massive, encyclopedic volume, relatively inexpensive. Of value to all teachers of conservation, geography, sociology, and history.

w. Tuleen, L. F., W. L. Meuhl, and G. S. Porter, *Test It Yourself!* (grades 7–12), Scott, Foresman and Company, Chicago, 1941. A laboratory manual of unusual experiments, such as soil testing, food analysis, properties of fuels. Especially suited to project work.

19-3. Conservation Education

Materials relating to conservation and resource use are issued by many branches of the U.S. government, including the following: Bureau of Mines; Bureau of Reclamation; Department of the Interior; the White House Executive Office; Senate and House Committees of Interior and Insular Affairs; Department of Health, Education, and Welfare; Tennessee Valley Authority; Rural Electrification Administration; National Park Service; Forest Service; Soil Conservation Service; Fish and Wildlife Service; Department of Agriculture in general; Agricultural Research Service; Bureau of Land Management; Atomic

Energy Commission. Materials issued by government agencies are available from the Superintendent of Documents, Washington.

Increasing numbers of state departments of education are issuing conservation teaching guides. At the end of Chapter 2 will be found a short listing.

a. Clark, Wilson F., *Conservation of Natural Resources,* Conservation Education Association, Eastern Montana College of Education, Billings, Mont., 1956. Although written for Montana teachers, this booklet contains more than 125 demonstrations and projects of use to teachers anywhere.

b. *Conservation and Nature Activities,* Audubon Society of Canada, Toronto, 1953, 256 pp. A guide for elementary teachers in integrating conservation into all subject areas. Of interest also to high school teachers and pupils. Describes specific school programs with emphasis on activities that give student something specific to do. Contains an extensive bibliography and an unusual chapter, Seventy-seven Nature Games. An excellent book to assist with activity-centered teaching.

c. *Conservation Education for American Youth,* Ohio State University Press, Columbus, Ohio, 1950, 35 pp. A report of a work conference on objectives and content of conservation education for American youth. Good in pointing out all sides of conservation and how each relates to human life.

d. Kauffman, Erle (ed.), *The Conservation Yearbook,* Washington, D.C., 1958. A directory and guide to agencies, commissions, boards, associations, foundations, and other organizations concerned with conservation of renewable resources. Gives up-to-date facts and figures in all fields of conservation.

e. Morholt, E., P. Brandwein, A. Joseph, *Teaching High School Science: A Sourcebook for the Biological Sciences* (teacher), Harcourt, Brace and Company, Inc., New York, 1958, 506 pp. Gives tested procedures and techniques for the teacher and student of general science and biology. Many of the experiments have conservation implications.

f. Mulaik, Stanley B., *Teachers' Guide for Conservation and Nature Study,* University of Utah, Salt Lake City, Utah, 1955. A University of Utah workshop session produced this useful guide, a "here's how" manual with many suggestions on integrating conservation and nature study into the regular subject-matter fields.

g. U.S. Soil Conservation Service, *An Outline for Teaching Conservation in High Schools,* 1952. A plan for interweaving the subject of conservation with other school subjects, with special emphasis on soil and water.

h. Weaver, Richard L., *Handbook for Teaching of Conservation and Resource Use* (teacher), Interstate Printers and Publishers, Inc., Danville, Ill., 1955, 499 pp. Prepared by the National Conservation Committee of the National Association of Biology Teachers with a grant from the American Nature Study Association. Deals largely with renewable resources and describes many actual activities throughout the country.

i. Wight, Edgar L., and others, *Classroom Activities Related to Natural Resources,* 2d ed., U.S. Bureau of Indian Affairs, 1956, 60 pp. (Purchase from Haskell Institute, Lawrence, Kans.) An excellent little booklet containing simple projects and demonstrations that can be started in the classroom by bringing in materials from out of doors. Equipment usually involves no cost. Includes experiments for all grades from 1 to 12.

19-4. Some Useful Bibliographies Including Free and Inexpensive Materials

Free and inexpensive materials are so numerous that only a few directories are included in this bibliography. Each teacher should obtain copies of the following references for locating this type of material.

a. *A Bibliography of Conservation,* National Wildlife Federation, Washington, D.C. Mimeographed lists of books, booklets, teaching aids, films and filmstrips.

b. *Bibliography: Outdoor Education;* and *School Camping.* An annotated bibliography of periodical articles, 1950 to 1956, available at Michigan State University Library.

c. Burda, E. J., *Applied Solar Energy Research: A Directory of World Activity and Bibliography of Significant Literature,* Stanford Research Institute, Stanford, Calif., 1955.

d. Burroughs, R. D., *Where and How to Obtain Free and Inexpensive Bulletins, Books and Visual Aids,* Education Division, Michigan Department of Conservation, Lansing, Mich., 1952. A carefully prepared bibliography with more annotation than most lists of free and inexpensive materials. Also contains much helpful information on how to obtain materials from governmental and private sources. Grade levels are indicated on much of the material.

e. Clark, Wilson F., *Selected References on Conservation Education for Teachers and Pupils,* Conservation Education Association, Eastern Montana College of Education, Billings, Mont., 1955. This bibliography has material for use in both elementary and secondary schools.

f. *The Conservation Directory,* National Wildlife Federation, Washington, D.C. A listing of organizations and officials concerned with the protection of wildlife and other natural resources. The public agencies of national, state, and territorial governments of the United States are listed, as well as those of neighboring nations in North and South America. Most of the nongovernment organizations within the United States that have a national or state-wide scope of interest are also included.

g. *Free and Inexpensive Literature Relating to Atomic Energy,* Education Section, American Museum of Atomic Energy, Oak Ridge, Tenn.

h. National Association of Biology Teachers, *Materials for Teaching Conservation and Resource Use,* Interstate Printers and Publishers, Danville, Ill., 1958, 55 pp. This useful bibliography, an enlarged edition of Muriel Beuschlein's *Free and Inexpensive Materials,* includes the following sources: private industry, nonprofit organizations of all kinds, government sources, state organizations, and lists of films and filmstrips.

i. National Research Council, *Catalogue of Publications,* National Academy of Sciences, Washington, D.C. This pamphlet lists those publications originating in or sponsored by the National Research Council that are presently available for general distribution. Among the topics are agriculture, chemistry and biochemistry, earth sciences, food and nutrition, manpower, nuclear science.

j. *Outdoor and Camping Education Bibliography,* Outdoor Education Association, New York. Mimeographed lists of books, periodicals, pamphlets, bulletins, unpublished materials, and films.

k. Stead, William H., *Government Publications Nucleus of a "Central Use Library" to Supplement Other Materials for the Use of Teachers in the "Resource Use Project,"* Joint Council of Economic Education, Resource-use Project, New York, 1956. A bibliography listing items by agencies and by types of resources. Very specific, with good descriptions of contents.

19-5. Renewable Resources

Water (See Also *Soil*)

a. Carhart, Arthur H., *Water—or Your Life* (grades 8–12), J. B. Lippincott Company, Philadelphia, 1951, 312 pp. A lively book. Jay N. Darling says, "If you want to read a book about water, this is it."

b. Ellis, Cecil B., and others, *Fresh Water from the Oceans: For Cities, Industry and Irrigation* (grade 12), The Ronald Press Company, New York, 1954, 220 pp. Discusses known methods (up to 1954) of converting salt water to fresh. This book should be supplemented with the most recent report on saline water conversion by the U.S. Department of the Interior.

c. Gaul, Albro, *The Pond Book* (grades 5–8), Coward-McCann, Inc., New York, 1955, 136 pp. Tells exciting life stories of pond creatures, where ponds come from, how they go, how the farmer and man in general make use of ponds.

d. Graham, Edward, and William R. Van Dersal, *Water Conservation* (grades 9–12; teacher), Oxford University Press, New York, 1956, 111 pp. A brief summary of the origin and source of water, its uses, the interdependence of all water uses, and citizen movements to bring about conservation of water. Fifty-three chapters on all phases of water; with photographs.

e. Hoyt, William G., and Walter B. Langhein, *Floods* (grade 12; teacher), Princeton University Press, Princeton, 1955, 469 pp. An impartial and thorough report on floods by members of the staff of the U.S. Geological Survey.

f. Kinf, Thomson, *Water—Miracle of Nature* (grades 9–12), The Macmillan Company, New York, 1953, 238 pp. Written in a popular style, telling the facts of the earth's water. Contains many interesting and little-known facts about water and the role it plays in the history of man.

g. Leopold, Luna B., and Thomas Maddock, Jr., *The Flood Control Controversy* (grades 10–12), The Ronald Press Company, New York, 1954, 278 pp. The study of national flood control programs with analysis of the current controversy on big dams, little dams, and land management.

h. Riedman, S. R., *Water for People* (grades 7–9), Henry Schuman, Inc., Publishers, New York, 1952, 141 pp. Water and its influence on life, utilization of water, water power. Also simple experiments.

i. U.S. Department of Agriculture, *Water,* The Yearbook of Agriculture (grades 7–12), 1955, 752 pp. Contains a wealth of information on all aspects of a subject that has become a major national concern.

Soil (See Also *Water*)

j. Bennett, Hugh Hammond, *Elements of Soil Conservation,* 2d ed. (teacher), McGraw-Hill Book Company, Inc., New York, 1955, 358 pp. Written by the chief of the Soil Conservation Service from 1935 to 1951. Discusses the more important aspects of soil and water wastage and the outstanding methods of soil and water conservation. Bibliography and list of visual aids are excellent.

k. Brink, Wellington, *Big Hugh: The Father of Soil Conservation* (grades 10–12), The Macmillan Company, New York, 1951, 167 pp., with a preface by Louis Bromfield. An interesting and informative biography. A good chance to work in outside reading in English or social studies.

l. Bromfield, Louis, *Pleasant Valley* (grades 10–12), Harper & Brothers, New York, 1945, 300 pp.; *Malabar Farm, ibid.*, 1948, 405 pp.; *Out of the Earth, ibid.*, 1950, 305 pp; *From My Experience, ibid.*, 1955, 355 pp. These widely read books deal with the transforming of the eroded Malabar Farm in Pleasant Valley into a farm with excellent productivity. They will be found in most libraries.

m. Cook, J. Gordon, *The Fight for Food* (grades 9–12; teacher), The Dial Press, Inc., New York, 1957, 208 pp. Tells what modern science is doing to meet the food problems of the world and how science can help in every aspect of food production and conservation.

n. Harris, Roger S., and Harold E. Jones, *4-H Soil and Water Conservation* (grades 7–12), University of Minnesota, Agricultural Extension Division, St. Paul, Minn. Single copies free; not available in quantities. A simple discussion of soil, keeping it productive, and controlling erosion. Contains many simple soil demonstrations that can be done in the classroom. Although some of the material deals specifically with Minnesota, most of it is applicable anywhere.

o. Kellogg, Charles Edwin, *Our Garden Soils* (grades 10–12), The Macmillan Company, New York, 1952, 232 pp. A book about gardening soils, not gardening in general. Gardens include the "kitchen," flower bed, lawn, trees, shrubs. Gives valuable tables, maps, and tests to help find specific soil-plant combinations.

p. Low, Julian W., *Geologic Field Methods* (grades 9–12), Harper & Brothers, New York, 1957, 489 pp. A do-it-yourself guide that makes it possible for the field tyro as well as the field veteran to follow the step-by-step procedures. Contains a chapter on living and working out of doors.

q. Sherman, Robert, *Life and Death of the Soil* (grades 7–12), Modern World of Science Series, Science Research Associates, Inc., Chicago, 1953,

48 pp. The story of land and its importance to man. An informative, thought-provoking booklet, written in a conversational style that will hold the interest of young people.

r. *Soil and Water Conservation* (grades 6–12), Boy Scouts of America, New York. A merit badge booklet. Fine material, simply presented.

s. Stallings, J. H., *Soil-use and Improvement* (grades 8–12), Prentice-Hall, Inc., Englewood Cliffs, N.J., 1957, 403 pp. This text, although designed for vocational agricultural courses, may well serve as an excellent reference for general science and conservation.

t. *The Story of Land—Its Use and Misuse* (grades 6–12), Soil Conservation Society of America, Des Moines, Iowa, 1955, 16 pp. Cartoon type. Less when purchased in quantity.

u. U.S. Department of Agriculture, *Land,* The Yearbook of Agriculture (grades 7–12), 1958, 686 pp. Leading authorities give a wealth of useful information on such topics as land in Alaska, government programs, Indian lands, highways, zoning and planning, our future need for food and fiber, conservation.

Forests

v. Carhart, Arthur, *Son of the Forest* (grades 9–12), J. B. Lippincott Company, Philadelphia, 1952, 244 pp. Good story by a one-time member of the U.S. Forest Service, about people and grazing problems in a western national forest. Contains authentic and numerous conservation messages. Recommended reading for teen-agers.

Timber in Your Life (grades 9–12), *ibid.,* 1955, 317 pp. Considered by many professional foresters as the best nontechnical book available on current forest conservation problems and their solution. Written in an informal, chatty style.

w. Collingwood, G. H., and Warren D. Brush, *Knowing Your Trees* (grades 6–12), The American Forestry Association, Washington, D.C., 1955, 312 pp. This new edition of an old favorite has 806 illustrations showing 162 of the most important trees and their leaves, bark, flowers, and fruits. Text describes range and habits of each tree, its use, and economic importance. Considered one of the best tree identification books.

x. *Facts about the Nation's Timber Industry* (grades 7–12), American Forest Products Industries, Inc., Washington, D.C., 1955. A booklet with helpful, nontechnical information.

y. *Forestry* (grades 6–12), Boy Scouts of America, New York. Merit badge booklet no. 3302. Excellent material, simply presented.

z. Frank, Bernard, *Our National Forests* (grades 7–12), University of Oklahoma Press, Norman, Okla., 1955, 238 pp. Fills a need for an up-to-date accounting of our 148 national forests. Handsomely illustrated.

aa. Lemmon, Robert S., *The Best Loved Trees of America* (grades 7–12), Doubleday & Company, Inc., New York, 1952, 254 pp. Facts about fifty-nine native trees in America. Concise, clearly written, nontechnical. Excellent photographs showing entire year's cycle for each tree.

bb. Moore, Alma Chesnut, *The Friendly Forests* (grades 6–8), The Viking Press, Inc., New York, 1954, 96 pp. A clear, readable discussion of the value of our forests, with a strong plea for their protection.

cc. Reed, H. J., *Purdue Forestry Publications* (grades 7–12), Purdue University Agricultural Extension Service, Lafayette, Ind. These pamphlets include 4-H Club forestry manuals as well as many special techniques of forestry.

dd. *The Story of the Forest* (grades 4–8), American Forest Products Industries, Inc., Washington, D.C., 1949, 12 pp. A booklet and filmstrip on wise use of forests.

ee. *Teachers' Manual*, American Forest Products Industries, Inc., Washington, D.C., revised 1959. Presents ways of integrating the study of forest conservation with various subject-matter areas from grades 4 to 12.

ff. U.S. Department of Agriculture, *Trees*, The Yearbook of Agriculture (grades 7–12), 1949, 944 pp. A rich source of information on trees, forests, and wood lots.

gg. U.S. Forest Service (teacher), *Suggestions for Integrating Forestry in the Modern Curriculum*, 1940; *Materials to Help Teach Forest Conservation*, 1949. Other conservation teaching aids are available to teachers on request.

hh. Zim, Herbert S., and Alexander Martin, *Trees* (grades 6–12), Simon and Schuster, Inc., New York, 1952, 157 pp. Illustrates 140 species of trees. Brief nontechnical but scientifically accurate discussion. Part of series sponsored by Wildlife Management Institute.

Other Land Cover

ii. Dickinson, Alice, *The First Book of Plants* (grades 4–7), Franklin Watts, Inc., New York, 1953, 93 pp. An excellent introduction to plants, from microscopic to high towering ones. Striking drawings.

jj. Riedman, Sarah T., *Grass: Our Greatest Crop* (grades 5–9), Thomas Nelson & Sons, New York, 1952, 127 pp. An outstanding story of the grass family. Teaches young people that grass is the indirect source of all food; that it should be protected and encouraged to grow. Unusually fine drawings.

kk. U.S. Department of Agriculture, *Crops in Peace and War*, The Yearbook of Agriculture (grades 7–12), 1950–1951, 941 pp. Note especially the two sections To Keep Us Well and Waste Not, Want Not.

Grass, The Yearbook of Agriculture (grades 7–12), 1948, 892 pp. Titles included are, among others: Grass in the Nation's Life; The Range—A Major Resource; The Search for Better Grass; Grass in the Ten Regions.

Wildlife (Including Ecology)

ll. Allen, Durward L., *Wildlife Management* (grades 6–12), Boy Scouts of America, New York, 1953, 95 pp. A merit badge booklet. Highly regarded by conservationists. Emphasizes improving habitat.

mm. Black, John D., *Biological Conservation* (grade 12; teacher), The Blakiston Division, McGraw-Hill Book Company, Inc., New York, 1954, 328 pp. A college textbook with particular emphasis on wildlife conservation related to environment. Discusses soil, water, forests, grasslands, fish and other aquatic animals, birds, mammals. Contains an annotated bibliography and film guide. Very useful to teachers and advanced readers.

nn. Buchsbaum, Ralph, and Mildred Buchsbaum, *Basic Ecology* (grades 10–12; teacher), Boxwood Press, Pittsburgh, 1957, 192 pp. This is an invaluable introduction to ecology, giving a concise account of the relationships between living plants and animals and their environment.

oo. Buck, Margaret Waring, *In Ponds and Streams* (grades 6–9), Abingdon Press, Nashville, Tenn., 1955, 72 pp. Descriptions and pictures of flowers, ferns, insects, fish, and other animal life in and around a pond.

pp. Eschmeyer, R. W., *Land, Water, and Fishing* (grades 7–12; teacher), Sport Fishing Institute, Washington, D.C., 1955, 15 pp.

Fish Conservation Fundamentals (grades 7–12; teacher), *ibid.*, 1955, 30 pp. These two booklets for secondary school students and for the teacher help to fill a need for educational material on this subject. Dr. Eschmeyer, for 12 years chief fisheries biologist for the TVA, was executive vice-president of the Sport Fishing Institute until his death in 1955.

qq. Gabrielson, Ira N., *Wildlife Management* (grades 11–12; teacher), The Macmillan Company, New York, 1950, 274 pp. Contains basic information on wildlife conservation.

rr. Martin, Alexander Campbell, and others, *American Wildlife and Plants* (grades 10–12), McGraw-Hill Book Company, Inc., 1951, 500 pp. A guide to wildlife food habits; the use of trees, shrubs, weeds, and herbs by birds and mammals of the United States. Prepared under the direction of the U.S. Fish and Wildlife Service.

ss. Moore, Clifford B., *Book of Wild Pets* (grades 7–12), Charles T. Branford Company, Boston, 1954, 553 pp. Identification and life habits of our native wildlife. Care and feeding of animals in the classroom.

tt. Murie, Olaus J., *A Field Guide to Animal Tracks* (grades 10–12), Houghton Mifflin Company, Boston, 1954, 374 pp. An excellent guide to animal identification presented with artistry and brevity.

uu. Odum, Eugene P., *Fundamentals of Ecology* (mature reader), W. B. Saunders Company, Philadelphia, 1953, 384 pp. One of the best basic textbooks on the relationships of plants and animals.

vv. Peterson, Roger T., and Edwin Teale, *Wildlife in Color* (grades 6–12), National Wildlife Federation, Washington, D.C., 1955, 192 pp. Colored illustrations of 453 birds, fish, animals, flowers, trees, and insects from the Wildlife Stamp Series. Nontechnical. Subjects grouped by habitat and area.

ww. Storer, John H., *The Web of Life: A First Book of Ecology* (grades 8–12), The Devin-Adair Company, New York, 1953, 144 pp. Also a Signet Key book, with an introduction by Fairfield Osborn. Probably the finest ecology book for secondary students. Discusses how all living things fit together into a single pattern. Easy vocabulary. Many fine photographs and numerous interesting incidents hold reader interest.

xx. Zim, Herbert S., and others, *Golden Nature Series,* Simon and Schuster, Inc., New York. Sponsored by the Wildlife Management Institute. Guides to birds, insects, reptiles, amphibians, mammals, etc. Answers the need for authentic yet inexpensive guides. Books use full-color plates.

19-6. Nonrenewable Resources (Minerals)

Resource-use material in this area is not as plentiful as in other fields of conservation. Probably the best and most up-to-date information for teachers and older pupils is to be found in government publications such as the U.S. Bureau of Mines' *Minerals Yearbook,* Vols. I, II, and III, and *Mineral Facts and Problems.* Another good source is the President's Materials Policies Commission's report, *Resources for Freedom,* Vol. I through V (Sec. 19-2).

This is a field in which you may wish to make extensive use of free materials. Many commercial organizations and industries will furnish not only booklets free, but also filmstrips and other visual aids.

a. Fawcett, Raymond, *Coal* (grades 5–9), *Where Does It Come From Series,* Robert Benchley, Inc., Boston, 1953, 48 pp. General discussion of how coal was formed, how it is mined, and how by-products are made from it.

Oil, ibid. Story of oil around the world.

b. Fenton, Carroll Lane, and Mildred Adam Fenton, *Riches from the Earth* (grades 5–9), The John Day Company, Inc., New York, 1953, 159 pp. Probably the best general discussion of minerals for older elementary and junior high students. In addition to common fuels it covers many other minerals such as salt, talc, tungsten, uranium, zinc.

Rocks and Their Stories (grades 5–9), Doubleday & Company, Inc., New York, 1951, 112 pp. Answers questions about most of the important rocks and minerals in clear, nontechnical terms.

c. Loomis, F. B., *Field Book of Common Rocks and Minerals* (grades 7–12), G. P. Putnam's Sons, New York, 1956, 352 pp. Identifies rocks and minerals of the United States and interprets their origins and meanings.

d. U.S. Bureau of Mines, *Mineral Facts and Problems,* 1956. An 85-chapter summary of the essential facts and problems concerning many mineral resources. Available in reprints of separate chapters and also in a bound volume.

Minerals Yearbook (published annually). Vol. I. *Metals and Minerals,* is a compendium of all the latest facts of production, prices, new methods, etc., with respect to minerals. Vol. II. *Fuels,* covers the fossil fuels (coal, peat, petroleum, natural gas, etc.). Vol. III. *Area Reports* discusses the mineral situation, primarily by states.

e. Van Royen, William, and Oliver Bowles, *The Mineral Resources of the World* (grades 10–12), Prentice-Hall, Inc., Englewood Cliffs, N.J., 1952,

181 pp. A very complete atlas of the major mineral deposits at mid-century and those which appear likely to play an important role in the near future. Not a statistical record but, rather, a discussion of economic, social, and political implications.

f. Voskuil, Walter H., *Minerals in World Industry* (grades 11–12), McGraw-Hill Book Company, Inc., New York, 1955, 324 pp. Takes the reader step by step from the functions of minerals in industry through the interests of the United States in the distribution and extent of the world's mineral resources. Discusses iron, coal, petroleum, natural gas, alternate fuels, copper, lead, zinc, aluminum and magnesium, building materials, mineral plant food, and sulfur.

g. Zim, Herbert S., P. R. Shaffer, and R. Perlman, *Rocks and Minerals* (grades 7–10), Simon and Schuster, Inc., New York, 1957. This small volume is of help in identifying and classifying rocks and minerals. Easy to use in the field.

19-7. Energy Sources

a. Ayres, Eugene, and Charles A. Scarlott, *Energy Sources: The Wealth of the World* (grades 11–12), McGraw-Hill Book Company, Inc., New York, 1952, 344 pp. A reevaluation of the nation's and the world's energy resources. Deals with nonrenewables and substitutes for them.

b. Beeler, Nelson F., and Franklin M. Branley, *Experiments with Atomics* (grades 6–12), Thomas Y. Crowell Company, New York, 1954, 160 pp. Explains the nature of the atom step by step. Presents easy experiments using common household objects.

c. Billings, Henry, *All Down the Valley* (grades 8–12), The Viking Press, Inc., New York, 1952, 208 pp. Story of TVA.

d. Bischof, George P., *Atoms at Work* (grades 6–12), Harcourt, Brace and Company, Inc., New York, 1951, 130 pp. In clear, direct language explains the basic principles of atom activity. Uses simple experiments a student can perform. Although written for young people, it will interest older readers also.

e. Hyde, Margaret O., *Atoms Today and Tomorrow* (grades 8–12), McGraw-Hill Book Company, Inc., New York, 1955, 143 pp. Demonstrates what atomic energy is, how it is being used today, and what may be expected in the near future for peacetime uses. Contains simple vocabulary, careful explanations, helpful illustrations.

f. Lewellen, John Bryan, *Exploring Atomic Energy* (grades 6–9), Science Research Associates, Inc., Chicago, 1951, 40 pp. Covers atomic structure, nuclear fission, operation of an atomic furnace, peaceful uses and control of atomic energy. Instructor's guide available.

The Mighty Atom, ibid. (grades 5–9), Alfred A. Knopf, Inc., New York, 1955, 59 pp. An unusually fine book to help young people understand the atom.

g. Potter, Robert D., *Young People's Book of Atomic Energy* (grades 7–12),

Dodd Mead & Company, Inc., New York, 1952, 201 pp. Contains fundamental data necessary to understanding the atomic age. Discusses uses for peace and war. An outstanding book for secondary students.

h. Schneider, Herman, and Nina Schneider, *More Power to You* (grades 5–8), William R. Scott, Inc., New York, 1953, 128 pp. Discusses power produced by wind, sun, water, electricity, and atomic energy.

i. Smith, F. G. Walton, and Henry Chapin, *The Sun, The Sea, and Tomorrow* (grades 10–12), Charles Scribner's Sons, New York, 1955, 210 pp. A fascinating book on the potential sources of food, energy, and minerals from the sea. Relation of food and fuel to the sun is clearly brought out. Discussion of energy use, abuse, and future needs.

j. *The Atom in Our Hands* (grades 7–12), Union Carbide Corporation, New York, 1955. An outstanding booklet with timely material, clearly presented. Gives insight into an atomic plant and stresses peacetime uses.

k. Williams, Albert N., *The Water and the Power* (grades 11–12), Duell, Sloan & Pearce, Inc., New York, 1951, 387 pp. Traces development of the five great rivers of the West. Shows the grave problems facing citizens when water supplies dwindle and municipal, industrial, and agricultural uses increase.

19-8. New and To-be-developed Resources

The Gifted Student as Resource Developer

a. Association for Supervision and Curriculum Development, *Educational Leadership,* January, 1956, National Education Association, Washington, D.C. The entire issue of this periodical is devoted to the subject of the Curriculum and the Gifted.

b. Brandwein, Paul F., *The Gifted Student as Future Scientist,* Harcourt, Brace and Company, Inc., New York, 1955, 107 pp. This book is useful for teachers and administrators who are working out a program in science for gifted high school students. There is also discussion of the type of teacher who appears to be successful with students of high ability in science.

c. Cutts, Norma E., and Nicholas Moseley, *Teaching the Bright and Gifted,* Prentice-Hall, Inc., Englewood Cliffs, N.J., 1957, 268 pp. The gifted are defined as "those whose performance in a worthwhile type of human endeavor is consistently remarkable," regardless of any arbitrary IQ score set as the criterion.

d. Havighurst, Robert J., Eugene Stivers, and Robert F. DeHaan, *A Survey of the Education of Gifted Children,* Supplementary Monographs no. 83. University of Chicago Press, Chicago, 1955, 114 pp. This survey can provide valuable assistance to those who wish to keep abreast of the variety of activity in recent years concerning gifted children. The longest part of the survey summarizes the major details of forty-five programs for serving gifted children. Also included is an excellent bibliography.

e. Jewett, Arno, and others, *Teaching Rapid and Slow Learners in High Schools* (The Status of Adaptation in Junior, Senior, and Regular High Schools Enrolling More than 300 Pupils), U.S. Department of Health, Education, and Welfare, Bulletin no. 5, 1954, 97 pp. Summarizes, largely in tabular form, administrative provisions for rapid and slow learners, techniques used in discovering them, and instructional provisions for them.

f. Passow, Harry, Miriam Goldberg, Abraham Tannenbaum, and Will French, *Planning for Talented Youth: Considerations for the Public Schools,* Talented Youth Project Publication 1, Horace Mann–Lincoln Institute of School Experimentation, Bureau of Publications, Teachers College, Columbia University, New York, 1955, 85 pp. This pamphlet summarizes past research in identifying gifted youth and the development of educational programs for them. Includes a bibliography.

g. Rockefeller Brothers Fund, *The Pursuit of Excellence: Education and the Future of America,* Panel Report V of the Special Studies Project, Doubleday & Company, Inc., New York, 1958, 49 pp. Discourse on the ability of a free people to identify, nurture, and wisely use its own talents.

h. Spencer, Lyle M., and Ruth Dunbar, *Making the Most of Your Intelligence,* Science Research Associates, Inc., Chicago, 1956, 48 pp. A Life Adjustment booklet. Written in excellent style for secondary pupils, this booklet is highly recommended for reading by the talented students themselves. It will assist greatly in making them aware of how they can best use their special abilities.

i. Super, Donald, and Paul Bachrach, *Scientific Careers: Vocational Development Theory,* Columbia University Press, New York, 1957, 135 pp. This monograph is a review and critique of research in the field of scientific giftedness. The authors suggest new research approaches in the light of current vocational development theory.

j. Witty, Paul (ed.), *The Gifted Child,* American Association for Gifted Children, D. C. Heath and Company, Boston, 1951, 338 pp. A compilation by various authors. Typical chapter headings are Progress in Educating the Gifted, Identifying Gifted Children, The Teacher of Gifted Children, Mental Hygiene of Gifted Children, Community Recognition of the Gifted, A High School of Science for Gifted Students, Administrative Problems in the Education of Gifted Children.

Career Guidance in the Field of Resources

In addition to the government pamphlets listed at the end of this section, information on conservation career opportunities may be obtained from the Department of the Army, Corps of Engineers; from the Bureau of Indian Affairs, Bureau of Land Management, Bureau of Mines, Bureau of Reclamation, Fish and Wildlife Service, and National Park Service of the Department of the Interior; the Bureau of Employment Security and the Employment Service of the Department of Labor; the Department of Health, Education and Welfare; and the Public Service Department of the Department of State.

k. *After High School What?* Engineers Council for Professional Development, New York, 1958. The purpose of this pamphlet is to help students decide on a career in engineering or in a related field of science, if they are interested and have the right qualifications.

l. Burroughs, R. D., *Careers in Conservation,* Michigan Department of Conservation, Lansing, Mich., 1956. This pamphlet answers such questions as: How can I get a job in the Conservation Department? What must I do to become a conservation officer? How much education and what kind is required of Department foresters, fish and game workers, forest fire officers?

m. *Career in Atomic Energy,* Atomic Energy Commission, 1957. For the student who is attracted to this new field on the science frontier.

n. Cole, Charles C., Jr., *Encouraging Scientific Talent,* College Entrance Examination Board, Princeton, N.J., 1956. A study of America's able students who are lost to college and of ways of attracting them to college and scientific careers.

o. *Encouraging Future Scientists: Keys to Careers,* National Science Teachers Association, Washington, D.C. This is an annual bibliography including career-guidance booklets and films in many scientific professions; information on scholarships; award programs for students; summer programs for students; awards, fellowships, and other programs for teachers; field trips (industrial plant and laboratory visits); career conferences and career consultants; agencies that can help.

p. National Manpower Council, *A Policy for Scientific and Professional Manpower,* Columbia University Press, New York, 1953, 263 pp. An over-all picture of what is happening to scientific and professional personnel. For everyone interested in the future security of the United States, this book supplies facts and policies. It discusses shortages and our undeveloped human resources, with guides for action.

A Policy for Skilled Manpower, ibid., 1954. This book deals with the resources of our nation in regard to the men who run the machines. It points out the problems and offers guides for action.

q. Neal, Harry Edward, *Nature's Guardians: Your Career in Conservation,* Julian Messner, Inc., Publishers, New York, 1956, 192 pp. This excellent book, often dramatic and amusing in its presentation, contains information about opportunities in conservation as well as in industrial and informational fields, private organizations, and universities. Suggests subjects for a young person to study in college to fit himself for a career in conservation.

r. Smith, Jean, *Find a Career in Conservation,* G. P. Putnam's Sons, New York, 1959, 160 pp. Young people will find in this book an interesting picture of the attractions—and the disadvantages—of careers in the field of renewable resources.

s. U.S. Department of Agriculture: *Career Service Opportunities in the USDA,* A1.76: 45/2.

Soil Conservation Service: A number of miscellaneous bulletins such as *Students—Start Your Career in SCS before You Graduate,* no. 714; *An Engineeing Career for You in SCS,* no. 715; *A Soil Science Career for You in SCS,* no. 716; *Careers in Soil Conservation Service,* no. 717. Forest Service: *A Forest Service Career,* MP-726; *Jobs with the Forest Service,* revised 1956.

Rural Electrification Administration: *A Challenging Career in Engineering for You,* no. 736.

The Role of Research in Resource Development

t. Baitsell, George A. (ed.), *Science in Progress* (grades 11–12), Yale University Press, New Haven, 1955, 343 pp. Authoritative reports on basic research by ten contributors.

u. Couzens, E. G., and V. E. Yarsley, *Plastics in the Service of Man* (grades 9–12), a Pelican Book, Penguin Books, Inc., Baltimore, 1956, 315 pp. Tells the story of modern substitution products and their usefulness to man.

v. Leyson, Burr W., *Marvels of Industrial Science* (grades 9–12), E. P. Dutton & Co., Inc., New York, 1955, 189 pp. The story of industrial chemical research as demonstrated by synthetic fabrics, atomic batteries, silicones, and transistors.

More Marvels of Industrial Science, ibid., 1958, 190 pp. Behind-the-scenes stories in laboratories like General Electric's to learn of revolutionary electrical research that affects all industry and modern life.

w. Soule, George, *The Shape of To-morrow,* (grades 9–12), The New American Library of World Literature, Inc., New York, 1958, 141 pp. A glimpse of the near future, when automation and atomic energy will transform economic life.

Tools for Future Resource Developers

x. Barr, George, *Research Ideas for Young Scientists,* Whittlesey House, McGraw-Hill Book Company, Inc., New York, 1959, 142 pp. All sorts of projects that are not repetitions of chemical demonstrations but new and "individual research."

y. Goldstein, Philip, and Paul Brandwein (gen. ed.), *How to Do an Experiment,* Harcourt, Brace and Company, New York, 1957. Telling the junior scientist about scientific methods and giving him ideas for science projects and exhibits for science fairs.

z. Patterson, Margaret E., and Joseph H. Kraus (eds.), *Thousands of Science Projects* (yearly editions), Science Service, Washington, D.C. Exhibits shown at science fairs and projects in connection with competition in the Science Talent Search.

aa. UNESCO, *Seven Hundred Science Experiments for Everyone,* Doubleday & Company, Inc., New York, 1959, 221 pp. Clear explanations and diagrams on how to make necessary equipment and how to perform many experiments to demonstrate "basic principles that govern the world."

19-9. Some Magazines

A number of states issue conservation periodicals. Check with your own State Department of Conservation to find out what it offers.

No school library or classroom would want all the following publications, but a careful selection will bring lively and up-to-date information to you and your students.

General

Conservation News (semimonthly), National Wildlife Federation, Washington, D.C.
Ecology (quarterly), Ecological Society of America, Duke University Press, Durham, N.C.
Junior Natural History (monthly), American Museum of Natural History, New York
Natural History (monthly), American Museum of Natural History, New York
Nature Magazine (monthly), American Nature Association, Washington, D.C.
New Horizons (three times yearly), Bulletin for the Junior Museum Field, National Foundation for Junior Museums, New York
Outdoor America (bimonthly), Izaak Walton League of America, Inc., Chicago
Ward's Natural Science Bulletin (bimonthly), Ward's Natural Science Establishment, Inc., Rochester, N.Y.
Weatherwise (bimonthly), American Meteorological Society, Boston

Water

Journal of Soil and Water Conservation (bimonthly), Soil Conservation Society of America, Des Moines.
Land and Water (quarterly), Friends of the Land, Hidden Acres, Zanesville, Ohio
Oceanus (quarterly), Woods Hole Oceanographic Institution, Woods Hole, Mass.
Watershed (monthly), American Watershed Council, Inc., Washington, D.C.

Soil

Desert Magazine (monthly), Desert Press, Inc., Palm Desert, Calif.
Farm Quarterly, F & W Publishing Corp., Cincinnati, Ohio
Horticulture (monthly), Massachusetts Horticultural Society, Boston
Plants and Gardens (quarterly), Brooklyn Botanic Garden, Brooklyn, N.Y.
Soil Conservation (monthly), U.S. Soil Conservation Service, Washington, D.C.
The Reclamation Era (monthly), U.S. Bureau of Reclamation, Washington, D.C.
What's New in Crops and Soils (nine issues), American Society of Agronomy, Madison, Wis.

Forests and Public Lands

American Forests (monthly), American Forestry Association, Washington, D.C.

Journal of Forestry (monthly), Society of American Foresters, Washington, D.C.

Journal of Range Management (bimonthly), American Society of Range Management, Portland, Ore.

National Parks Magazine (quarterly), National Parks Association, Washington, D.C.

Our Public Lands (quarterly), U.S. Bureau of Land Management, Washington, D.C.

The Living Wilderness (quarterly), The Wilderness Society, Washington, D.C.

Wildlife

Animal Kingdom (bimonthly), New York Zoological Society, New York

Audubon Junior News (five times yearly), National Audubon Society, New York

Audubon Magazine (bimonthly), National Audubon Society, New York

FAO Fisheries Bulletin (quarterly), FAO Rome, Italy

Wildlife Review (irregular), Fish and Wildlife Service, Wildlife Review, Patuxent Refuge, Laurel, Md.

Minerals and Energy Sources

Bulletin of the Atomic Scientists (monthly), Educational Foundation for Nuclear Science, Inc., Chicago

Chemical and Engineering News (weekly), American Chemical Society, Washington, D.C.

Chemical Week (weekly), McGraw-Hill Publishing Company, Inc., New York

Earth Science (six issues), Midwest Federation of Minerological Societies, Chicago

The Sun at Work (quarterly), Association for Applied Solar Energy, Phoenix, Ariz.

For Future Resource Developers

Science Newsletter (weekly), Science Service, Inc., Washington, D.C.

Science World: The Magazine for High School Science Students (16 issues per school year), Street and Smith Publications, Inc., New York.

For Teachers

American Biology Teacher (eight issues), National Association of Biology Teachers, Bryan, Ohio

Conservation Education Association Newsletter (four issues sent to members), Eastern Montana College of Education, Billings, Mont.

National Wildlife Federation Conservation News (twenty-six issues to those who buy Wildlife Conservation Stamps), National Wildlife Federation, Washington, D.C.

Nature Conservancy Newsletter (four issues sent to members), Washington, D.C.

Outdoor Education Newsletter (issued three times a year), College of Education, Michigan State University, East Lansing, Mich.

19-10. Films

This list, prepared by The Conservation Foundation, is highly selective; it includes only a few of the many films screened during the last ten years. Each film listed below maintains, in our opinion, a high standard of production, in regard to both quality and ingenuity of presentation. The films are appropriate for the high school level. Each is as "timeless" as a film can be. The list is not a long one, or an inclusive one; it is simply *our* list.[1]

Where to Order Films

This will give you addresses of distributors whose films we have mentioned more than once in our listings. The addresses of distributors mentioned only once will be found directly on the listed films.

Association Films, Inc., Broadway at Elm, Ridgefield, N.J.

Contemporary Films, Inc., 267 W. 25th St., New York

Encyclopaedia Britannica Films, Inc. (address the film library and order from the nearest source):

Region I: 1150 Wilmette Ave., Wilmette, Ill.

Region II: 202 East 44th St., New York

Region III: 1414 Dragon St., Dallas

Region IV: 5625 Hollywood Blvd., Hollywood, Calif.

Region V: 277 Pharr Road, N.E., Atlanta, Ga.

Modern Talking Picture Service, 3 East 54th St., New York

U.S. Bureau of Mines, Central Experiment Station, 4800 Forbes St., Pittsburgh

Conservation Education (for the Teacher)

Conservation Vistas (Color, sound, 14 min, U.S. Forestry Service, free loan). Emphasizing that new methods of teaching conservation are being developed, this film tells the story from the teacher's point of view. It stresses the fact that firsthand contact with the out-of-doors can be one of the best ways of creating interest in conservation. The accent is on forestry, with the suggestion that this area is rich in career opportunities.

Outdoor Education, Cook County (Ill.) (Color, sound, 28 min, Forest Reserve District, Conservation Department, Cook County, Ill.). How one large urban school system organizes and handles an outdoor experience for its students is illustrated in this film. A bus load of young people, traveling through the countryside, visits a lake maintained by the Chicago public schools. The values of this experience are made evident. Other city school systems might find useful suggestions in this film.

[1] A more complete listing, including elementary films as well, may be found in the pamphlet, *A Critical Index of Films and Filmstrips in Conservation,* The Conservation Foundation, 30 East 40th St., New York.

The Window (Color, sound, 17 min, National Audubon Society, 1130 Fifth Ave., New York, rental or sale). This film shows the experience of one teacher in relating her students to the world of nature outside the classroom window. The film may help other teachers to find their own way of bridging the gap between textbook learning and living experience. New dimensions may thus be added to the teaching of science, social studies, language, and art.

Renewable Resources

A Way of Life (Color, sound, 27 min, Missouri Conservation Commission, Jefferson City, Mo., sale; inquire for rental). Predators, such as coyotes and foxes, have always been among the less sympathetic and most misunderstood of earth's creatures. This film stresses their importance in the web of life. Although the story is restricted to the Missouri countryside, discussion might bring to light the role of predation in any other region.

In the Beginning (Color, sound, 28 min, Modern Talking Picture Service, free loan). This film depicts the five great eras of earth building as recorded in the walls of the Grand Canyon. Examples of the erosive action of water, wind, and frost are made evident. The film points out the great spans of geologic time necessary for major changes in the earth's form and structure.

Living Earth Series (Color, sound, 11 min per reel, Encyclopaedia Britannica Films, Inc., sale or rental).

Part I. *Birth of the Soil.* This reel illustrates the age-long process by which soil is produced from bare rock. Emphasis is on the roles played by water, air, and sunlight and by plants and animals in the creation of topsoil.

Part II. *This Vital Earth.* The theme of this reel is an ecological one—the interrelationship of plants and animals and their linkage to the soil. The film makes clear why it is necessary for man to replace nutrients in order to keep the soil fertile.

Part III. *Arteries of Life.* Emphasizing the fact that soil without water cannot maintain life, this reel shows how the storage of water and control of its flow depend on forest and grass cover.

Part IV. *Seeds of Destruction.* This film dramatizes what happens when a single link in the "chain of life" is broken, and what man may still do to help solve the problems thus created.

For a forum version of the Living Earth Series, see *Yours Is the Land.*

Living Forest Series (Color, sound, 11 min per reel, Encyclopaedia Britannica Films, Inc., sale or rental).

Part I. *The Forest Grows.* This film analyzes the growth of tree species, their interrelationship with one another, and their ultimate development into a healthy climax forest.

Part II. *The Forest Produces.* This reel describes man's reliance on the forest to meet three of his needs: a lumber supply, a source of water, and a place of beauty for recreation.

Part III. *Forest Conservation.* By showing the results of sound and unsound lumbering practices, the film emphasizes the necessity for wise management of our forest resources.

The Living Forest (Color, sound, 1 reel, 44 min). This film, forum version of the Living Forest Series, describes in detail the growth of a forest, its importance to man, and the ways in which it may be wisely managed.

Living Water Series (Color, sound, 1 min per reel, Encyclopaedia Britannica Films, Inc., sale or rental).

Part I. *Nature's Plan.* The first of the two films in this series portrays the principles and importance of the water cycle. In illustrating the movement of water from sea to air to earth and back to sea again, the film makes evident the roles of the sun and wind. It also points out the part played by watersheds in storing and distributing water.

Part II. *Man's Problem.* This sequel tells the story of the problems confronting communities in obtaining and protecting their water supply. The story of water for the growing city of Los Angeles is used as an example. Portrayed also are the construction of dams with attendant problems, the dangers of water pollution, and the twin headaches of "too much" and "too little" water.

Muddy Waters (B&W, sound, 19 min, Motion Picture Service, Office of Information, USDA, free loan). This is an early government conservation film telling the story of land use and abuse in the Southwest. With the advent of the white man this area was transformed into a vast farming and stock-raising region. Erosion and floods followed on the heels of excessive grazing. Remedial measures are depicted and the need for long-range planning emphasized.

Water for a Nation (Color, sound, 19 min, Motion Picture Service, Office of Information, USDA, free loan). This film brings up to date the problems and problem solving of the earlier film, *Muddy Waters.* Again, it shows the farmer's dependence on water to raise his crops and livestock. The film deals also with the dilemmas of "too much" and "too little" water and demonstrates how conservation practices not only aid the individual farmer but also help to guard the entire nation's water supply.

Waters of Coweeta (Color, sound, 20 min, Motion Picture Service, Office of Information, USDA, free loan). Students, teachers, and engineers are conducted on a tour through the Coweeta Experimental Hydrologic Laboratory in North Carolina, to see the results of 20 years of basic research. There is striking evidence of the effects of different kinds of farming, lumbering, and grazing practices on stream flow and on the health of the watershed. This documentary might well be used as an introduction to the problems of any watershed and the need for its proper management.

Watershed Wildfire (Color or B&W, sound, 21 min, Motion Picture Service, Office of Information, USDA). This film pictures the nine-day battle to control a forest fire which ravaged the Santa Inez watershed in California. In addition to showing the results of man's carelessness and his skill in organizing to stop the conflagration, the film stresses the importance of immediate reseeding to protect the watershed and restore it to health.

Web of Life Series (Color, sound, 16 min per reel, Encyclopaedia Britannica Films, Inc., sale or rental).

Elementary grades: *What We Need; Where We Find It;* and *How We Get It.*

Junior high school: *The Demand; The Supply;* and *Balancing the Supply and Demand.*

Senior high school: *Can the Biologist Meet the Demand?; Can the Chemist Renew the Supply?;* and *Can the Physicist-Engineer Strike a Balance?*

Index